ALGEBRA I

Student Text

Pittsburgh, PA
Phone 888.851.7094
Fax 412.690.2444

www.carnegielearning.com

Acknowledgements

We would like to thank those listed below who helped to prepare the Cognitive Tutor® ***Algebra I*** Student Text.

William S. Hadley
Jessica Pflueger
Michele Covatto
The Carnegie Learning Development Team

Algebra was used in a variety of ways to design the building and surrounding grounds on the front cover. Architects designed the sides of the pyramid with slopes that were structurally sound and pleasing to the eye. Stone masons calculated the number of bricks needed for the sidewalk and designed the pattern in which they were laid. Landscapers mixed the fertilizer for the grass and shrubbery with the correct ratio of water and chemicals. As you work through the Cognitive Tutor® ***Algebra I*** text and software, you will see additional opportunities for using Algebra in your everyday activities.

ISBN-13 978-1-932409-60-4
ISBN-10 1-932409-60-2
Student Text

Printed in the United States of America
1-2006-VH
2-2006-VH
3-2006-VH
4-2006-VH
5-2006-VH
6-2007-VH
7-2007-VH
8-4/2008 HPS

Dear Student,

You are about to begin an exciting adventure using mathematics, the language of science and technology. As you sit in front of a computer screen or video game, ride in an automobile, fly in a plane, talk on a cellular phone, or use any of the tools of modern society, realize that mathematics was critical in its invention, design, and production.

The workplace today demands that employees be technologically literate, work well in teams, and be self-starters. At Carnegie Learning, we have designed a mathematics course that uses state-of-the-art computer software with collaborative classroom activities.

As you use the Cognitive Tutor® ***Algebra I*** software, it actually learns about you as you learn about mathematics. As you work, you will receive "just-in-time" instruction so that you are always ready for the next problem. In the classroom, you will work with your peers to solve real-world problem situations. Working in groups, you will learn to use multiple representations to analyze questions and write or present your answers.

Throughout the entire process, your teacher will be a facilitator and guide in support of your learning. As a result, you will become a self-sufficient learner, moving through the software and Student Text at your own rate and discovering solutions to problems that you never thought were possible to solve.

Throughout this year, have fun while Learning by Doing!

The Cognitive Tutor® *Algebra I* Development Team

Contents

Contents

Contents

Looking Ahead to Chapter 1

1

Focus In Chapter 1, you will work with patterns and sequences, find terms in sequences, and use sequences and patterns to solve problems. You will also learn how to represent problem situations in different ways using tables, graphs, and algebraic equations.

Chapter Warmup

Answer these questions to help you review the skills that you will need in Chapter 1.

Find each sum, difference, product, or quotient.

1. 7(31) **2.** 124 + 18 **3.** 54 − 29

4. 342 ÷ 6 **5.** 8 • 8 • 8 **6.** 0.78 + 6.05

7. 16.95 ÷ 0.5 **8.** 13(12.45) **9.** 139.05 − 12.4

Compare the two numbers using the symbol < or >.

10. 951 ◯ 876 **11.** 48.2 ◯ 48.7 **12.** $\frac{2}{3}$ ◯ $\frac{2}{5}$

Read the problem scenario below.

You grow your own vegetables. To keep the rabbits from eating all your carrots, you decide to build a rectangular wire fence around your garden. How much fencing will you need to enclose each garden described below? What is the area of each garden described below? Be sure to include the correct units in your answers. Write your answers using a complete sentence.

13. The length of the garden is 7 feet and the width is 9 feet.

14. The length of the garden is 21 meters and the width is 14 meters.

15. The length of the garden is 65 inches and the width is 140 inches.

Key Terms

pattern ■ p. 5
sequence ■ p. 6
term ■ p. 6
area ■ p. 7
profit ■ p. 10
power ■ p. 11
base ■ p. 11
exponent ■ p. 11
order of operations ■ p. 12
numerical expression ■ p. 13
algebraic expression ■ p. 13
variable ■ p. 13
coefficient ■ p. 14
evaluate ■ p. 14
value ■ p. 14
*n*th term ■ p. 16
sum ■ p. 23
labels ■ p. 26
units ■ p. 26
bar graph ■ p. 27
bounds ■ p. 28
graph ■ p. 28
algebraic equation ■ p. 30
solution ■ p. 30
dependent variable ■ p. 35
independent variable ■ p. 35
estimation ■ p. 42
point of intersection ■ p. 47

CHAPTER

1

Patterns and Multiple Representations

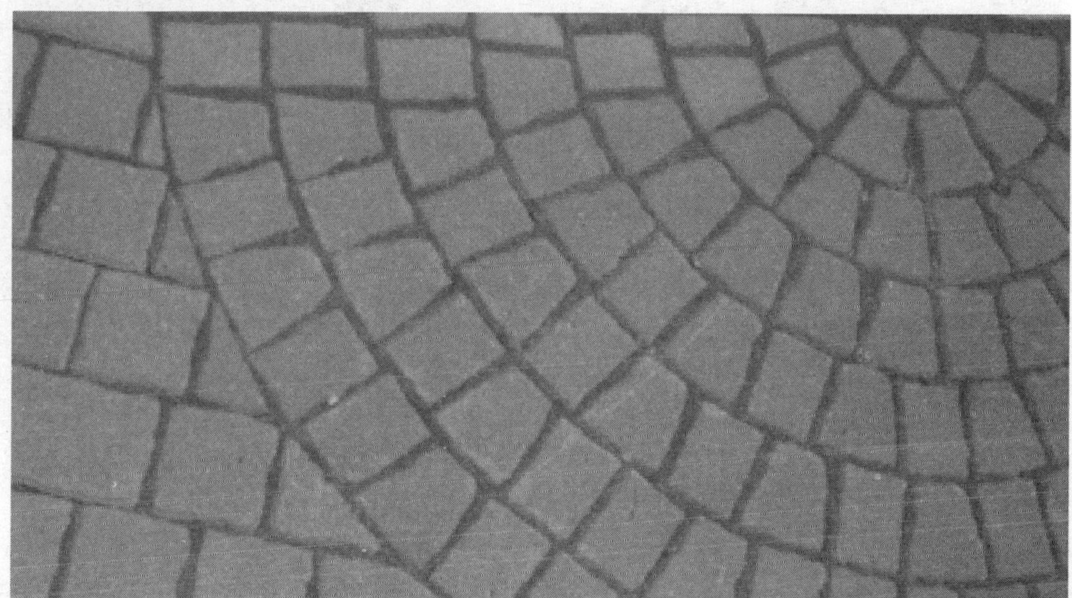

Tiled sidewalks can be seen around public parks, swimming pools, monuments, and other outdoor sites. The tiles provide a decorative backdrop on which visitors can walk without harming the natural surroundings. In Lesson 1.1, you will continue a pattern to create a tiled sidewalk.

Mathematical Representations

1

INTRODUCTION Mathematics is a human invention, developed as people encountered problems that they could not solve. For instance, when people first began to accumulate possessions, they needed to answer questions such as: How many? How many more? How many less?

People responded by developing the concepts of numbers and counting. Mathematics made a huge leap when people began using symbols to represent numbers. The first "numerals" were probably tally marks used to count weapons, livestock, or food.

As society grew more complex, people needed to answer questions such as: Who has more? How much does each person get? If there are 5 members in my family, 6 in your family, and 10 in another family, how can each person receive the same amount?

During this course, we will solve problems and work with many different representations of mathematical concepts, ideas, and processes to better understand our world. The following processes can help you solve problems.

Discuss to Understand

- Read the problem carefully.
- What is the context of the problem? Do you understand it?
- What is the question that you are being asked? Does it make sense?

Think for Yourself

- Do I need any additional information to answer the question?
- Is this problem similar to some other problem that I know?
- How can I represent the problem using a picture, diagram, symbols, or some other representation?

Work with Your Partner

- How did you solve the problem?
- Show me your representation.
- This is the way I thought about the problem—how did you think about it?
- What else do we need to solve the problem?
- Does our reasoning and our answer make sense to one another?

Work with Your Group

- Show me your representation.
- This is the way I thought about the problem—how did you think about it?
- What else do we need to solve the problem?
- Does our reasoning and our answer make sense to one another?
- How can we explain our solution to one another? To the class?

Share with the Class

- Here is our solution and how we solved it.
- We could only get this far with our solution. How can we finish?
- Could we have used a different strategy to solve the problem?

1.1 Designing a Patio

Patterns and Sequences

Objectives

In this lesson, you will:

- Predict the next term in a sequence.
- Identify particular terms of sequences.
- Write sequences of numbers.
- Describe patterns of sequences.

Key Terms

- pattern
- sequence
- term
- area

SCENARIO As the owner of a landscaping company, you have been hired to design a patio. The customer wants the patio floor to be made of concrete blocks called "pavers." For the patio design, you are considering the different paver shapes shown below.

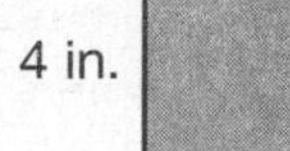

Problem 1 Design Patterns

A. One way to arrange the pavers is to place them in a **pattern** called a Spanish bond design. The first three steps in the design are shown below. What are the next two steps? Draw a separate picture of each step.

Step 1

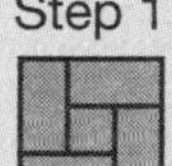

Step 2

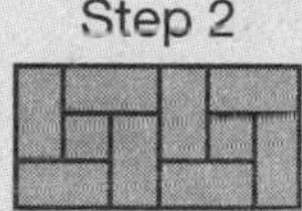

Step 3

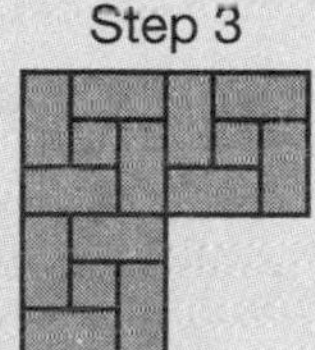

B. Another arrangement that you are considering is a double basket weave design. The first three steps in the design are shown below. What are the next two steps? Draw a separate picture of each step.

Step 1

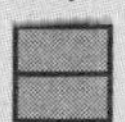

Step 2

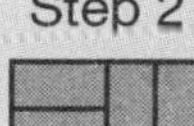

Step 3

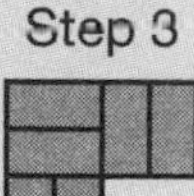

1

Problem 1 Design Patterns

C. After considering these two designs, you decide to create your own design. The first three steps in your design are shown below. What are the next two steps? Draw a separate picture of each step.

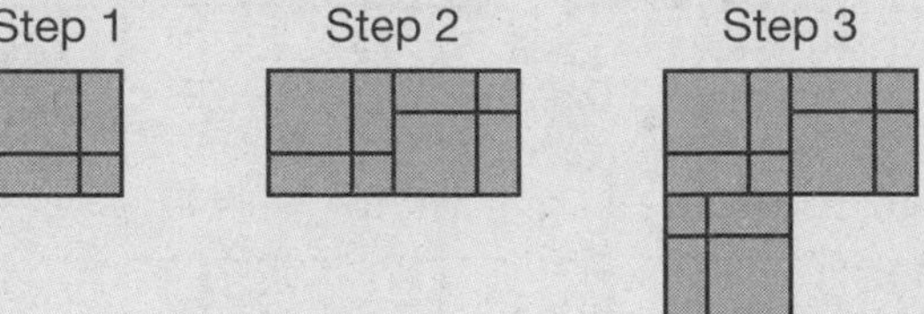

D. **Just the Math: Sequences** The figures in each paver pattern form a *sequence* of figures. A **sequence** is an ordered set of objects or numbers. The steps in each paver pattern form the **terms,** or members, of the sequence. The first term is the first object or number in the sequence; the second term is the second object or number in the sequence; and so on.

In the Spanish bond design below, circle the third term of the sequence.

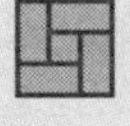  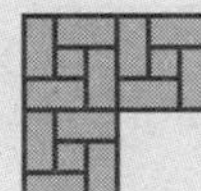 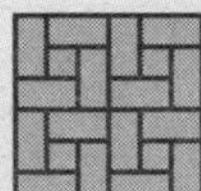 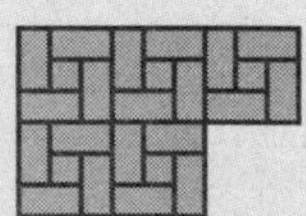

In the Spanish bond design, identify the term that is given by the figure at the right.

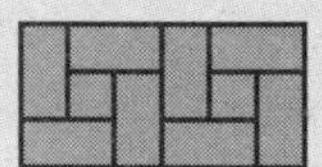

Draw the fifth term of the sequence in the double basket weave design.

Identify the term from the double basket weave design shown at the right.

1

Investigate Problem 1

1. After you choose a design for the patio, you need to find the number of pavers needed to complete the job. You will also need to know the area that is covered by the pavers. Complete each table below for the three designs.

Spanish bond design					
Number of pavers	5				
Area (square inches)	144				

Double basket weave design					
Number of pavers	2				
Area (square inches)	64				

Your design					
Number of pavers	4				
Area (square inches)	144				

Take Note

Recall that the **area** of a square is equal to the side length of the square mutiplied by itself. For instance, the area of a square paver with a side length of 12 inches is (12 inches)(12 inches) = 144 square inches. The area of two of these pavers is twice the area of one paver, or 2(144 square inches) = 288 square inches.

2. A sequence can be made up of numbers as well as objects. The numbers of pavers and the areas in the tables above form sequences of numbers. Write the sequences of numbers given in the tables above.

Spanish bond design

Numbers of pavers:

Areas:

Double basket weave design

Numbers of pavers:

Areas:

Your design

Numbers of pavers:

Areas:

1

Investigate Problem 1

3. Find the next two terms of the sequence of the number of pavers in the Spanish bond design. Use complete sentences to explain how you found your answers.

4. Find the next two terms of each sequence. Use complete sentences to explain how you found your answers.

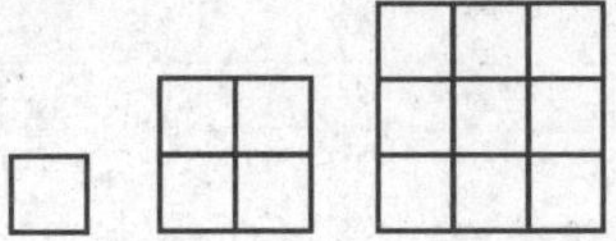

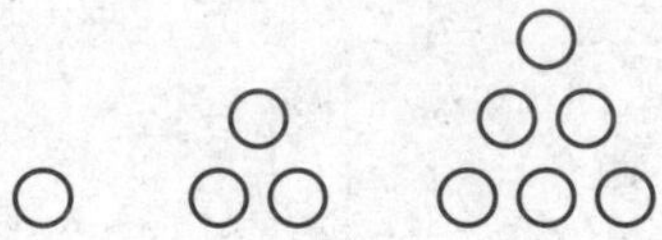

1, 12, 123, 1234, ________, ________, ...

6, 11, 16, 21, ____, ____, ...

12, 10, 8, ____, ____, ...

1, 3, 9, 27, 81, 243, ________, ________, ...

Take Note

Whenever you see the share with the class icon, your group should prepare a short presentation to share with the class that describes how you solved the problem. Be prepared to ask questions during other groups' presentations and to answer questions during your presentation.

1.2 Lemonade, Anyone?

Finding the 10th Term of a Sequence

Objectives

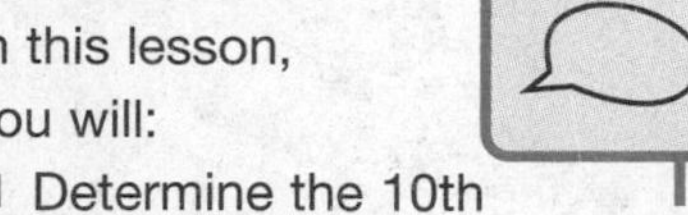

In this lesson, you will:

- Determine the 10th term of sequences.
- Write sequences.
- Write powers.
- Use the order of operations.

Key Terms

- profit
- power
- base
- exponent
- order of operations

SCENARIO Your community is planning a street fair to raise money for the local soup kitchen. You are helping by selling lemonade. You need a lemonade recipe, ingredients to make the lemonade, and a sign for your lemonade stand.

Problem 1 Setting Up the Stand

A. When creating the sign for the lemonade stand, you decide to decorate the sign's border with a pattern of lemons. Your design creates a sequence of figures, as shown below. Draw the 10th term of the sequence. Then use a complete sentence to explain how you found your answer.

B. You find a recipe for lemonade that includes the table below which shows the number of lemons needed for different numbers of pitchers of lemonade. The numbers of lemons form a sequence: 8, 16, 24, 32, 40, ...

Amount of lemonade (pitchers)	1	2	3	4	5
Number of lemons	8	16	24	32	40

Complete each statement below to write the number of lemons needed in terms of the number of pitchers of lemonade that you want to make.

Number of lemons needed for 2 pitchers of lemonade:

2 × (___) = 16

Number of lemons needed for 3 pitchers of lemonade:

3 × (___) = 24

How many lemons are needed for 10 pitchers of lemonade? Use a complete sentence in your answer.

1

Investigate Problem 1

1. It costs $5 to make the sign and $2 for the ingredients for one pitcher of lemonade. You can use a sequence to model the total cost of making different numbers of pitchers of lemonade. Complete each statement below to find the total cost.

   Total cost in dollars to make 1 pitcher of lemonade:
   $5 + 2(\_\_\_) = \_\_\_$

   Total cost in dollars to make 2 pitchers of lemonade:
   $5 + 2(\_\_\_) = \_\_\_$

   Total cost in dollars to make 3 pitchers of lemonade:
   $5 + 2(\_\_\_) = \_\_\_$

   Write the sequence of numbers formed by the total cost of making 1 pitcher of lemonade, 2 pitchers of lemonade, 3 pitchers of lemonade, and so on.

   What is the 10th term of this sequence? Show all your work.

   Use a complete sentence to explain what the 10th term represents.

2. You can pour 14 glasses of lemonade from one pitcher. If you sell the lemonade for $.50 per glass, how much money do you receive from one pitcher of lemonade? Use a complete sentence to explain how you found your answer.

3. Write the sequence of numbers that represents the amount of money that you receive from selling 1 pitcher of lemonade, 2 pitchers of lemonade, 3 pitchers of lemonade, and so on.

4. The **profit** is the amount of money that you have left after you subtract the costs from the amount of money that you receive. What is your profit from selling 1 pitcher of lemonade? What is your profit from selling 2 pitchers of lemonade?

   Write the sequence that represents the profit from 1 pitcher of lemonade, 2 pitchers of lemonade, 3 pitchers of lemonade, and so on.

Take Note

Whenever you see the share with the class icon, your group should prepare a short presentation to share with the class that describes how you solved the problem. Be prepared to ask questions during other groups' presentations and to answer questions during your presentation.

Problem 2 Kids' Booth

At the street fair, there are activity booths for young children. In one of the booths, children can create sand art by layering different colors of sand in a clear plastic cube. One local company is donating the sand and another company is donating the plastic cubes.

1

Take Note

A cube is a box whose length, width, and height are the same measurement. The volume, or amount of space, inside a cube is found by multiplying the cube's length, width, and height.

Volume is measured in cubic units. For instance, if the side lengths are measured in feet, then the volume is measured in cubic feet.

A. You need to contact the sand company and tell them the amount of sand that you will need. If the cubes are six inches long, six inches wide, and six inches tall, then the amount of sand needed to fill one plastic cube can be found by multiplying the length, width, and height of the cube. Write and simplify an expression for the amount of sand needed for one cube.

B. Suppose that the cubes are eight inches long, eight inches wide, and eight inches tall. Write and simplify an expression for the amount of sand needed for one cube.

C. Suppose that the cubes are ten inches long, ten inches wide, and ten inches tall. Write and simplify an expression for the amount of sand needed for one cube.

Investigate Problem 2

1. **Just the Math: Powers** When factors are repeated, you can represent the product by using **powers.** For instance, the product 6(6)(6) has only one factor, 6, which is repeated 3 times. You can write this product as the power 6^3.

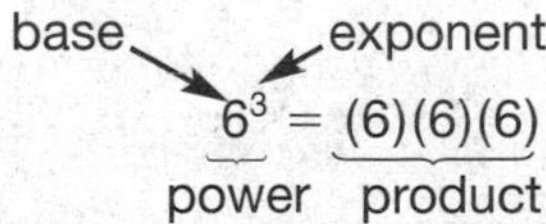

The **base** of a power is the repeated factor and the **exponent** of the power is the number of times that the factor is repeated.

Write each power as a product.

2^5 $\quad$ 4^2 $\quad$ 6^5

1

Investigate Problem 2

Write each product as a power.

3(3) 1(1)(1) 5(5)(5)(5)

2. **Just the Math: Order of Operations** When finding the 10th term of a sequence, you may have used the **order of operations.** These rules ensure that the result of combining numbers and operations, such as addition and multiplication, is the same every time.

Order of Operations

1. Evaluate expressions inside grouping symbols such as ( ) or [ ].
2. Evaluate powers.
3. Multiply and divide from left to right.
4. Add and subtract from left to right.

Perform the indicated operations. Show your work.

$22 - 3(4)$ $9(3) + 2(4)$ $30 - 4^2$

$2^3 + 4(5)$ $(7 - 3)5 - 2^2$ $8(5) - 3(2 + 5)$

3. Suppose that you will have 80 cubes for the street fair and each cube is 9 inches wide, 9 inches long, and 9 inches tall. Write an expression for the number of cubic inches of sand that you will need for the fair.

Find the value of the expression and use a complete sentence to describe the amount of sand that you will need.

1.3 Dinner with the Stars

Finding the *n*th Term of a Sequence

1

Objectives

In this lesson, you will:

- Write numerical and algebraic expressions.
- Evaluate algebraic expressions.
- Use the *n*th term to write the terms of sequences.

Key Terms

- numerical expression
- algebraic expression
- variable
- evaluate
- value
- coefficient
- *n*th term

SCENARIO Your school is planning a charity dinner where people eat with local celebrities. Your job is to find a caterer to provide the meal, have invitations printed and mailed, buy and set up decorations in the dining area, and provide door prizes to be awarded during the dinner.

Problem 1 Catering Costs

A. The caterer gives you the dinner costs based on the number of people attending the event. You can represent the total catering cost for different numbers of people with the sequence 22, 44, 66, ...

Number of people	1	2	3	4
Total catering cost (dollars)	22	44	66	88

What is the total catering cost if 5 people attend the event? Use a complete sentence to explain your answer.

What is the total catering cost if 10 people attend the event? Use a complete sentence to explain your answer.

Use a complete sentence to describe the mathematical process that is being repeated to find the total catering cost.

B. Just the Math: Expressions Whenever we perform the same mathematical process over and over again, we can write a mathematical phrase, called an *expression,* to represent the situation. A **numerical expression** consists of numbers and operations to be performed. An **algebraic expression** consists of numbers, variables, and operators. A **variable** is a letter or symbol that can represent one or more numbers.

In part (A), you described a process for finding the total catering cost. You can write an algebraic expression for this process. Let the variable *n* represent the number of people that attend the event. What algebraic expression can you write to represent the total catering cost in dollars if *n* people attend?

Total catering cost in dollars for *n* people:

Take Note

Common names for variables are *x* and *y*. All other letters except for *e*, *i*, *l*, *I* and *O* can be used as variables.

1

Investigate Problem 1

1. You mail invitations for the charity dinner. You spend $20 on invitations. You also spend $0.39 for a stamp on each invitation.

   Write the sequence of numbers that represents the total cost of mailing 10, 20, 30, 40, and 50 invitations, and so on.

   Use a complete sentence to describe the mathematical process that is being repeated to find the total mailing cost.

   Write an expression to find the total mailing cost for different numbers of invitations plus the $20 cost of the invitations.

   Total mailing cost in dollars for 1 invitation:

   Total mailing cost in dollars for 2 invitations:

   Total mailing cost in dollars for 3 invitations:

   Write an expression for the total mailing cost for n invitations.

2. **Just the Math: Evaluating Expressions** You can use the expression from Question 1 to find the total mailing cost for any number of invitations. To do this, you can **evaluate** the expression by first replacing the variable with a number and then finding the **value** of the expression. For instance, evaluate the expression $0.39n$ when n is 100 to find the total cost of mailing 100 invitations.

   0.39(____) + 20 = ____ + 20 = _____

   It will cost _____ to mail 100 invitations.

   Evaluate each expression for the given value of the variable.

   Evaluate $p - 16$ when p is 20. Evaluate $\frac{b}{3}$ when b is 18.

   Evaluate $3c - 1$ when c is 2. Evaluate $5d + 2$ when d is 0.

Take Note

When a variable is multiplied by a number, the number is called the **coefficient.** For instance, in the algebraic expression $0.37n$, 0.37 is the coefficient of n.

Investigate Problem 1

3. You decorate by placing one large decoration at the entrance of the dining area and one decoration on each dining table. The large decoration costs $40 and each table decoration costs $20. The total decorating cost for different numbers of tables can be modeled by a sequence.

Number of dining tables	1	2	3	4	5
Total decorating cost (dollars)	60	80			

Write an expression for the total decorating cost for different numbers of dining tables. Then complete the table above.

Total decorating cost in dollars with 3 dining tables:

Total decorating cost in dollars with 4 dining tables:

Total decorating cost in dollars with 5 dining tables:

Write an expression for the total decorating cost when n dining tables are needed.

4. You will also give away door prizes at the charity dinner. You will do this by taping numbered slips of paper underneath some of the chairs. The chairs all have identification numbers stamped on them. You use a sequence to determine the chairs on which you will tape the slips of paper. The sequence you use is shown in the table.

Paper slip number	1	2	3	4	5
Chair ID number	5	16	27	38	49

Write an expression for the chair number in terms of the paper slip number.

Chair ID number for paper slip 6:

Chair ID number for paper slip 7:

Chair ID number for paper slip 8:

Write an expression for the chair number for paper slip n.

Take Note

Whenever you see the share with the class icon, your group should prepare a short presentation to share with the class that describes how you solved the problem. Be prepared to ask questions during other groups' presentations and to answer questions during your presentation.

1

Investigate Problem 1

5. Just the Math: *n*th Term In Questions 1, 3, and 4, you wrote expressions in terms of n for each sequence. Each expression is called the ***n*th term** of the sequence, represented by a_n. You can use the nth term to *generate* the terms of a sequence. Complete each statement to find the first five terms of the sequence given by $a_n = 7n$.

First term: $a_1 = 7(1) = 7$

Second term: $a_2 = 7(2) =$ ____

Third term: $a_3 =$ ____ $=$ ____

Fourth term: $a_4 =$ ____ $=$ ____

Fifth term: $a_5 =$ ____ $=$ ____

6. Use the nth term to list the first five terms of each sequence. Show all your work.

$a_n = 10n$

$a_n = \frac{1}{2}n$

$a_n = n + 8$

$a_n = 14 - n$

$a_n = 4n - 3$

$a_n = 3n + 1$

1.4 Working for the CIA

Using a Sequence to Represent a Problem Situation

Objectives

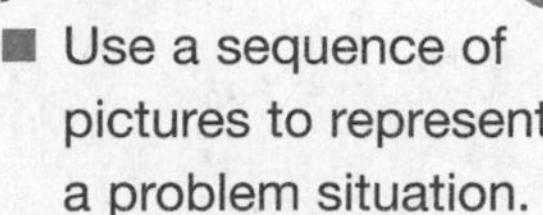

In this lesson, you will:

- Use a sequence of pictures to represent a problem situation.
- Use a sequence of numbers to represent a problem situation.
- Solve a problem by first solving a simpler problem.

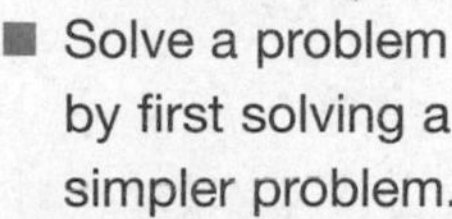

Key Term

- expression

SCENARIO The Central Intelligence Agency (CIA) headquarters in Langley, Virginia, employs scientists, engineers, economists, linguists, mathematicians, secretaries, accountants, and computer specialists. You want to work for the CIA someday.

Problem 1 Pathways Problem

Suppose that there is a plan to build a new complex of buildings at the CIA headquarters. The plan requires that every building be directly connected to every other building by a pathway.

A. You can draw a diagram to help you solve this problem. Use the figures below to determine the number of pathways that are needed to connect 2 buildings, 3 buildings, and 4 buildings.

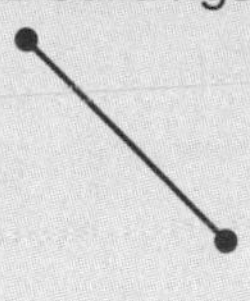

2 buildings

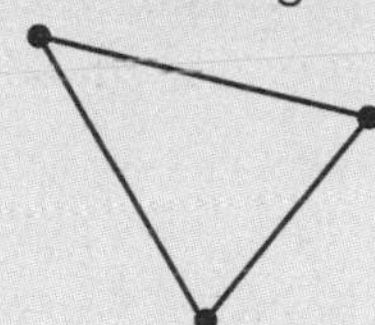

3 buildings

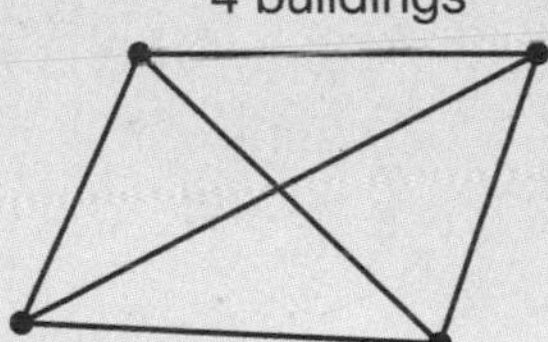

4 buildings

B. Draw diagrams that represent the pathways needed to connect 5 buildings, 6 buildings, and 7 buildings. In each case, determine the number of pathways that are needed.

C. Complete the table below to show your results so far.

Number of buildings	2	3	4	5	6	7
Number of pathways						

1

Investigate Problem 1

1. How many pathways will be needed if there are 8 buildings? Use a complete sentence to write your answer.

   How many pathways will be needed if there are 10 buildings? Use a complete sentence to write your answer.

2. Would it be difficult to find the number of pathways needed if there are 25 buildings? Use complete sentences to explain.

3. Suppose that the CIA wants to have 6 buildings in the complex. How many pathways are needed to connect the first building to the other buildings?

   How many pathways are needed to connect the second building to the other buildings, not including any of the pathways already counted?

   How many pathways are needed to connect the third building to the other buildings, not including any of the pathways already counted?

   How many pathways are needed to connect the fourth building to the other buildings, not including any of the pathways already counted?

   How many pathways are needed to connect the fifth building to the other buildings, not including any of the pathways already counted?

   How many pathways are needed to connect the sixth building to the other buildings, not including any of the pathways already counted?

4. Use the information in Question 3 to write a numerical expression for the number of pathways needed for 6 buildings.

Take Note

Whenever you see the share with the class icon, your group should prepare a short presentation to share with the class that describes how you solved the problem. Be prepared to ask questions during other groups' presentations and to answer questions during your presentation.

Investigate Problem 1

5. Write each number in Question 3 in terms of 6, the number of buildings. For instance: $5 = 6 - 1$.

6. Use the results of Questions 4 and 5 to write a numerical expression in terms of 6 for the number of pathways needed for 6 buildings.

7. Use the result of Question 6 to write an expression for the number of pathways needed for *n* buildings. Then check your expression by verifying the results of Question 1.

Problem 2 Telephone Network Problem

You have been hired by the CIA to design a secure telephone network. The network must be set up so that every person is connected to every other person by a direct line. Your task is to determine the number of different lines that will be needed for different numbers of employees.

A. Use the figures below to determine the number of lines that you need to connect a set of 2 employees, 3 employees, and 4 employees.

2 employees 3 employees 4 employees

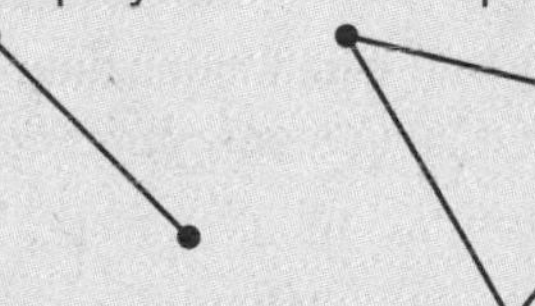

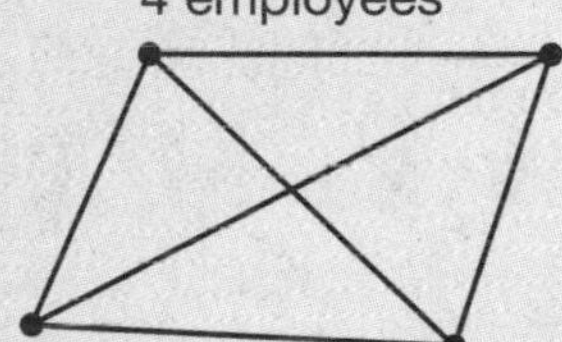

B. Draw figures that represent the number of lines needed for 5 employees, 6 employees, and 7 employees. In each case, determine the number of lines that are needed.

C. Complete the table below to show your results so far.

Number of employees	2	3	4	5	6	7
Number of lines						

1

Investigate Problem 2

1. How many lines does it take to connect 9 employees? Use a complete sentence in your answer.

   How many lines does it take to connect 11 employees? Use a complete sentence in your answer.

2. Would it be difficult to find the number of lines needed for 30 employees? Use a complete sentence to explain why or why not.

3. Suppose that the CIA wants to set up a telephone network for 5 employees. How many direct lines are required for the first person?

   How many direct lines are required for the second person, not including any of the lines already counted?

   How many direct lines are required for the third person, not including any of the lines already counted?

   How many direct lines are required for the fourth person, not including any of the lines already counted?

   How many direct lines are required for the fifth person, not including any of the lines already counted?

4. Use the information in Question 3 to write a numerical expression for the number of lines required for 5 employees.

5. Write each number in Question 3 in terms of 5, the number of employees. For instance, $4 = 5 - 1$.

6. Use the results of Questions 4 and 5 to write a numerical expression in terms of 5 for the number of lines required for 5 employees.

7. Use the result of Question 6 to write an expression for the number of lines required for n employees. Then check your expression by verifying the results of Question 1.

Problem 3 Handshake Problem

Suppose that there is a monthly meeting at CIA headquarters for all employees. How many handshakes will it take for every employee at the meeting to shake the hand of every other employee at the meeting once?

A. Use the figures below to determine the number of handshakes that will occur between 2 employees, 3 employees, and 4 employees.

2 employees

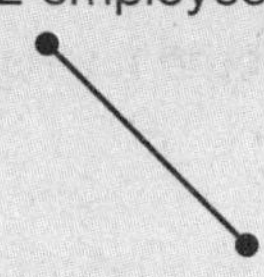

3 employees

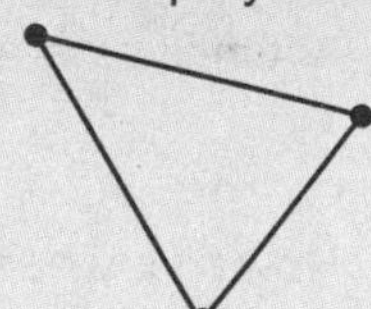

4 employees

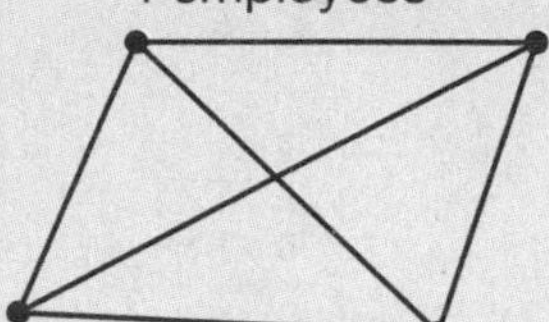

B. Draw figures that represent the number of handshakes that occur between 5 employees, 6 employees, and 7 employees and determine the number of handshakes that will occur in each situation.

C. Complete the table to show your results so far.

Number of employees	2	3	4	5	6	7
Number of handshakes						

Investigate Problem 3

1. How many handshakes will occur between 12 employees? Use a complete sentence to write your answer.

   How many handshakes will occur between 13 employees? Use a complete sentence to write your answer.

2. Would it be difficult to find the number of handshakes that occur between 45 employees? Use complete sentences to explain.

1

Investigate Problem 3

3. Suppose that there are 7 employees at the meeting. How many handshakes will the first person make?

   How many handshakes occur with the second person, not including any of the handshakes already counted?

   How many handshakes occur with the third person, not including any of the handshakes already counted?

   How many handshakes occur with the fourth person, not including any of the handshakes already counted?

   How many handshakes occur with the fifth person, not including any of the handshakes already counted?

   How many handshakes occur with the sixth person, not including any of the handshakes already counted?

   How many handshakes occur with the seventh person, not including any of the handshakes already counted?

4. Use the information in Question 3 to write a numerical expression for the number of handshakes that occur between 7 employees.

5. Write each number in Question 3 in terms of 7, the number of employees. For instance, $6 = 7 - 1$.

6. Use the results of Questions 4 and 5 to write a numerical expression for the number for handshakes that occur between 7 employees.

7. Use the result of Question 6 to write an expression for the number of handshakes that occur between n employees. Then check your expression by verifying the results of Question 1.

1.5 Gauss's Formula

Finding the Sum of a Finite Sequence

Objectives

In this lesson, you will:

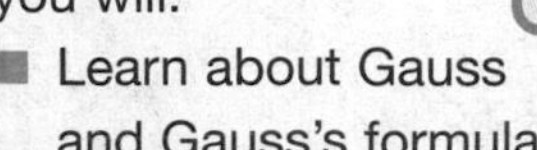

- Learn about Gauss and Gauss's formula.

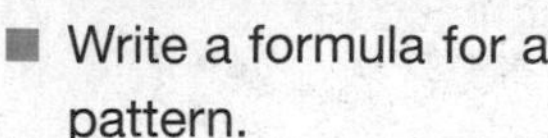

- Write a formula for a pattern.
- Solve a problem by first solving a simpler problem.

Key Terms

- sum
- expression

SCENARIO Carl Friedrich Gauss was perhaps the world's greatest mathematician. When Carl was in third grade, his teacher was annoyed with him because he finished his lessons too quickly. The teacher gave him the problem below to solve, because the teacher thought that it would take Carl a long time to find the answer.

Add the numbers from 1 through 100.

As Carl walked back to his desk, he immediately found the answer. How did he do it?

Problem 1 Solve a Simpler Problem

A. Consider the **sum** below, which is the sum of the numbers from 1 through 9, written twice. Find the total sum of all of the numbers. To do this, first add the numbers in each column.

$$\begin{array}{r} 9 + 8 + 7 + 6 + 5 + 4 + 3 + 2 + 1 \\ \underline{+\ 1 + 2 + 3 + 4 + 5 + 6 + 7 + 8 + 9} \end{array}$$

What do you notice about the arrangement of the numbers?

What is the relationship between the total sum and the sum of the numbers from 1 through 9? Use a complete sentence in your answer.

How can you find the sum of the numbers from 1 through 9? Use a complete sentence in your answer.

B. The method in part (A) is the method that Gauss used. Use this method to find the sum of the numbers from 1 through 20. Show all your work.

Investigate Problem 1

1. Complete the statement: The sum of the numbers from 1 through 20 can be written as

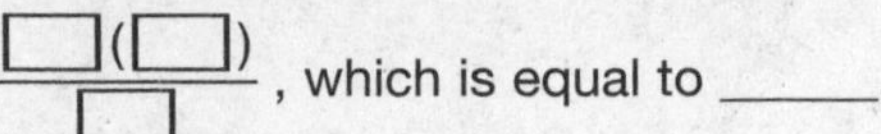

, which is equal to ______.

2. What is the sum of the numbers from 1 through 50? Show all your work.

3. What is the sum of the numbers from 1 through 100? Show all your work.

4. Write an expression for the sum of the numbers from 1 through n.

5. In Lesson 1.4, you discovered a formula for finding the number of pathways required to connect n buildings, the number of phone lines required to connect n people, and the number of handshakes that occur between n people. Is the sum of the numbers from 1 through 100 the same as the number of pathways required to connect 100 buildings? Why or why not? Use complete sentences in your answer.

Take Note

Whenever you see the share with the class icon, your group should prepare a short presentation to share with the class that describes how you solved the problem. Be prepared to ask questions during other groups' presentations and to answer questions during your presentation.

Problem-Solving Strategies Finding a Pattern

Finding and generalizing patterns is an important problem-solving strategy. Even though the problem situations in Lesson 1.4 were different, they represented the same mathematical problem. To find the patterns in this lesson and Lesson 1.4, you completed the following steps:

- First, you considered a similar problem with smaller numbers.
- Then you looked for a pattern to help you predict the answer for larger numbers.
- Next, you wrote an expression to model the pattern for any number n.
- Finally, you used the expression to find the result for any number.

The ability to model a variety of situations will continue to be an important part of this course.

1.6 $8 an Hour Problem

Using Multiple Representations, Part 1

1

Objectives

In this lesson, you will:

- Investigate different representations for problem situations.
- Determine values from graphs.
- Write equations.
- Identify variable quantities.

Key Terms

- labels
- units
- bar graph
- bounds
- graph
- algebraic equation
- solution

SCENARIO You are looking for a part-time job. Pat-E-Oh Furniture is hiring furniture assemblers. The job, to remove furniture parts from shipping containers and assemble furniture, pays $8 an hour. After your interview, the company offers you the job and you decide to take it.

Problem 1 Earnings at Pat-E-Oh Furniture

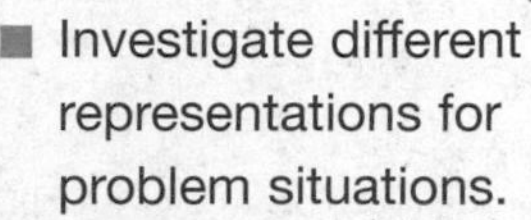

A. During the summer, you can work eight hours per day for 5 days each week. How much money will you earn after one week of work? Use a complete sentence in your answer.

B. During the school year, you can only work 4 hours each day. How much money will you earn after one day? Use a complete sentence in your answer.

C. You want to buy a bicycle for $372. If you save every cent you earn, how many hours must you work in order to make enough money to buy the bicycle? Use a complete sentence to explain how you found your answer.

D. If you save only half of the money you earn, how many hours must you work to make enough money to buy the bicycle? Use a complete sentence to explain how you found your answer.

If you could work 6 hours each day, how many days would it take you to earn enough money to buy the bicycle? Use a complete sentence to explain how you found your answer.

1

Investigate Problem 1

1. You can keep track of the amount of money that you earn in a table. Whenever you create a table, begin by creating a row of **labels** that contains written descriptions for each column of numbers. You should also include a row of **units** that identifies the standard measurements in which each column of numbers is measured.

   The table below shows the number of hours that you have worked for the first five weeks on the job. Complete the table. Copy the dollar values into the table on page 28.

Quantity Name	**Week**	**Time worked**	**Earnings**
Unit		**hours**	**dollars**
	Week 1	11.5	
	Week 2	20	
	Week 3	16	
	Week 4	10	
	Week 5	9.5	

   Use a complete sentence to explain how you found your earnings for each week.

Use the information in the table to answer Questions 2 through 5.

2. During which week did you earn the greatest amount of money? Use a complete sentence in your answer.

   During which week did you earn the least amount of money? Use a complete sentence in your answer.

3. How much more money did you earn during Week 2 than during Week 3? Use a complete sentence in your answer.

4. How much money did you earn during the first five weeks on the job? Use a complete sentence in your answer.

Take Note

Recall that to find the average of a set of numbers, find the sum of the numbers and divide the sum by the number of elements in the set.

Take Note

Whenever you see the share with the class icon, your group should prepare a short presentation to share with the class that describes how you solved the problem. Be prepared to ask questions during other groups' presentations and to answer questions during your presentation.

Investigate Problem 1

1

5. What were your average earnings per week?

How did you find your answer? Use a complete sentence to explain.

6. Use the space below to create a **bar graph** of the data from the table in Question 1. The bar graph should display the earnings for each week. Clearly label the graph and add a title.

(label) (units)

7. What information can you determine immediately from the bar graph?

8. Can you use the bar graph to determine the number of hours that you need to work to earn $100? Use complete sentences to explain.

9. What information does a bar graph illustrate well? Use complete sentences to explain.

10. What information does a bar graph not illustrate well? Use complete sentences to explain.

1

Investigate Problem 1

11. Create a **graph** of the data in the second and third columns of the table in Question 1. First, set the **bounds** of the graph. The *lower and upper bounds* determine the portion of the graph that you will see.

    The data that you are graphing should be greater than the lower bounds and less than the upper bounds. Decide whether this is true for the bounds chosen below. Use complete sentences to explain your decision.

Week	Time worked	Earnings
	hours	dollars
1	11.5	
2	20	
3	16	
4	10	
5	9.5	

12. Use the grid and the numbers in the "Interval" column to write a sentence that describes an interval.

13. Use the bounds and intervals to label the grid below. Then create a graph of the data from the table in Question 1.

Variable quantity	Lower bound	Upper bound	Interval
Time worked	0	30	2
Earnings	0	300	20

(label) (units)

(label) (units)

Take Note

In order for someone to better understand a graph that you create, you may want to add a title to your graph. The title should describe what the graph is showing.

Take Note

When you approximate, you find a result that is nearly, but not exactly, the value.

Investigate Problem 1

Use the graph to answer the following questions.

14. Approximate the amount of money that you would earn if you worked 10 hours. Use a complete sentence to explain how you found your answer.

Approximate the amount of money that you would earn if you worked 22 hours. Use a complete sentence to explain how you found your answer.

Approximate the amount of money that you would earn if you worked $3\frac{1}{2}$ hours. Use a complete sentence to explain how you found your answer.

Are any of your answers in Question 14 exact answers? Use complete sentences to explain your reasoning.

15. In this problem situation, what information does the graph illustrate well? Use a complete sentence in your answer.

16. Use the graph to determine whether there is a number pattern in this problem. If there is a pattern, use complete sentences to describe the pattern.

1

Investigate Problem 1

17. Write an expression that you can use to find the earnings for any number of hours worked. Let h represent the number of hours worked. Use a complete sentence in your answer.

18. You want to determine your exact earnings for 40 hours of work. Would you use your graph or the expression in Question 17? Use complete sentences to explain your reasoning.

19. Just the Math: Writing Equations In Question 17, you wrote an algebraic expression to represent the earnings for any number of hours of work. You can also write an *algebraic equation* to generalize a problem situation. You can create an **algebraic equation** by writing an equals sign (=) between two algebraic expressions.

In this problem situation, suppose the earnings are \$120. Write an algebraic equation for this situation by using the expression that you wrote in Question 17.

Suppose the earnings are \$200. Write an algebraic equation for this situation by using the expression that you wrote in Question 17.

20. Just the Math: Solutions of Equations When you replace the variable in an equation with a number, you create a statement that is either true or false. If you create a true statement, the number that you used is a **solution** of the equation. Replace the variable in the equation $200 = 8h$ with the number 25. Then decide whether 25 is a solution of the equation $200 = 8h$. Show all your work. Write a complete sentence that explains your answer.

Decide whether the value of the variable is a solution of the equation.

$225 = 5x$	$204 = 32w$	$108 = 12c$
$x = 45$	$w = 6$	$c = 9$

1.7 The Consultant Problem

Using Multiple Representations, Part 2

Objectives

In this lesson, you will:

- Use different methods to represent a problem situation.
- Determine a value from a graph.
- Convert units of measure.
- Write an equation in one variable.
- Write an equation in two variables.

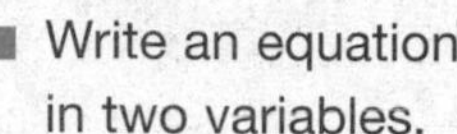

- Identify independent and dependent variables.

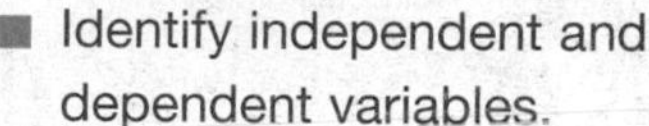

Key Terms

- dependent variable
- independent variable

SCENARIO Your aunt works as an architectural consultant, advising a variety of companies on building design. She recently opened her own firm. As is typical with any consulting firm, your aunt charges her customers for each hour that she works on a project. During the last two months, your aunt worked on four projects. She earns $112.75 for each hour that she works.

Problem 1 Project Earnings

A. Your aunt's first project was for the company USY. It took her 31 hours to complete the project. How much money did she earn for this project? Use a complete sentence to explain how you found your answer.

B. Her second project was for the company TTG. It took her 23 hours to complete the project. How much money did she earn for this project? Use a complete sentence to explain how you found your answer.

C. Her third project was for the Barbara Hanna Company. It took her 39 hours to complete the project. How much money did she earn for this project? Use a complete sentence to explain how you found your answer.

D. Her fourth project was for the company ALCOM. It took her 19 hours to complete the project. How much money did she earn for this project? Use a complete sentence to explain how you found your answer.

Investigate Problem 1

1. Keep track of the amount of money that your aunt earned by using your results from Problem 1 to complete the table below with the number of hours she worked on each project and the amount of money she earned.

Quantity Name	Project		
Unit			
	USY		
	TTG		
	Barbara Hanna Company		
	ALCOM		

Use a complete sentence to explain how you found the earnings for each project.

2. Your aunt wants to buy a car that costs $33,000. Has she earned enough money from all four projects to buy the car? Use complete sentences to explain how you found your answer.

3. On which project did your aunt earn the greatest amount of money? Use a complete sentence in your answer.

On which project did your aunt earn the least amount of money? Use a complete sentence in your answer.

4. How much more money did your aunt earn from working on the Barbara Hanna Company project than on the USY project? Use a complete sentence in your answer.

Investigate Problem 1

5. Use the grid below to create a graph of the data from the table in Question 1. First, use the table to help you choose the upper and lower bounds. What is the least number of hours that your aunt could work? What is the greatest number of hours that your aunt has worked? Add these bounds to the table below.

What are the least and greatest amounts of money that your aunt has earned? Add an upper bound for earnings of 4500 to the table below.

Find the difference between the upper and lower bounds for each quantity. Then choose an interval that divides evenly into this number. This will ensure even spacing between the grid lines. Add these intervals to the table below.

Variable quantity	Lower bound	Upper bound	Interval
Time worked			
Earnings			

6. Use the bounds and intervals to label the grid below. Then create a graph of the data from the table in Question 1 on the grid.

Take Note

Remember to label your graph clearly and add a title to the graph.

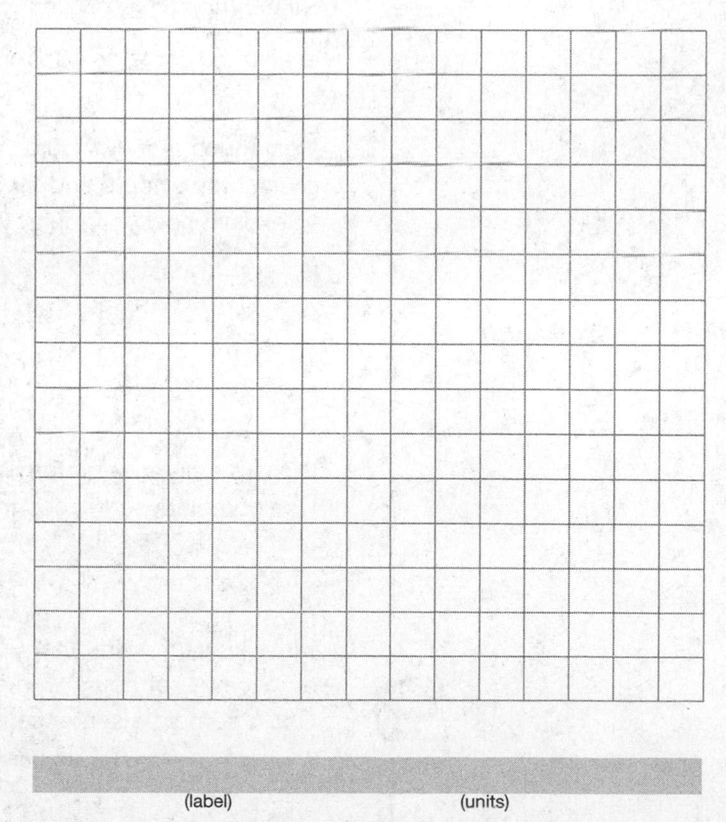

1

1

Investigate Problem 1

Use the graph to answer Questions 7 and 8.

7. Approximately how much money would your aunt earn if she worked on a project for 10 hours? Use a complete sentence in your answer.

   Approximately how much money would your aunt earn if she worked on a project for 22 hours? Use a complete sentence in your answer.

   Approximately how much money would your aunt earn if she worked on a project for 5 hours and 15 minutes? Use a complete sentence in your answer.

8. **Just the Math: Changing Units of Measure** Whenever you are solving a problem that involves units for time, distance, and so on, all similar measurements should be in the same units. For instance, four hours and 45 minutes is the same as 4.75 hours because $4 + \frac{45}{60} = 4.75$. Four hours and 45 minutes is also the same as 285 minutes because $4(60) + 45 = 285$.

   How much money would your aunt earn if she worked on a project for 6 hours and 20 minutes? Use complete sentences to explain how you found your answer.

9. Is there a number pattern in your table in Question 1? Use complete sentences to explain your reasoning.

10. Write an expression that you could use to find the earnings for any number of hours worked. Let h represent the time worked. Use a complete sentence in your answer.

Investigate Problem 1

Suppose that your aunt earned $112.75. Write an algebraic equation for this situation by using the expression that you wrote on the previous page.

Suppose that your aunt earned $225.50. Write an algebraic equation for this situation.

Suppose that your aunt earned $563.75. Write an algebraic equation for this situation.

Suppose that your aunt earned $1691.25. Write an algebraic equation for this situation.

In the previous equations, identify the numbers that change from equation to equation. What do these numbers represent? Use a complete sentence in your answer.

11. From Question 10, you should see that the time worked and the earnings change; that is, they are variable quantities. So, we can write an equation in *two variables* that you can use to find the earnings for any number of hours worked and to find the number of hours worked for any amount of earnings. Let E represent the earnings in dollars. Write an equation that relates E and h for this problem situation. Use a complete sentence in your answer.

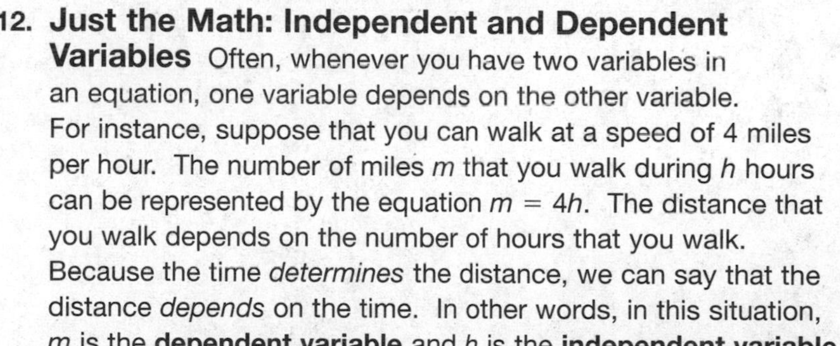

12. Just the Math: Independent and Dependent Variables Often, whenever you have two variables in an equation, one variable depends on the other variable. For instance, suppose that you can walk at a speed of 4 miles per hour. The number of miles m that you walk during h hours can be represented by the equation $m = 4h$. The distance that you walk depends on the number of hours that you walk. Because the time *determines* the distance, we can say that the distance *depends* on the time. In other words, in this situation, m is the **dependent variable** and h is the **independent variable.**

Determine which of the variable quantities in your equation in Question 11 depends on the other. Use complete sentences to explain your reasoning.

Identify the independent and dependent variables in your equation. Use a complete sentence in your answer.

Take Note

Whenever you see the share with the class icon, your group should prepare a short presentation to share with the class that describes how you solved the problem. Be prepared to ask questions during other groups' presentations and to answer questions during your presentation.

1.8

U.S. Shirts

Using Tables, Graphs, and Equations, Part 1

1

Objectives

In this lesson, you will:

- Use different methods to represent a problem situation.
- Determine an initial value when given a final result.
- Identify the advantages and disadvantages of using a particular representation.

Key Terms

- independent variable
- dependent variable

SCENARIO This past summer you were hired to work at a custom T-shirt shop, U.S. Shirts.

Problem 1 Cost Analysis

A. One of your responsibilities is to find the total cost of customers' orders. The shop charges $8 per shirt plus a one-time charge of $15 to set up the T-shirt design. Use complete sentences to describe the problem situation in your own words.

B. How does this problem situation differ from the problem situations in Lesson 1.6 and Lesson 1.7? Use a complete sentence in your answer.

C. What is the total cost of an order for 3 shirts? Use a complete sentence in your answer.

What is the total cost of an order for 10 shirts? Use a complete sentence in your answer.

What is the total cost of an order for 100 shirts? Use a complete sentence in your answer.

D. Use complete sentences to explain how you found the total costs.

1

Investigate Problem 1

1. A customer has $50 to spend on T-shirts. How many shirts can the customer buy? Use a complete sentence in your answer.

   A customer has $60 to spend on T-shirts. How many shirts can the customer buy? Use a complete sentence in your answer.

   A customer has $220 to spend on T-shirts. How many shirts can the customer buy? Use a complete sentence in your answer.

   Use complete sentences to explain how you found the number of shirts that can be ordered.

2. Complete the table of values for the problem situation.

Quantity Name	Number of shirts ordered	Total cost
Unit	shirts	dollars

Investigate Problem 1

1

3. What are the variable quantities in this problem situation? Assign letters to represent these quantities including each quantity's units. Use a complete sentence in your answer.

4. What are the constant quantities in this problem situation? Include the units that are used to measure these quantities. Use a complete sentence in your answer.

5. Which variable quantity depends on the other variable quantity?

6. Which of the variables from Question 3 is the independent variable and which is the dependent variable?

7. Use the grid below to create a graph of the data from the table in Question 2. First, choose your bounds and intervals.

Variable quantity	Lower bound	Upper bound	Interval
Number of shirts			
Total cost			

(label) (units)

(label) (units)

Take Note

Remember to label your graph clearly and add a title to the graph.

1

Investigate Problem 1

8. Write an algebraic equation for the problem situation. Use a complete sentence in your answer.

9. In this lesson, you have represented the problem situation in four different ways: as a sentence, as a table, as a graph, and as an equation. Explain the advantages and disadvantages of each representation by writing a paragraph. Use complete sentences. Be prepared to share your answers with the class.

Take Note

Whenever you see the share with the class icon, your group should prepare a short presentation to share with the class that describes how you solved the problem. Be prepared to ask questions during other groups' presentations and to answer questions during your presentation.

1.9 Hot Shirts

Using Tables, Graphs, and Equations, Part 2

1

Objectives

In this lesson, you will:

- Use different methods to represent a problem situation.
- Estimate values of expressions that involve decimals.
- Determine an initial value when given a final result.

Key Term

- estimation

SCENARIO In Lesson 1.8, you explored a job at U.S. Shirts. One of U.S. Shirt's competitors, Hot Shirts, advertises that they make custom T-shirts for $5.50 each with a one-time set-up fee of $49.95.

Problem 1 Analyzing the Competition

A. Your boss brings you the advertisement from Hot Shirts and asks you to figure out how the competition might affect business. Use complete sentences to describe the problem situation in your own words.

B. What is the total cost of an order for 3 shirts from Hot Shirts? Use a complete sentence in your answer.

What is the total cost of an order for 10 shirts from Hot Shirts? Use a complete sentence in your answer.

What is the total cost of an order for 50 shirts from Hot Shirts? Use a complete sentence in your answer.

What is the total cost of an order for 100 shirts from Hot Shirts? Use a complete sentence in your answer.

C. Use complete sentences to explain how you found the total costs.

1

Investigate Problem 1

1. **Just the Math: Estimation** When you do not need to know the exact value of an expression, you can use **estimation** to find the approximate value. One way to estimate is to use rounding.

   For instance, to estimate the difference of 125.35 and 84.95, you could round each number to the nearest whole number and subtract. So, round 125.35 down to 125 and round 84.95 up to 85. Then find the difference of 125 and 85. In this way, you can estimate the difference of 125.35 and 84.95 to be approximately equal to $125 - 85 = 40$. You can write this as $125.35 - 84.95 \approx 40$. The symbol $\approx$ means "is approximately equal to."

   Estimate the value of each expression.

   $748.75 + 60.22$　　　　$345 - 214$　　　　45.13×20.44

2. Estimate the number of shirts that a customer can purchase from Hot Shirts for \$50. Use a complete sentence in your answer.

   Estimate the number of shirts that a customer can purchase from Hot Shirts for \$60. Use a complete sentence in your answer.

   Estimate the number of shirts that a customer can purchase from Hot Shirts for \$220. Use a complete sentence in your answer.

3. Use complete sentences to explain how you estimated the number of shirts that can be purchased.

4. Complete the table of values on the next page for the problem situation.

Investigate Problem 1

Quantity Name	Number of shirts ordered	Total cost
Unit	shirts	dollars

5. Use the grid below to create a graph of the data from the table in Question 4. First, choose your bounds and intervals.

Variable quantity	Lower bound	Upper bound	Interval
Number of shirts			
Total cost			

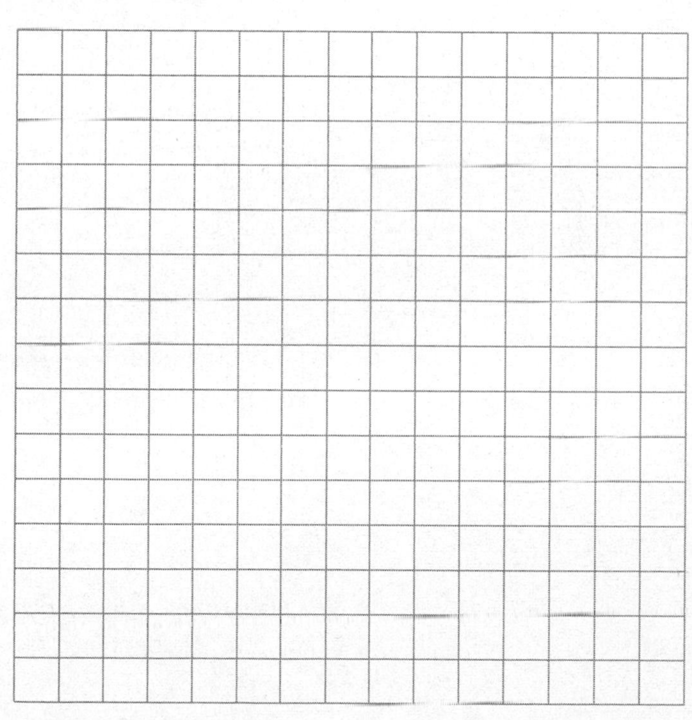

Take Note

Remember to label your graph clearly and add a title to the graph.

Take Note

Whenever you see the share with the class icon, your group should prepare a short presentation to share with the class that describes how you solved the problem. Be prepared to ask questions during other groups' presentations and to answer questions during your presentation.

6. Write an algebraic equation for the problem situation.

1.10 Comparing U.S. Shirts and Hot Shirts

Comparing Problem Situations Algebraically and Graphically

1

Objectives

In this lesson, you will:

- Compare two problem situations algebraically.
- Compare two problem situations graphically.

Key Term

- point of intersection

SCENARIO In Lessons 1.8 and 1.9, you explored the costs of ordering T-shirts from two companies, U.S. Shirts and Hot Shirts.

Problem 1 Which Is the Better Buy?

A. Your boss asks you to determine which company has the better price for T-shirts in different situations. For an order of fewer than five shirts, is U.S. Shirts or Hot Shirts the better buy? What would each charge for exactly five shirts? Use complete sentences in your answer.

Use a complete sentence to describe how you found your answer.

B. For an order of 18 shirts, which company's price is better? How much better is the price? Use complete sentences in your answer.

Use complete sentences to describe how you found your answer.

C. For an order of 80 shirts, which company's price is better? How much better is the price? Use complete sentences in your answer.

Use a complete sentence to describe how you found your answer.

1

Investigate Problem 1

1. Use the grid below to draw the graphs for the total cost for U.S. Shirts and Hot Shirts. Use the bounds and intervals shown in the table below.

Variable quantity	Lower bound	Upper bound	Interval
Number of shirts	0	150	10
Total cost	0	1500	100

2. Estimate the number of T-shirts for which the total costs are the same. Use a complete sentence in your answer.

   Use a complete sentence to explain how you found the number of T-shirts.

3. For how many T-shirts is U.S. Shirts more expensive to order from? Use a complete sentence in your answer.

Investigate Problem 1

4. For how many T-shirts is Hot Shirts more expensive to order from? Use a complete sentence in your answer.

5. Look back to your graph on the previous page. Use complete sentences to describe the graphs in your own words.

Notice that the graphs *intersect* at about (14, 127). This **point of intersection** indicates where the total cost for each company is the same. So, when U.S. Shirts sells 14 shirts, the total cost is \$127 and when Hot Shirts sells 14 shirts, the total cost is \$127. You will learn more about finding points of intersection in Chaper 7.

6. Write a report for your boss that compares the costs of ordering from each company. Try to answer your boss's question, "Will Hot Shirts' prices affect the business at U.S. Shirts?"

Take Note

Whenever you see the share with the class icon, your group should prepare a short presentation to share with the class that describes how you solved the problem. Be prepared to ask questions during other groups' presentations and to answer questions during your presentation.

1

Looking Ahead to Chapter 2

Focus In Chapter 2, you will learn how to use ratios, rates, and proportions to solve problems. You will use proportions in similar triangles to find measurements indirectly and use proportions to solve percent problems. You will also develop an understanding of the direct variation relationship between two quantities.

Chapter Warm-up

Answer these questions to help you review skills that you will need in Chapter 2.

2

Use mental math to solve each equation.

1. $4x = 36$
2. $6x = 42$
3. $8x = 96$
4. $10x = 110$
5. $14x = 84$
6. $13x = 39$

In each pair of fractions, determine the fraction that is greater.

7. $\frac{2}{3}, \frac{5}{6}$
8. $\frac{7}{10}, \frac{3}{5}$
9. $\frac{3}{8}, \frac{1}{3}$

Read the problem scenario below.

Shauna, Kevin, and Lee are avid sports fans who love hockey. They all collect sports cards and want to find out who has the largest collection of hockey cards. Seven-twelfths of Shauna's collection is hockey cards. One-fourth of Kevin's collection is hockey cards. Two-thirds of Lee's collection is hockey cards.

10. Write the fractions of the three sports fans' hockey cards in order from least to greatest.

11. Who has the smallest fraction of hockey cards in his or her collection?

12. Who has the largest fraction of hockey cards in his or her collection?

Key Terms

CHAPTER

2

Proportional Reasoning, Percents, and Direct Variation

2

It is not feasible to use a ladder and a tape measure to measure a very tall tree. But, you can use the shadow that is cast by the tree and mathematics to find the height. In Lesson 2.3, you will measure the height of a tree indirectly.

2

2.1 Left-Handed Learners

Using Samples, Ratios, and Proportions to Make Predictions

Objectives

In this lesson, you will:

- Write ratios.
- Write and solve proportions.
- Use a survey to make predictions.
- Identify biased samples.
- Identify sampling methods.

Key Terms

- sample
- ratio
- proportion
- means
- extremes
- biased
- randomly chosen
- sampling methods

SCENARIO You are writing a report about whether people use their right hand or their left hand to write and perform tasks. In the first part of your report, you will investigate the number of people in your school who are left-handed, right-handed, or ambidextrous (equally skillful with each hand).

Because you only have two weeks to complete the report, you cannot ask every person in the school which hand is his or her dominant hand. Instead, you can survey, or ask a portion of the students in your school, which hand is dominant. The students that you survey are a **sample** of the student population.

Problem 1 Survey Says

A. For this study, we will assume that there are the same number of students in each grade in your school. Choose ten students from each grade and ask them whether they are right-handed, left-handed, or ambidextrous. Record your results in the table below.

Grade	Number of left-handed students	Number of right-handed students	Number of ambidextrous students
Total number of students			

B. How many students did you survey? Use a complete sentence in your answer.

Investigate Problem 1

1. **Just the Math: Ratios** You can compare the results in your survey by using ratios. A **ratio** is a way to compare two quantities that are measured in the *same* units by using division. For instance, if you have 4 red marbles and 5 blue marbles, the ratio of red marbles to blue marbles is $\frac{\text{4 red marbles}}{\text{5 blue marbles}}$. You can also write this ratio by using a colon as 4 red marbles : 5 blue marbles.

   Write each ratio below by using division and by using a colon. Be sure to include units in your ratios.

   Write a ratio of the number of left-handed students to the total number of students surveyed.

   Write a ratio of the number of right-handed students to the total number of students surveyed.

   Write a ratio of the number of left-handed students to the number of right-handed students surveyed.

   Write a ratio of the number of ambidextrous students to the total number of students surveyed.

Take Note

Another way to write a ratio of two numbers is to use words. For instance, if you have 4 red marbles and 5 blue marbles, you can write the ratio as 4 red marbles to 5 blue marbles.

2

2. **Just the Math: Proportions** You can use the results of your survey and *proportions* to predict the number of left-handed, right-handed, and ambidextrous students there are in your school. A **proportion** is an equation that states that two ratios are equal. You write a proportion by placing an equals sign between two *equivalent* ratios. You can also write a proportion by placing a double colon in place of the equals sign.

   $\frac{\text{4 students}}{\text{8 students}} = \frac{\text{1 student}}{\text{2 students}}$ or

   4 students : 8 students :: 1 student : 2 students

   Complete the following proportions. Use complete sentences to explain how you found your results.

   $\frac{1}{4} = \frac{\square}{12}$ $\qquad$ $\frac{2}{3} = \frac{10}{\square}$ $\qquad$ $\frac{12}{32} = \frac{\square}{8}$

Take Note

Recall that two fractions are *equivalent* when they represent the same amount or quantity.

Investigate Problem 1

3. Just the Math: Means and Extremes When you completed the proportions in Question 2, you were *solving* them. Another way to solve a proportion is to use the proportion's *means and extremes.* In the proportion 4 students : 8 students :: 1 student : 2 students, the **means** are the quantities in the middle of the proportion (8 students and 1 student) and the **extremes** are the two quantities at the beginning and end of the proportion (4 students and 2 students).

Identify the means and extremes of the proportions in Question 2. Then, find the product of the means and the product of the extremes for each proportion. What do you notice? Use complete sentences to explain.

2

4. Assume that there are 120 students in your school. Complete the proportion below to find the number of left-handed students that are in your school. Let the variable x represent the number of left-handed students that are in your school.

$$\frac{\square \text{ left-handed students}}{40 \text{ students}} = \frac{x \text{ left-handed students}}{120 \text{ students}}$$

Complete the following, which states that the product of the means is equal to the product of the extremes.

$40x = \square(120)$

$40x = \square$

To solve the proportion, we need to find a number that we can multiply by 40 to get the product on the left of the equals sign, 1440. Use mental math to find this number.

$40x = \square$

$x = \square$

When we find the number, we have solved the proportion.

There should be about _____ left-handed students in the school.

Take Note

The property of proportions that states that the product of the means is equal to the product of the extremes is called the *Cross Product Property* of proportions.

Investigate Problem 1

5. Determine the actual number of students in your school. Then use proportions and the results of your survey to predict the number of left-handed, right-handed, and ambidextrous students that there are in your school. Show all your work and use complete sentences in your answer.

Take Note

Whenever you let a variable represent a quantity, it is a good idea to write a statement that indicates what quantity the variable stands for.

2

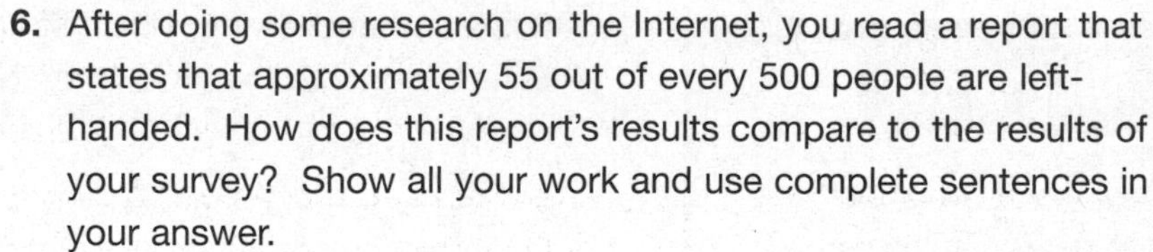

6. After doing some research on the Internet, you read a report that states that approximately 55 out of every 500 people are left-handed. How does this report's results compare to the results of your survey? Show all your work and use complete sentences in your answer.

Take Note

Whenever you see the share with the class icon, your group should prepare a short presentation to share with the class that describes how you solved the problem. Be prepared to ask questions during other groups' presentations and to answer questions during your presentation.

Problem 2 Which Sample Is the Best?

A. After talking to other students, you learn that one person formed the sample in Problem 1 by surveying different students during lunchtime. Another person surveyed students working out in the gym. Some samples will be more representative of a population than others, depending on the sampling method used. How did you choose the students in your survey? Use complete sentences in your answer.

2

Investigate Problem 2

1. **Just the Math: Biased Samples** A sample that does not accurately represent all of a population is **biased.** Determine whether the following samples of your school's population are biased. Use complete sentences to explain your reasoning.

   A sample consists of some of the females in your school.

   A sample consists of students randomly chosen from all students who take a foreign language class.

Take Note

To be **randomly chosen** means that no particular rule was used to choose a person.

2. **Just the Math: Sampling Methods** Some different sampling methods are listed below. Determine which sampling method you used in your survey. Was your sample biased? Use complete sentences to explain your reasoning.

   Random sample: A sample is chosen by using a method in which each person in the population has an equally likely chance of being chosen.

   Stratified sample: After dividing the population into groups, people are chosen at random from each group.

   Systematic sample: A sample is chosen by using a pattern, such as choosing every third person from a list.

   Convenience sample: A sample is chosen by using people that are easily accessible.

   Self-selected sample: A sample is chosen by using volunteers.

Take Note

A sampling method can be formed from one or more of the methods shown at the right.

2

2.2 Making Punch

Ratios, Rates, and Mixture Problems

Objectives

In this lesson, you will:

- Use ratios to make comparisons.
- Use rates and proportions to solve mixture problems.

Key Terms

- ratio
- rate
- proportion

SCENARIO Each year, your class presents its mathematics portfolio to parents and community members. This year, your homeroom is in charge of the refreshments for the reception that follows the presentations.

Problem 1 May the Best Recipe Win

A. Four students in the class give their recipes for punch. The class decides to analyze the recipes to determine which punch recipe will make the punch with the strongest grapefruit flavor. The recipes are shown below. How many total parts are there in each recipe?

Adam's Recipe
4 parts lemon-lime soda
8 parts grapefruit juice

Bobbi's Recipe
3 parts lemon-lime soda
5 parts grapefruit juice

Carlos' Recipe
2 parts lemon-lime soda
3 parts grapefruit juice

Zeb's Recipe
1 part lemon-lime soda
4 parts grapefruit juice

Investigate Problem 1

1. For each recipe, write a ratio that compares the number of parts of grapefruit juice to the total number of parts in each recipe. Then simplify each ratio, if possible.

Adam's recipe:

Bobbi's recipe:

Carlos' recipe:

Zeb's recipe:

Which recipe has the strongest taste of grapefruit? Show all your work and use complete sentences to explain your reasoning.

2

Adam's Recipe
4 parts lemon-lime soda
8 parts grapefruit juice

Bobbi's Recipe
3 parts lemon-lime soda
5 parts grapefruit juice

Carlos' Recipe
2 parts lemon-lime soda
3 parts grapefruit juice

Zeb's Recipe
1 part lemon-lime soda
4 parts grapefruit juice

Investigate Problem 1

2. For each recipe, write a ratio that compares the number of parts of lemon-lime soda to the total number of parts in each recipe. Then simplify each ratio, if possible.

Adam's recipe:

Bobbi's recipe:

Carlos' recipe:

Zeb's recipe:

Which recipe has the strongest taste of lemon-lime soda? Show all your work and use complete sentences to explain your reasoning.

Problem 2 Making the Refreshments

A. You are borrowing glasses from the cafeteria to serve the punch. Each glass will hold 6 fluid ounces of punch. Your class expects that 70 students and 90 parents and community members will attend the reception. You decide to make enough punch so that every person who attends can have one glass of punch. How many fluid ounces of punch will you need for the reception? Show all your work and use a complete sentence in your answer.

Investigate Problem 2

1. Just the Math: Rates In Problem 1, you wrote ratios to compare parts of each punch recipe to total parts. Recall that in a ratio, the units of the numbers being compared are the same, for instance, parts to parts. A **rate** is a ratio in which the *units* of the parts being compared are different.

For Adam's recipe, write a rate to find the number of fluid ounces of punch there are in one part of the recipe. Use a complete sentence in your answer.

Investigate Problem 2

How many fluid ounces of lemon-lime soda and grapefruit juice are needed to make enough punch for the reception if you use Adam's recipe? Show all your work.

2. How many fluid ounces of lemon-lime soda and grapefruit juice are needed to make enough punch for the reception if you use Bobbi's recipe? Show all your work.

3. How many fluid ounces of lemon-lime soda and grapefruit juice are needed to make enough punch for the reception if you use Carlos' recipe? Show all your work.

Adam's Recipe
4 parts lemon-lime soda
8 parts grapefruit juice

Bobbi's Recipe
3 parts lemon-lime soda
5 parts grapefruit juice

Carlos' Recipe
2 parts lemon-lime soda
3 parts grapefruit juice

Zeb's Recipe
1 part lemon-lime soda
4 parts grapefruit juice

2

Investigate Problem 2

4. How many fluid ounces of lemon-lime soda and grapefruit juice are needed to make enough punch for the reception if you use Zeb's recipe? Show all your work.

5. Summarize the work that you have done so far in the table below.

	Amount of lemon-lime soda (fluid ounces)	Amount of grapefruit juice (fluid ounces)	Total amount of punch (fluid ounces)
Adam's recipe			
Bobbi's recipe			
Carlos' recipe			
Zeb's recipe			

Problem 3 Changing the Glass

A. A cafeteria worker tells you that you could instead use a glass that holds 8 fluid ounces of punch. Your class decides to consider this option. For any of the recipes, what would you expect the number of parts of grapefruit juice and the number of parts of lemon-lime soda to be in one glass of punch? Use complete sentences to explain your reasoning.

Investigate Problem 3

1. Write a rate for Zeb's recipe that compares the number of fluid ounces in one 8-ounce glass to the total number of parts in the recipe.

   How many fluid ounces of lemon-lime soda and grapefruit juice are in one 8-ounce glass of punch? Show all your work and write your answers as decimals.

2. For Carlos' recipe, how many fluid ounces of lemon-lime soda and grapefruit juice are in one 8-ounce glass of punch? Show all your work and write your answers as decimals.

2

Adam's Recipe
4 parts lemon-lime soda
8 parts grapefruit juice

Bobbi's Recipe
3 parts lemon-lime soda
5 parts grapefruit juice

Carlos' Recipe
2 parts lemon-lime soda
3 parts grapefruit juice

2

Zeb's Recipe
1 part lemon-lime soda
4 parts grapefruit juice

Investigate Problem 3

3. For Bobbi's recipe, how many fluid ounces of lemon-lime soda and grapefruit juice would be in one 8-ounce glass of punch? Show all your work and write your answers as decimals.

4. For Adam's recipe, how many fluid ounces of lemon-lime soda and grapefruit juice would be in one 8-ounce glass of punch? Show all your work and write your answers as decimals.

5. Use complete sentences to explain how ratios and rates helped you to solve the problems in this lesson.

6. Explain how you could use any of the recipes to make exactly 100 glasses of punch. Use complete sentences in your answer.

2.3

Shadows and Proportions

Proportions and Indirect Measurement

Objectives

In this lesson,
you will:

- Use similar figures to write and solve a proportion.
- Write unit rates.
- Use rates to convert units.
- Use a rate to write an equation.

Key Terms

- similar
- corresponding sides
- unit rate
- rate

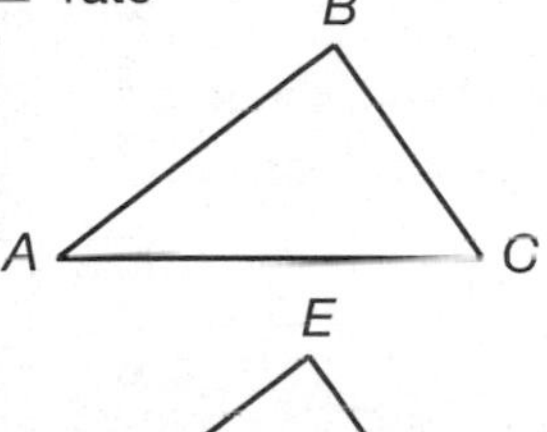

Take Note

One way to simplify a ratio that involves a decimal is to multiply the numerator and denominator by an appropriate multiple of 10 to eliminate decimals in the ratio. Then simplify the result as you normally would. For instance,

$$\frac{1.2}{4} = \frac{1.2(10)}{4(10)} = \frac{12}{40} = \frac{3}{10}.$$

SCENARIO You and your friends are discussing the height of a tall pine tree that is near your school. Your friend Kirk suggests that you can determine the height of the tree by measuring the shadow cast by the tree. He thinks that the shadow's length will be the same as the tree's height.

Problem 1 Trees and Their Shadows

A. You measure the shadow's length and find that it is about 8 meters long, but the tree appears to be a lot taller than that. You notice that Kirk appears to be taller than his shadow. You measure both Kirk and his shadow and find that Kirk is 1.5 meters tall and his shadow is 0.6 meter long.

You can use *similar figures* to help you solve this problem. Two figures are **similar** if they have the same shape, but not necessarily the same size. A property of similar figures is that the ratios of their ***corresponding sides*** are equal.

Triangles *ABC* and *DEF* at the left are similar. Their corresponding sides are sides *AB* and *DE*, sides *BC* and *EF*, and sides *AC* and *DF*. Because the triangles are similar,

$$\frac{AB}{DE} = \frac{BC}{EF} = \frac{AC}{DF}.$$

Visualize the problem by completing the diagram below that shows the tree, its shadow, Kirk, and his shadow. Record any measurements that you know on the diagram.

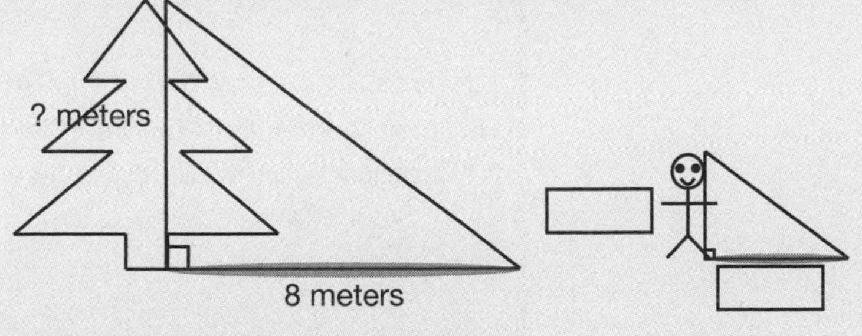

Investigate Problem 1

1. Write a ratio that compares Kirk's height to his shadow's length. Then simplify the ratio.

2

Investigate Problem 1

2. Use a complete sentence to explain why the proportion is true.

$$\frac{\text{Kirk's height}}{\text{Kirk's shadow's length}} = \frac{\text{tree height}}{\text{tree shadow length}}$$

3. If the tree's height is 3 meters, what is the length of the tree's shadow? Show all your work and use a complete sentence in your answer.

4. If the length of the tree's shadow is 6 meters, what is the tree's height? Show all your work and use a complete sentence in your answer.

5. Find the height of the tree that is described in the original part (A) scenario. Show all your work and use a complete sentence in your answer.

Problem 2 Tree Growth

A. As you finish finding the tree's height, an elderly woman comes out of her house nearby and asks what you are doing. You explain that you found the tree's height by using the length of its shadow.

Upon hearing this, the woman tells you that she and her husband planted the tree on their wedding day 50 years ago. When they planted the tree, it was about 1 meter tall. She tracked its growth until it was too tall to measure directly. According to the woman, the tree has grown about 30 centimeters each year.

Take Note

When the word "per" is used in this way, it means "in one."

Recall that a rate is a ratio in which the units of the numbers being compared are different. A **unit rate** is a **rate** per one given unit, such as 43 miles per 1 gallon.

It takes 2 hours to ride your bike 24 miles. Complete the statement to write a unit rate that represents your average speed in miles per hour.

$$\frac{24 \text{ miles}}{2 \text{ hours}} = \frac{\square}{1 \text{ hour}}$$

A pump is draining 20 gallons of water out of a pool in 5 minutes. Write a unit rate that represents the amount of water drained in gallons per minute.

B. Write a rate that represents the tree's growth rate in centimeters per year.

Investigate Problem 2

Take Note

Unit analysis is the process by which you determine appropriate units for your answer to a problem. In Question 1, you used unit analysis to determine that 30 centimeters is equivalent to 0.3 meter.

1. **Just the Math: Unit Conversion** You can use a proportion to convert units. Solve the proportion below to write the tree's growth rate in meters per year. Then complete the rate.

$$\frac{1 \text{ meter}}{100 \text{ centimeters}} = \frac{x \text{ meters}}{30 \text{ centimeters}}$$

The tree's growth is $\frac{\square \text{ meter}}{1 \text{ year}}$.

Investigate Problem 2

2. Use a complete sentence to explain how you could use the rate that you found in Question 1 to determine how much the tree grows in five years.

Take Note

When you are working on a problem that uses different units from the same system (length, weight, etc.), it is a good idea to convert to the same units (convert all lengths to feet, convert all weights to grams, and so on).

2

3. If the tree continued to grow the same amount each year, how tall was the tree after 10 years? Use a complete sentence in your answer.

How tall was the tree after 20 years?

How tall was the tree after 40 years?

4. Use your results from Question 3 to complete the table below to relate the tree height to the amount of time passed.

Quantity Name	**Amount of time since tree was planted**	**Tree height**
Unit	**years**	**meters**
	0	
	10	
	20	
	40	
	70	
	75	

Take Note

When you are choosing your bounds, use your table as a guide. Also remember that an interval should divide its set of bounds equally.

5. Use the grid on the next page to create a graph of the data from the table in Question 4. First, choose your bounds and intervals. Be sure to label your graph clearly.

Variable quantity	Lower bound	Upper bound	Interval
Time			
Height			

Investigate Problem 2

(units)

(label)

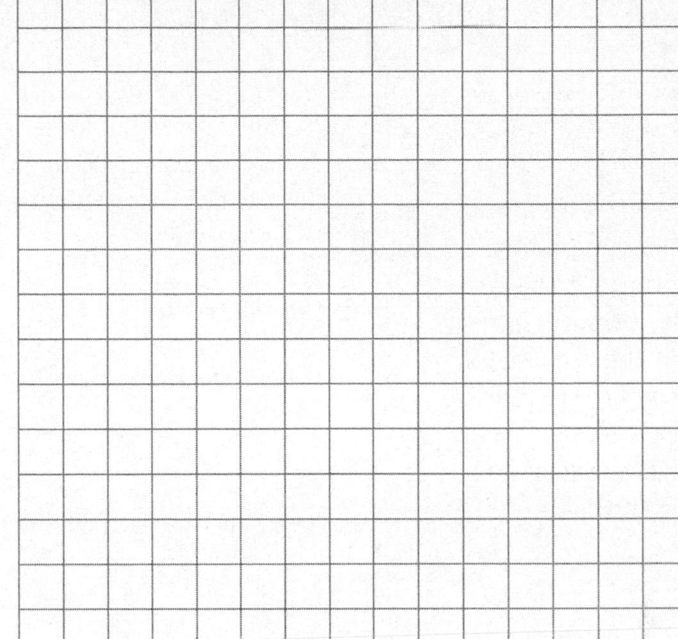

(label) (units)

6. Write an **equation** that models the growth of the tree over time. Let h represent the height of the tree in meters and let t represent the amount of time in years.

7. Use your equation to estimate the tree's height after 50 years. Show all your work and use a complete sentence in your answer.

8. How does the 50-year-old tree height you found in Problem 1 compare to the 50-year-old tree height you found above? Use a complete sentence in your answer.

9. What factors might account for any differences between the two heights? Use a complete sentence in your answer.

10. Which method do you think is more accurate? Use complete sentences to explain your reasoning.

2

2.4 TV News Ratings

Ratios and Part-to-Whole Relationships

Objectives

In this lesson, you will:

- Use ratios to model part-to-whole relationships.
- Write an equation that models a part-to-whole relationship.

Key Terms

- ratio
- equation

SCENARIO The cost of running a commercial on television during a particular program depends on the number of people that watch the program. The greater the number of people that watch the program, the higher the cost of running the commercial.

Problem 1 Do You Watch the Evening News?

A. A recent survey of the local news programs in your area indicates that two out of every five people that watch a news program watch *Channel 11 News at Six*.

Write a **ratio** that compares the number of people who watch *Channel 11 News at Six* to the number of people who watch a news program.

Investigate Problem 1

1. Use the survey results to answer the following questions. Use complete sentences in your answers.

How many people are watching *Channel 11 News at Six* if there are 10 people watching a news program?

How many people are watching *Channel 11 News at Six* if there are 1000 people watching a news program?

Investigate Problem 1

How many people are watching *Channel 11 News at Six* if there are 10,000 people watching a news program?

2

2. Use the survey results to answer the following questions. Use complete sentences in your answers.

How many people are watching any news program if there are 20 people watching *Channel 11 News at Six*?

How many people are watching a news program if there are 200 people watching *Channel 11 News at Six*?

How many people are watching a news program if there are 20,000 people watching *Channel 11 News at Six*?

Investigate Problem 1

3. Let p represent the number of people that watch a news program and let t represent the number of people that watch *Channel 11 News at Six*. Use the description to write an equation for t in terms of p.

$$\frac{t}{p} = \frac{2}{5}$$

$\square = \square$ Set the means equal to the extremes.

$\square = \square$ Divide each side by 5.

4. Use complete sentences to explain how you can use the information you have so far to determine the number of people who are watching *Channel 11 News at Six*.

5. Complete the table that represents the problem situation.

Quantity Name	**All news watchers**	
Unit	**people**	**people**
Expression		$\frac{2}{5}p$
	250	
	800	
	1500	
	5000	
	10,000	

6. Use the grid on the next page to create a graph of the data from the table in Question 5. First, choose your bounds and intervals. Be sure to label your graph clearly.

Variable quantity	Lower bound	Upper bound	Interval

Investigate Problem 1

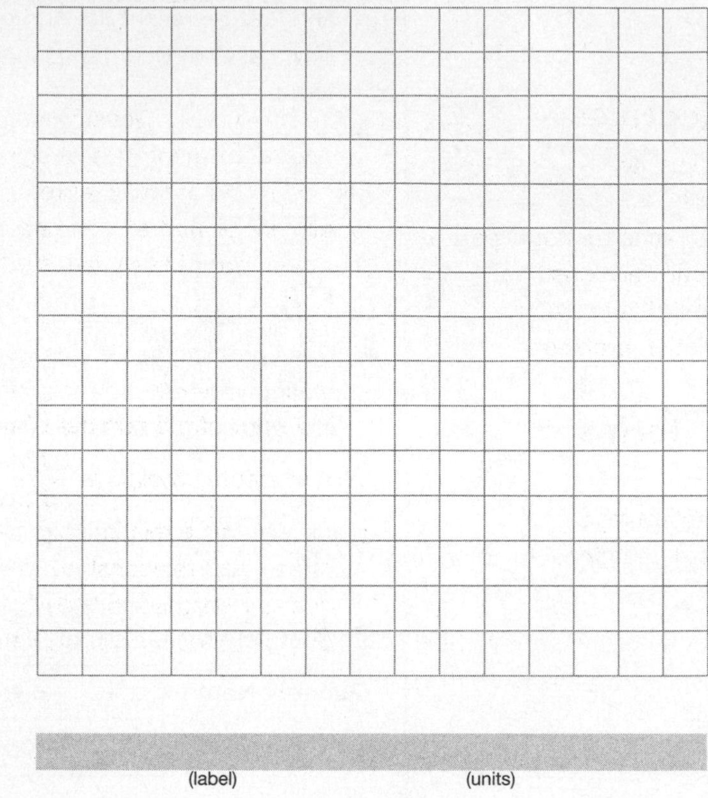

7. What are the variable quantities in this problem situation? Identify the letters that represent these quantities and include the units that are used to measure these quantities. Use a complete sentence in your answer.

8. Which variable quantity depends on the other variable quantity?

9. Which variable from Question 7 is the independent variable and which variable is the dependent variable?

10. The news producers on Channel 4 tell the commercial sponsors that their news at 6 PM is watched by one of every three news viewers. With which news program should the advertisers place their commercial if they want to reach the largest viewing audience? Use complete sentences to explain.

2.5 Women at a University

Ratios, Part-to-Part Relationships, and Direct Variation

Objectives

In this lesson, you will:

- Use ratios to model part-to-part relationships.
- Use ratios in a direct variation problem.

Key Terms

- ratio
- constant ratio
- direct variation

SCENARIO Government agencies and civil rights groups monitor enrollment data at universities to ensure that different ethnic groups are fully represented. One study focused on the enrollment of women at a certain university. The study found that three out of every five students enrolled were women.

2

Problem 1 Enrollment Numbers

A. The **ratio** of the number of women enrolled to the total number of students enrolled is $\frac{\text{3 female students}}{\text{5 total students}}$. This ratio represents a part-to-whole relationship. We can also use a ratio to represent a part-to-part relationship. What is the ratio of the number of male students enrolled to the number of female students enrolled? Use complete sentences to explain how you found your answer.

Investigate Problem 1

1. How many *male* students are enrolled if there are 1000 female students enrolled? Use a complete sentence in your answer.

   How many *male* students are enrolled if there are 10,000 female students enrolled? Use a complete sentence in your answer.

Take Note

When you need to use rounding to find your answer, consider the type of quantity that the number represents. For instance, if the number represents the amount of time that it takes you to complete a race, you may want to round your answer to the nearest tenth. If the number represents the number of pieces of paper that you will need to complete a project, you may want to round your answer to the nearest whole number.

Investigate Problem 1

How many *male* students are enrolled if there are 5000 female students enrolled? Use a complete sentence in your answer.

Use complete sentences to explain how you found your answers in Question 1.

2. How many *female* students are enrolled if there are 3000 male students enrolled? Use a complete sentence in your answer.

How many *female* students are enrolled if there are 1800 male students enrolled? Use a complete sentence in your answer.

How many *female* students are enrolled if there are 27,000 male students enrolled? Use a complete sentence in your answer.

Use complete sentences to explain how you found your answers in Question 2.

Investigate Problem 1

3. Did the way that you found the answers to Questions 1 and 2 in this lesson differ from the way you answered Investigate Problem 1 Questions 1 and 2 in Lesson 2.4? Use complete sentences to explain your reasoning.

4. Let *w* represent the number of female students that are enrolled and let *m* represent the number of male students that are enrolled. Follow the instructions to write an equation for *m* in terms of *w*.

$\frac{m}{w} = \frac{[\ ]}{[\ ]}$

$[\ ] = [\ ]$ Set the means equal to the extremes.

$[\ ] = [\ ]$ Use mental math to solve for *m*.

5. Use complete sentences to explain how you can use the information that you have to determine the number of male students who are enrolled.

6. Complete the table that represents the problem situation.

Quantity Name	**Female students**	
Unit	**students**	**students**
Expression	*w*	
	1000	
		1800
		3000
	5000	
	10,000	
		27,000

Investigate Problem 1

Take Note

When you are choosing your bounds, use your table as a guide. Also remember that an interval should divide its set of bounds equally.

2

7. Use the grid below to create a graph of the data from the table in Question 6. First, choose your bounds and intervals. Be sure to label your graph clearly.

Variable quantity	Lower bound	Upper bound	Interval

8. Use the Internet to gather enrollment information about a college or university in your state. What is the ratio of the number of male students enrolled to the number of female students enrolled? What is the ratio of the number of minority students enrolled to the total number of students enrolled? Find other ratios that interest you.

Investigate Problem 1

9. Now, we will return to a ratio that represents a part-to-whole relationship, the ratio that compares the number of female students to the total number of students enrolled at the university. How many female students are at a university if there are 1000 students enrolled? Use a complete sentence in your answer.

How many female students are at a university if there are 10,000 students enrolled? Use a complete sentence in your answer.

How many female students are there if there are 5000 students enrolled? Use a complete sentence in your answer.

Use complete sentences to explain how you found your answers in Question 9.

10. How many students are enrolled if there are 3000 female students enrolled? Use a complete sentence in your answer.

Investigate Problem 1

How many students are enrolled if there are 1800 female students enrolled? Use a complete sentence in your answer.

2

How many students are enrolled if there are 27,000 female students enrolled? Use a complete sentence in your answer.

Use complete sentences to explain how you found your answers in Question 10.

11. Let t represent the total number of students enrolled and let w represent the number of female students enrolled. Write an equation for w in terms of t. Show all your work.

12. Just the Math: Direct Variation A **constant ratio** is a ratio that has a constant value. When two quantities x and y have a constant ratio, their relationship is called **direct variation.** It is said that one quantity "varies directly" with the other. In direct variation, the constant ratio is commonly labeled k and the ratio is written as $\frac{y}{x} = k$ or $y = kx$. Is the relationship of the quantities represented by the variables w and t in Question 11 direct variation? Use complete sentences to explain why or why not.

Investigate Problem 1

13. Complete the table of values for parts 9–11 of Problem 1.

Quantity Name		
Unit		
Expression		

14. Use the grid below to create a graph of the data from the table in Question 13. First, choose your bounds and intervals. Be sure to label your graph clearly.

Variable quantity	Lower bound	Upper bound	Interval

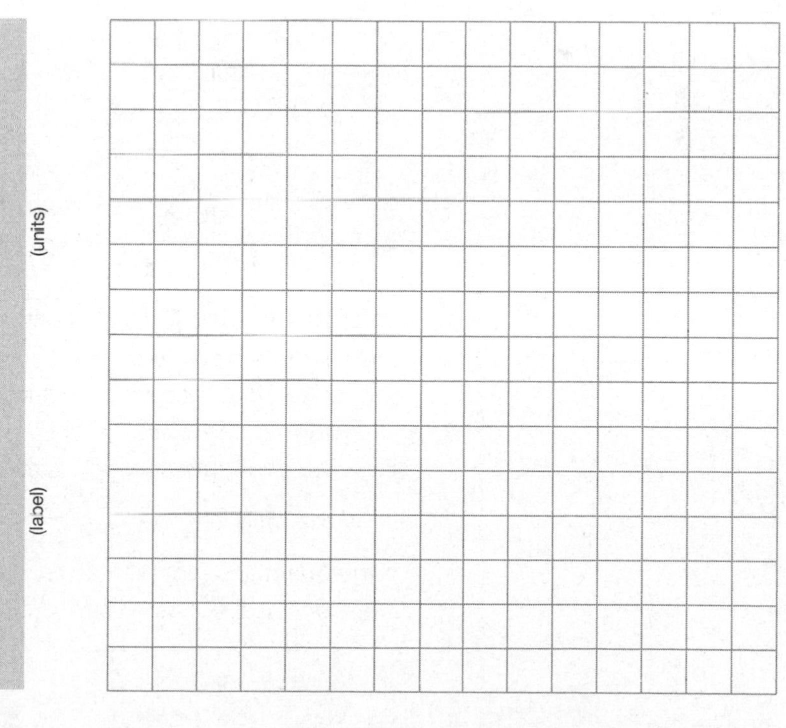

2

2

2.6 Tipping in a Restaurant

Using Percents

Objectives

In this lesson, you will:

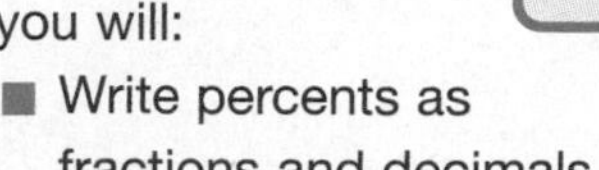

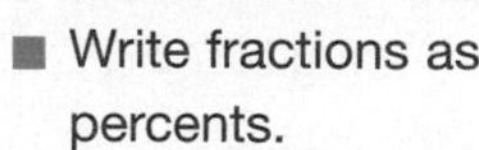

- Write percents as fractions and decimals.
- Write fractions as percents.
- Find percents of tips.
- Find amounts of tips.
- Find amounts of total bills.

Key Terms

- percent
- proportion

SCENARIO The earnings of servers in restaurants are made up of a small hourly wage and tips from customers. It is customary to tip 15% of the total bill for average service and 20% of the total bill for excellent service.

Problem 1 Going Out!

A. You go to a restaurant with some of your friends. Your bill is \$25 and you leave a \$5 tip. Write a ratio that compares the amount left for the tip to the total amount of the bill.

B. The word percent means "per cent" or "per hundred," so a **percent** is a ratio whose denominator is 100. For instance, 9% or 9 per hundred can be written as the ratio $\frac{9}{100}$. We can also write a percent as a decimal by writing the percent first as a fraction, then as a decimal.

Write each percent as a fraction and as a decimal. Simplify the fraction, if possible.

11%   24%   75%

You can write a fraction as a percent by writing the fraction with a denominator of 100 and then writing the fraction as a percent. Write each fraction as a percent. Show all your work.

$\frac{17}{100}$ $\frac{4}{50}$ $\frac{3}{10}$

You can also write a fraction first as a decimal and then as a percent. Write each fraction as a percent by first writing it as a decimal.

$\frac{10}{40}$ $\frac{9}{15}$ $\frac{3}{8}$

Take Note

Besides being whole numbers, percents can be decimals, such as 12.5%. As a fraction, 12.5% is $\frac{12.5}{100} = \frac{125}{1000} = \frac{1}{8}$ and as a decimal, 12.5% is 0.125.

Investigate Problem 1

1. Complete the proportion below.

$$\frac{5}{25} = \frac{\square}{100}$$

So, 5 out of 25 is the same as what percent? _____

What percent tip did you leave? Write your answer using a complete sentence.

2

2. Different restaurant bills and the tips that were left are given below. Use a proportion to find the percent tip that was left. Show all your work and use a complete sentence in your answer.

Bill: $50
Tip: $8

Bill: $120
Tip: $18

Bill: $65
Tip: $13

Bill: $12
Tip: $2.16

Problem 2

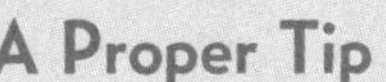

A. Your friend's bill is $22. He wants to leave a 20% tip. Complete and then solve the proportion below to find the amount of the tip that he should leave. Let x represent the tip amount. Use a complete sentence in your answer.

$$\frac{20}{100} = \frac{\square}{\square}$$

Investigate Problem 2

1. Use a proportion to find the tip amount that will be left if the tip is a 20% tip. Show all your work and use a complete sentence in your answer.

Bill: $30

Bill: $55

Bill: $14

Bill: $60

2. Use a proportion to find the amount of the *bill* if you know that each tip amount given below represents a 20% tip. Show all your work and use a complete sentence in your answer.

Tip: $8

Tip: $11

Tip: $3.60

Tip: $7.20

3. Use complete sentences to describe how your solutions to Investigate Problem 1 Question 2 and Investigate Problem 2 Questions 1 and 2 are similar.

2

Investigate Problem 2

4. Complete the table of values that describes the relationship between the amount of the bill and the tip amount if the tip is a 20% tip.

Quantity Name	**Bill**	**Tip**
Unit		
Expression		
	14	
		3.60
		6.00
	36	
	40	

5. Let b represent the amount of the bill in dollars and let t represent the tip amount in dollars. Write an equation for t in terms of b.

What is the independent variable in the equation? Use a complete sentence in your answer.

What is the dependent variable in the equation? Use a complete sentence in your answer.

Is there a constant in the equation? If so, what is it? Use a complete sentence in your answer.

Do the variables in the equation have direct variation? Use complete sentences to explain your reasoning.

2

Investigate Problem 2

6. Use the grid below to create a graph of the data from the table in Question 4. First, choose your bounds and intervals. Be sure to label your graph clearly.

Variable quantity	Lower bound	Upper bound	Interval

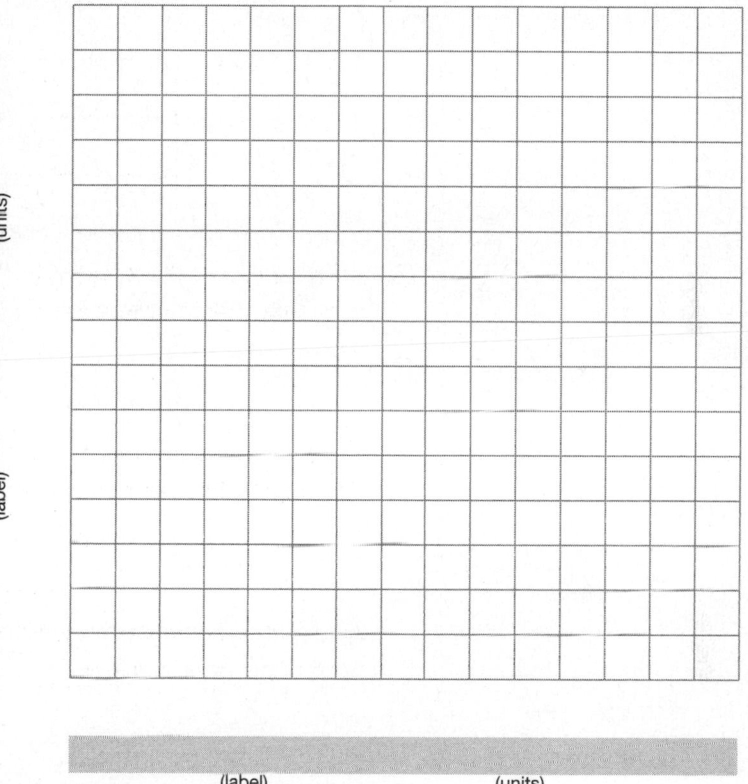

7. Members of a wait staff are predicting their tips if all of their tips are exactly 20% of each bill. One person writes an equation to model his tips. Another person creates a table of values to model her tips. Yet another person uses a graph to display his tips. The three people are discussing which representation is the best representation. Which representation do you think is the best? Use complete sentences to explain your reasoning.

2

2

2.7 Taxes Deducted From Your Paycheck

Percents and Taxes

Objectives

In this lesson,
you will:

- Find different tax rates.
- Find amounts of gross pay.
- Find amounts of paid taxes.
- Write an equation that relates gross pay and net pay.

Key Terms

- gross pay
- tax rate
- net pay

SCENARIO The amount of money that you earn at a job is your **gross pay.** When you start your first job, you will notice that the amount of money that you are directly paid is less than your gross pay. This is because taxes, paid to the government, are taken from your gross pay. The amount taken out depends on the amount of money that you earn and the *tax rate.* The **tax rate** is a percent. The amount of money that you take home after taxes have been taken out is your **net pay.**

Problem 1 What Is Your Tax Rate?

A. The amount that you pay in taxes is a percentage of your gross pay. If you know the ratio of the taxes paid to the gross pay, how can you use a proportion to find the percent of gross pay that is taken out as taxes? Write the proportion and use a complete sentence to explain how to find the percent taken out as taxes.

Investigate Problem 1

1. Different gross pay amounts and the taxes paid on the amounts are given below. Find the tax rate for the taxes paid. Show all your work and use complete sentences in your answers.

Gross pay: \$250
Taxes paid: \$75

Gross pay: \$600
Taxes paid: \$144

Gross pay: \$120
Taxes paid: \$21.60

Gross pay: \$500
Taxes paid: \$165

2

Problem 2 How Much Do You Have to Pay?

A. Some people pay 37% of their gross pay in federal, state, and local taxes. This means that their tax rate is 37%. If you know a person's gross pay, explain how you can use a proportion to find 37% of the gross pay. Write the proportion and use a complete sentence to explain how to find 37% of the gross pay.

Investigate Problem 2

1. For each amount of gross pay below, find the amount paid in taxes if the tax rate is 37%. Show all your work and use complete sentences in your answer.

Gross pay: \$1200

Gross pay: \$60,000

2. For each amount of tax paid below, find the gross pay if the tax rate is 37%. Show all your work and use complete sentences in your answer.

Tax paid: \$37

Tax paid: \$185

Tax paid: \$462.50

Tax paid: \$370

Investigate Problem 2

3. Complete the table of values that describes the relationship between the amount of gross pay and the amount paid in taxes if the tax rate is 37%. Let x represent the amount of gross pay.

Quantity Name		
Unit		
Expression		

4. Use the grid below to create a graph of the data from the table in Question 3. First, choose your bounds and intervals. Be sure to label your graph clearly.

Variable quantity	Lower bound	Upper bound	Interval

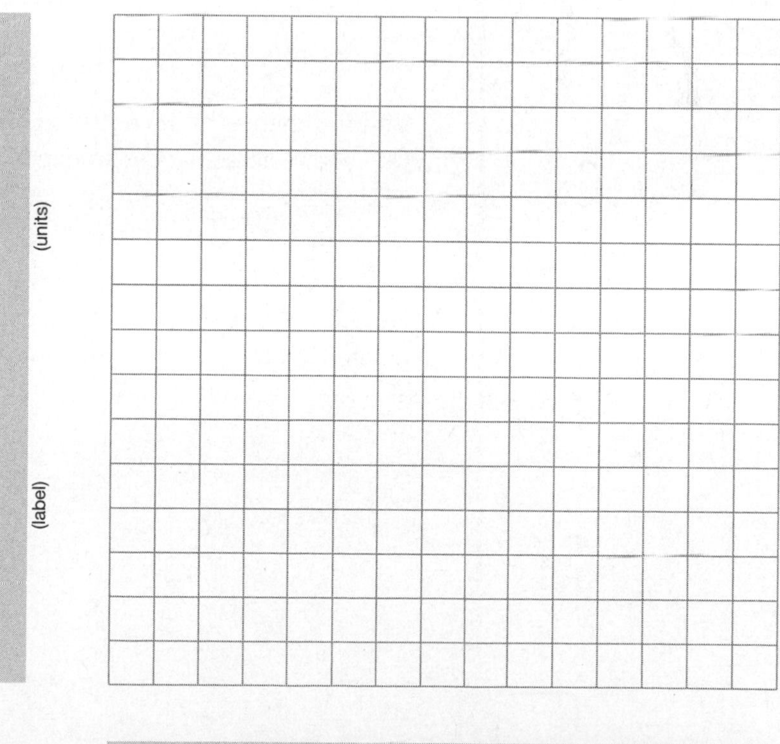

2

2

Investigate Problem 2

5. If you are taxed 37% of your gross pay, what percent of your gross pay is your net pay? Use complete sentences to explain how you found your answer.

6. Let x represent the amount of gross pay (in dollars) and let n represent the amount of net pay (in dollars). Write an equation for n in terms of x.

   What is the independent variable in the equation? Use a complete sentence in your answer.

   What is the dependent variable in the equation? Use a complete sentence in your answer.

   Is there a constant in the equation? If so, what is it? Use a complete sentence in your answer.

   Do the variables in the equation have direct variation? Use complete sentences to explain your reasoning.

7. Use complete sentences to describe the similarities and differences between the problems in this chapter.

Looking Ahead to Chapter 3

Focus In Chapter 3, you will learn how to solve one-and two-step equations and use them in real-life situations. You will also work with integers and graph equations in the coordinate plane using the Cartesian coordinate system.

Chapter Warm-up

Answer these questions to help you review skills that you will need in Chapter 3.

Perform the indicated operation.

1. $48 + 18$

2. $\frac{8}{9} - \frac{3}{4}$

3. $78 - 39$

4. $12 \cdot 10$

5. $5(8)$

6. $324 \div 4$

Use mental math to find the value of *x*.

3

7. $\frac{x}{6} = 8$

8. $30x = 120$

9. $\frac{x}{100} = 0.23$

Read the problem scenario below.

You start a new job and make $44 each week. Your goal is to save enough money to buy a new television set that costs $352.

10. Can you buy the television after 6 weeks of working?

11. How many weeks do you need to work so that you have enough money to buy the television?

12. Suppose that you have saved 75% of the money needed to buy the television. How much money have you saved?

Key Terms

CHAPTER

3

Solving Linear Equations

Most plastic containers are made using polyethylene, which was discovered in 1933. Polyethylene is also used to make soda bottles and milk jugs. In Lesson 3.5, you will design shipping boxes for plastic containers.

3.1 Collecting Road Tolls

Solving One-Step Equations

Objectives

In this lesson, you will:

- Write one-step equations.
- Solve one-step equations.
- Check solutions algebraically.
- Check solutions graphically.

Key Terms

- solve an equation
- equivalent equations
- one-step equation
- inverse operations
- algebraic check of a solution
- graphical check of a solution

SCENARIO When you travel on certain bridges or roadways in the United States, you are charged a toll or a fee to use the bridge or roadway. The tolls are used to pay for road maintenance and safety.

Problem 1 Paying a Toll

In Virginia, travelers who cross the George P. Coleman Bridge going northbound on Route 17 pay a toll. A two-axle vehicle pays \$2 to cross the bridge.

A. How much money is collected in tolls if 40 two-axle vehicles cross the bridge? Use a complete sentence in your answer.

How much money is collected in tolls if 55 two-axle vehicles cross the bridge? Use a complete sentence in your answer.

How much money is collected in tolls if 59 two-axle vehicles cross the bridge? Use a complete sentence in your answer.

How much money is collected in tolls if 65 two-axle vehicles cross the bridge? Use a complete sentence in your answer.

Use complete sentences to explain how you found your answers in part (A).

B. Let v represent the number of two-axle vehicles that cross the bridge. Write an algebraic expression that represents the amount of money collected in tolls.

C. How many two-axle vehicles crossed the bridge if \$20 in tolls were collected from two-axle vehicles? Use a complete sentence in your answer.

3

Problem 1 Paying a Toll

How many two-axle vehicles crossed the bridge if $50 in tolls were collected from two-axle vehicles? Use a complete sentence in your answer.

How many two-axle vehicles crossed the bridge if $190 in tolls were collected from two-axle vehicles? Use a complete sentence in your answer.

How many two-axle vehicles crossed the bridge if $220 in tolls were collected from two-axle vehicles? Use a complete sentence in your answer.

Use complete sentences to explain how you found your answers in part (C).

3

Investigate Problem 1

1. **Just the Math: Solutions of Equations** In part (C), you were actually *writing and solving equations.* To **solve an equation** means to find the value or values of the variable that make the equation true. Suppose that $800 were collected in tolls from two-axle vehicles and you want to know how many two-axle vehicles crossed the bridge. From part (B), you know that an expression for the amount collected in tolls from two-axle vehicles is given by $2v$.

   To determine v, the number of two-axle vehicles that crossed the bridge when $800 were collected, you can write and solve the equation $800 = 2v$.

   What is the value of v that makes the equation $800 = 2v$ true? Use a complete sentence in your answer.

Investigate Problem 1

2. **Just the Math: Solving One-Step Equations** You may have used mental math to solve the equation in Question 1, but in some cases you will want to solve an equation by writing an *equivalent equation* that has the variable by itself on one side of the equation. Two equations are **equivalent** if they have the same solution or solutions. There are many ways to write equivalent equations.

Solve $x - 5 = 8$ by writing an equivalent equation. You can do this by *adding* 5 to each side of the equation.

$x - 5 = 8$	Original equation
$x - 5 + \square = 8 + \square$	Add 5 to each side.
$\square = \square$	Equivalent equation

The solution of $x - 5 = 8$ is $x =$ _____.

Solve $x + 7 = 10$ by writing an equivalent equation. You can do this by *subtracting* 7 from each side of the equation.

$x + 7 = 10$	Original equation
$x + 7 - \square = 10 - \square$	Subtract 7 from each side.
$\square = \square$	Equivalent equation

The solution of $x + 7 = 10$ is $x =$ _____.

Solve $\frac{x}{4} = 6$ by writing an equivalent equation. You can do this by *multiplying* each side of the equation by 4.

$\frac{x}{4} = 6$	Original equation
$\frac{x}{4} \cdot \square = 6 \cdot \square$	Multiply each side by 4.
$\square = \square$	Equivalent equation

The solution of $\frac{x}{4} = 6$ is $x =$ _____.

Solve $3x = 24$ by writing an equivalent equation. You can do this by dividing each side of the equation by 3.

$3x = 24$	Original equation
$\frac{3x}{\square} = \frac{24}{\square}$	Divide each side by 3.
$\square = \square$	Equivalent equation

The solution of $3x = 24$ is $x =$ _____.

3

Investigate Problem 1

3. The equations in Question 2 are **one-step equations.** Write a complete sentence to explain why you think this is so.

4. In Question 2, you solved the equation $x - 5 = 8$ by using the operation of addition, which undoes the operation of subtraction. Operations that undo each other are **inverse operations.** For each equation below, use a complete sentence to identify the operation you would use to get the variable by itself on one side of the equation. Then solve the equation.

$\frac{x}{6} = 5.5$

$x + 9 = 14$

$x - 15 = 45$

$2x = 450$

3

5. Complete the table of values that shows the relationship between the amount collected in tolls and the number of two-axle vehicles that cross the bridge.

Quantity Name	Number of two-axle vehicles	Tolls collected
Unit	vehicles	dollars
Expression		
		40
		200
		350
		480
		600

Investigate Problem 1

6. Use the grid below to create a graph of the data from the table in Question 4. First, choose your bounds and intervals. Be sure to label your graph clearly.

Variable quantity	Lower bound	Upper bound	Interval

(label) (units)

(label) (units)

7. Just the Math: Algebraic Check of a Solution

A toll taker collected $250 in tolls. The toll taker thinks he counted 125 two-axle vehicles crossing the bridge. Did he count correctly? The answer can be determined by checking the solution of an equation. To algebraically check whether 125 is a solution of the equation $2v = 250$, substitute the value for the variable in the equation.

Substitute 125 for v: $2(125) \stackrel{?}{=} 250$

$250 = 250$

Because both sides of the equations are equal, 125 is a solution.

Algebraically determine whether 169 is a solution of the equation $2v = 358$. Then, algebraically determine whether 179 is a solution of the equation $2v = 358$. Show all your work.

Investigate Problem 1

8. Just the Math: Graphical Check of a Solution
To graphically check whether 125 is a solution of the equation $2v = 250$, find the point on your line that corresponds to 125 vehicles. This point also corresponds to 250 dollars in tolls. So, 125 is a solution of the equation $2v = 250$ because the tolls collected for 125 two-axle vehicles is \$250.

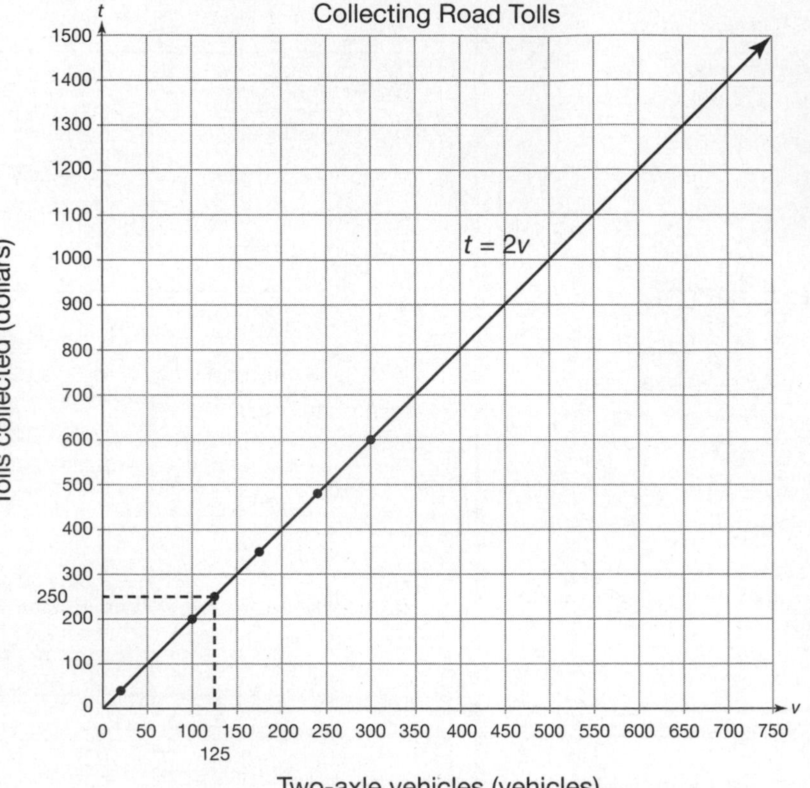

Graphically determine whether 250 is a solution of the equation $2v = 500$. Use a complete sentence to explain your reasoning.

Graphically determine whether 375 is a solution of the equation $2v = 800$. Use a complete sentence to explain.

9. Use complete sentences to explain which method of checking the solution of an equation is better, algebraic or graphical.

Take Note

Draw straight lines to help you determine whether a value is a solution of an equation. Draw a vertical line up from the value of the number of two-axle vehicles until it intersects the line. Then draw a horizontal line over from the amount of tolls collected until it intersects the line. If you intersect the line at the same place, then the value is a solution of the equation.

Take Note

Whenever you see the share with the class icon, your group should prepare a short presentation to share with the class that describes how you solved the problem. Be prepared to ask questions during other groups' presentations and to answer questions during your presentation.

3

3.2 Decorating the Math Lab

Solving Two-Step Equations

Objectives

In this lesson, you will:

- Solve two-step equations.
- Check solutions algebraically.
- Check solutions graphically.

Key Terms

- two-step equation
- inverse operations
- algebraic check of a solution
- graphical check of a solution

SCENARIO Your class will decorate the walls of your math computer lab with posters of great mathematicians. Your teacher finds a catalog that sells posters for $2 each. There is an additional charge of $4 to ship an order.

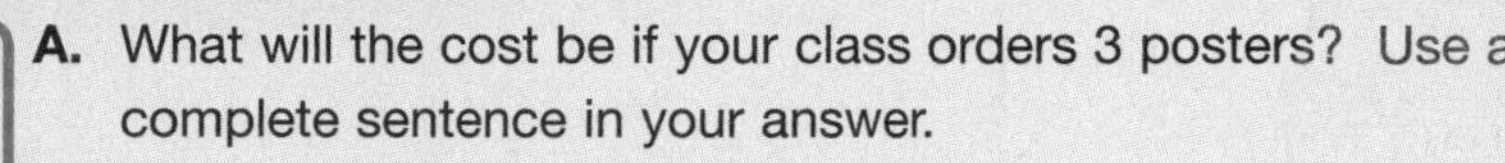

Problem 1 Finding the Total Cost

A. What will the cost be if your class orders 3 posters? Use a complete sentence in your answer.

What will the cost be if your class orders 5 posters? Use a complete sentence in your answer.

What will the cost be if your class orders 8 posters? Use a complete sentence in your answer.

What will the cost be if your class orders 12 posters? Use a complete sentence in your answer.

Use complete sentences to explain how you found your answers in part (A).

B. Let p represent the number of posters ordered. Write an algebraic expression that represents the total cost of the order.

3

Problem 1 Finding the Total Cost

C. How many posters were ordered if the cost of the order was \$8? Use a complete sentence in your answer.

How many posters were ordered if the cost of the order was \$16? Use a complete sentence in your answer.

How many posters were ordered if the cost of the order was \$32? Use a complete sentence in your answer.

How many posters were ordered if the cost of the order was \$44? Use a complete sentence in your answer.

3

Use complete sentences to explain how you found your answers in part (C).

Investigate Problem 1

1. **Just the Math: Solving Two-Step Equations** When you were finding the number of posters ordered in part (C), you were solving a *two-step equation*. Suppose that your class paid \$54 for posters and you want to know how many posters were ordered. From part (B), you know that an expression for the total cost of an order is $2p + 4$.

   To determine p, the number of posters ordered when the total cost was \$54, you can write and solve the two-step equation $2p + 4 = 54$.

   This equation is a **two-step equation** because it requires two steps in order to solve it. To solve a two-step equation, you need to perform operations together that "undo" each other. What operations do you need to undo in the equation $2p + 4 = 54$ to get the variable by itself on the right side? What are the inverse operations of these operations?

Investigate Problem 1

The first step is to undo the addition. Write the equivalent equation that is created when you undo the addition with the inverse operation of subtraction. Then simplify each side of the equation.

Take Note

When you undo operations to solve an equation, you must follow the order of operations in reverse order. This is why you first undo the addition and then you undo the multiplication to solve the equation $2p + 4 = 54$.

The second step is to undo the multiplication. Write the equivalent equation created when you undo the multiplication with the inverse operation of division. Then simplify each side of the equation.

3

So, _____ posters were ordered.

2. For each equation below, use a complete sentence to identify the operations that you would use to get the variable by itself on one side of the equation and the order in which you would perform these operations. Then solve the equation.

$5x - 3 = 2$

$1 + 2x = 7$

$\frac{x}{3} + 2 = 4$

$\frac{x}{3} - 5 = 1$

3

Investigate Problem 1

3. Complete the table of values that shows the relationship between the number of posters ordered and the total cost of the order.

Quantity Name	Number of posters ordered	Total cost
Unit	posters	dollars
Expression		
		14
		18
		22
		30
		40

4. Use the grid below to create a graph of the data from the table above. First, choose your bounds and intervals. Be sure to label your graph clearly.

Variable quantity	Lower bound	Upper bound	Interval

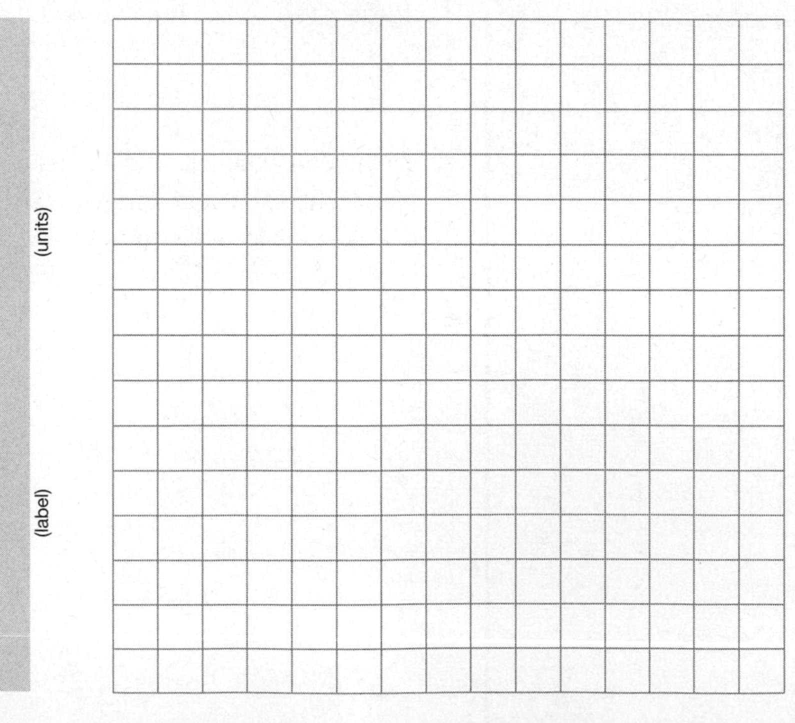

Investigate Problem 1

5. Your teacher tells you that it cost \$70 for the posters. One of your fellow classmates claims that 32 posters were ordered. Another classmate claims that 35 posters were ordered. You think that 33 posters were ordered.

   Algebraically determine whether 32 and 33 are solutions of the equation $2p + 4 = 70$. Use complete sentences to explain.

   Graphically determine whether 35 is a solution of the equation $2p + 4 = 70$. Use complete sentences to explain.

   Graphically determine whether 50 is a solution of the equation $2p + 4 = 50$. Use complete sentences to explain.

6. Determine whether 11 is a solution of the equation $2p + 4 = 26$ graphically or algebraically. Use complete sentences to explain the reasons for the choice of your method.

3

3.3 Earning Sales Commissions

Using the Percent Equation

Objectives

In this lesson, you will:

- Find commissions.
- Solve percent equations.
- Solve two-step equations.

Key Terms

- commission
- commission rate
- percent equation

SCENARIO Often, part of a salesperson's pay is made up of a *commission*. A **commission** is an amount based on a percent of the salesperson's total sales. The percent is called the **commission rate.**

You have started working at a car dealership as a salesperson. You earn a commission that is 2% of your total sales.

Problem 1 What Is My Commission?

A. During your first week, your total sales are $10,000.
Use a proportion to find your commission for your first week.
Show your work and use a complete sentence in your answer.

B. During your second week, your total sales are $15,000.
Use a proportion to find your commission for your second week.
Show your work and use a complete sentence in your answer.

C. During your third week, your total sales are $25,000.
Use a proportion to find your commission for your third week.
Show your work and use a complete sentence in your answer.

D. During your fourth week, your total sales are $32,000.
Use a proportion to find your commission for your fourth week.
Show your work and use a complete sentence in your answer.

Investigate Problem 1

1. Write a proportion that relates the commission, the total sales, and the commission rate. Use the variable t to represent your total sales and c to represent the amount of money that you earn in commission.

   Now, use means and extremes to solve the proportion. Then, write the equation that you can use to find the commission earned c on the total sales for any value of t. Show all your work.

2. **Just the Math: The Percent Equation** The equation you wrote in Question 1 is a *percent equation.* Recall that a percent is a ratio that compares two numbers. A **percent equation** is an equation of the form $a = \frac{p}{100}b$ where p is the percent and the numbers being compared are a and b. Use complete sentences to explain how the percent equation is equivalent to the proportion $\frac{a}{b} = \frac{p}{100}$.

3. In each statement below, identify a, b, and p. Then write a percent equation that represents the situation.

   18 is 40% of 45.

   Sixty percent of 35 is 21.

Take Note

It is common to write the expression $\frac{p}{100}$ as a decimal when using the percent equation. For instance, when the percent is 35%, the percent equation can be written as $a = 0.35b$.

Investigate Problem 1

4. Write and solve a percent equation to answer each question. Use a complete sentence in your answer.

Fifty is what percent of 200?

What is 20% of 160?

Eight is 5% of what number?

What is 40% of 85?

Problem 2 How Much Money Did I Earn?

You are working at a car dealership as a salesperson. In addition to your 2% commission, you also earn a base salary of $215 each week.

A. How much money will you earn if your total sales for a week are $10,000? Show all your work and use a complete sentence in your answer.

B. How much money will you earn if your total sales for a week are $25,000? Show all your work and use a complete sentence in your answer.

C. How much money will you earn if your total sales for a week are $100,000? Show all your work and use a complete sentence in your answer.

D. How much money will you earn if your total sales for a week are $200,000? Show all your work and use a complete sentence in your answer.

E. Let t represent your total sales for a week and let E represent your earnings. Write an equation for your earnings in terms of your total sales.

Investigate Problem 2

1. Use your equation to find your total sales for a week if your earnings are $300. Show all your work and use a complete sentence in your answer.

   What are your total sales for a week if your earnings are $215? Show all your work and use a complete sentence in your answer.

   What are your total sales for a week if your earnings are $220? Show all your work and use a complete sentence in your answer.

   What are your total sales for a week if your earnings are $400? Show all your work and use a complete sentence in your answer.

   What are your total sales for a week if your earnings are $1000? Show all your work and use a complete sentence in your answer.

   Use complete sentences to explain how you found your answers in Question 1.

2. What is the independent variable quantity in your equation? What is the dependent variable quantity in your equation?

3

Investigate Problem 2

3. Complete the table of values that shows the relationship between the earnings and the total sales for a week.

Quantity Name	Total sales	Earnings
Unit		
Expression		
	0	
		235
	5000	
	12,000	
		635

4. Use the grid below to create a graph of the data from the table above. First, choose your bounds and intervals. Be sure to label your graph clearly.

Variable quantity	Lower bound	Upper bound	Interval

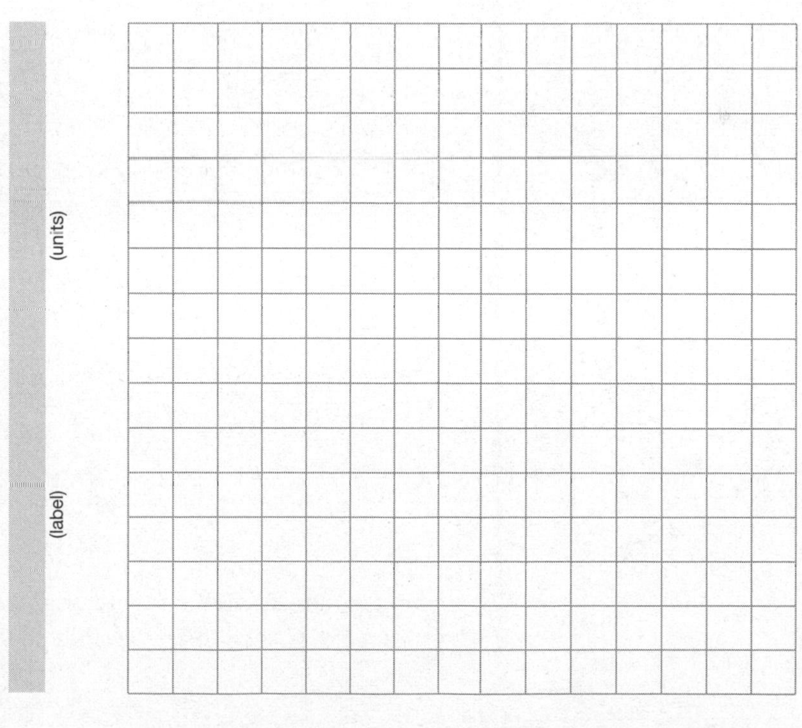

Investigate Problem 2

5. You have heard that a different sales job offers a base salary that is lower than your base salary, but the commission rate is higher. Yet another sales job offers a base salary that is higher than your base salary, but the commission rate is lower. A third sales job offers only a straight salary. Under which conditions will each amount of pay be the best? Would you stay at the dealership that you are at, or try to get a job at a different dealership? Write a paragraph to answer the questions.

3.4 Rent a Car from Go-Go Car Rentals, Wreckem Rentals, and Good Rents Rentals

Using Two-Step Equations, Part I

Objectives

In this lesson, you will:

- Write and solve two-step equations.
- Determine the better deal.
- Compare three problem situations.

Key Term

- two-step equation

SCENARIO You are taking a road trip and you need to rent a car. You look on the Internet to compare car rental prices. The first company you find, Go-Go Car Rentals, charges $28 each day along with a charge of $.25 per mile.

Problem 1 Renting from Go-Go Car Rentals

A. What will the cost be for one day if you drive the car 10 miles? Show your work and use a complete sentence in your answer.

B. What will the cost be for one day if you drive the car 50 miles? Show your work and use a complete sentence in your answer.

C. What will the cost be for one day if you drive the car 536 miles? Show your work and use a complete sentence in your answer.

D. What will the cost be for one day if you drive the car 750 miles? Show your work and use a complete sentence in your answer.

E. Use complete sentences to explain how you determined the cost of the car rental in parts (A) through (D).

F. Let t represent the total cost of the car rental in dollars and let m represent the number of miles driven. Write an equation that gives the total cost in terms of the number of miles driven.

Investigate Problem 1

1. Use the equation that you wrote in part (F) to find the number of miles driven in one day if the total rental cost is $30. Show all your work and use a complete sentence in your answer.

Investigate Problem 1

Find the number of miles driven in one day if the total rental cost is $45. Show your work and use a complete sentence in your answer.

Find the number of miles driven in one day if the total rental cost is $67.50. Show your work and use a complete sentence in your answer.

Find the number of miles driven in one day if the total rental cost is $121.25. Show your work and use a complete sentence in your answer.

Use complete sentences to explain how you found your answers in Question 1.

2. Complete the table of values that shows the relationship between the total cost and the number of miles driven.

Quantity Name	Miles driven	Total cost
Unit	miles	dollars
Expression		

3. Use the grid below to create a graph of the data from the table above. First, choose your bounds and intervals. Be sure to label your graph clearly.

Variable quantity	Lower bound	Upper bound	Interval

Take Note

When you create your table, be sure to only consider distances that are reasonably traveled in one day.

3

Investigate Problem 1

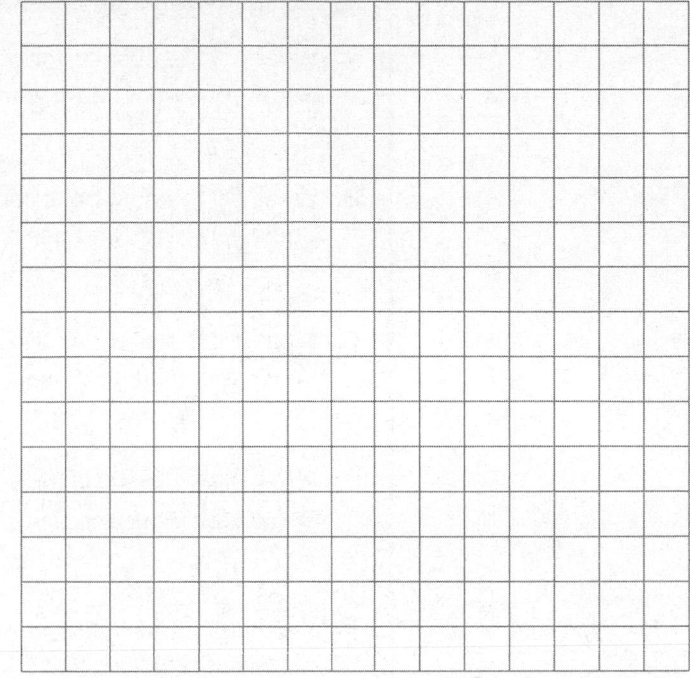

4. Go-Go Car Rentals offers you a special deal. The cost for each day is $35, but you get 500 miles for free. For any number of miles driven above 500, you pay $.25 per mile. If you plan to drive 20 miles in one day, is this deal better? Show all your work and use complete sentences to explain your reasoning.

If you plan to drive 400 miles in one day, is the special deal better? Show all your work and use complete sentences to explain.

If you plan to drive 600 miles in one day, is the special deal better? Show your work and use complete sentences to explain.

3

Problem 2 Renting from Wreckem Rentals

Another rental company, Wreckem Rentals, charges $29.95 each day along with a charge of $.23 per mile.

A. What will the cost be for one day if you drive the car 10 miles? Show your work and use a complete sentence in your answer.

B. What will the cost be for one day if you drive the car 50 miles? Show your work and use a complete sentence in your answer.

C. What will the cost be for one day if you drive the car 536 miles? Show your work and use a complete sentence in your answer.

D. What will the cost be for one day if you drive the car 2500 miles? Show your work and use a complete sentence in your answer.

3

E. Use complete sentences to explain how you determined the cost of the car rental in parts (A) through (D).

F. Let t represent the total cost of the car rental in dollars and let m represent the number of miles driven. Write an equation that gives the total cost in terms of the number of miles driven.

Investigate Problem 2

1. Use the equation that you wrote in part (F) to find the number of miles you drove in one day if the total cost of the rental is $30.64. Show all your work and use a complete sentence in your answer.

Find the number of miles driven in one day if the total rental cost is $33.17. Show your work and use a complete sentence in your answer.

Investigate Problem 2

Find the number of miles driven in one day if the total rental cost is $46.28. Show your work and use a complete sentence in your answer.

Find the number of miles driven in one day if the total rental cost is $83.77. Show your work and use a complete sentence in your answer.

Use complete sentences to explain how you found your answers in Question 1.

3

2. Complete the table of values that shows the relationship between the total cost and the number of miles driven.

Take Note

Remember that when you create your table, you should only consider distances that are reasonably traveled in one day.

Quantity Name		
Unit		
Expression		

3. Use the grid on the next page to create a graph of the data from the table above. First, choose your bounds and intervals. Be sure to label your graph clearly.

Variable quantity	Lower bound	Upper bound	Interval

Investigate Problem 2

4. Wreckem Rentals offers you a special deal. The cost for each day is \$32, but you get 250 miles for free. For any number of miles driven above 250, you pay \$.23 per mile. If you plan to drive 20 miles in one day, is this deal better? Show all your work and use complete sentences to explain your reasoning.

If you plan to drive 400 miles in one day, is the special deal better? Show your work and use complete sentences to explain.

If you plan to drive 600 miles in one day, is the special deal better? Show your work and use complete sentences to explain.

Problem 3 Renting from Good Rents Car Rentals

The last rental company you consider, Good Rents Car Rentals, charges $21.65 each day along with a charge of $.27 per mile.

A. What will the cost be for one day if you drive the car 10 miles? Show your work and use a complete sentence in your answer.

B. What will the cost be for one day if you drive the car 50 miles? Show your work and use a complete sentence in your answer.

C. What will the cost be for one day if you drive the car 536 miles? Show your work and use a complete sentence in your answer.

D. What will the cost be for one day if you drive the car 2500 miles? Show your work and use a complete sentence in your answer.

E. Use complete sentences to explain how you determined the cost of the car rental in parts (A) through (D).

F. Let t represent the total cost of the car rental in dollars and let m represent the number of miles driven. Write an equation that gives the total cost in terms of the number of miles driven.

Investigate Problem 3

1. Use the equation that you wrote in part (F) to find the number of miles you drove in one day if the total cost of the rental is $29.75. Show all your work and use a complete sentence in your answer.

Find the number of miles driven in one day if the total rental cost is $33.26. Show all your work and use a complete sentence in your answer.

3

Investigate Problem 3

Find the number of miles driven in one day if the total rental cost is $39.74. Show all your work and use a complete sentence in your answer.

Find the number of miles driven in one day if the total rental cost is $51.62. Show all your work and use a complete sentence in your answer.

Use complete sentences to explain how you found your answers in Question 1.

3

2. Complete the table of values that shows the relationship between the total cost and the number of miles driven.

Take Note

Remember that when you create your table, you should only consider distances that are reasonably traveled in one day.

Quantity Name		
Unit		
Expression		

3. Use the grid on the next page to create a graph of the data from the table above. First, choose your bounds and intervals. Be sure to label your graph clearly.

Variable quantity	Lower bound	Upper bound	Interval

Investigate Problem 3

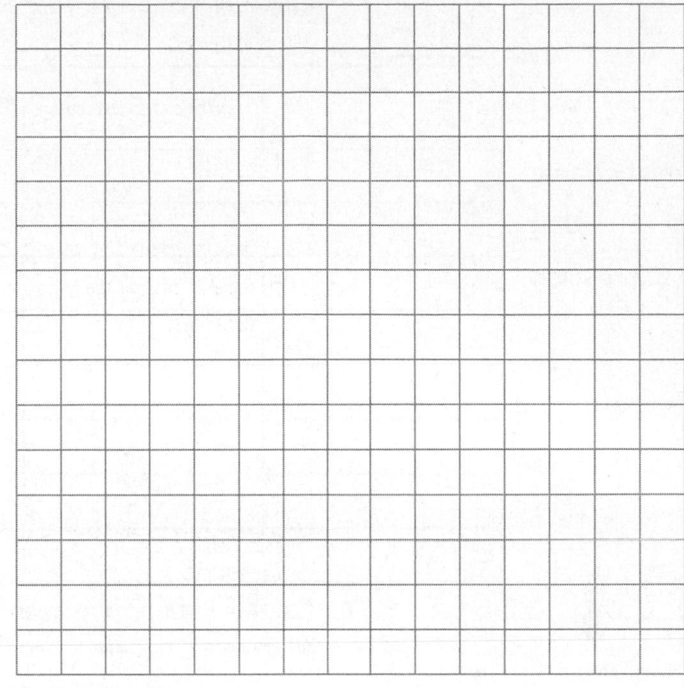

4. Good Rents Car Rentals offers you a special deal. The cost for each day is $28, but you get 150 miles for free. For any number of miles driven above 150, you pay $.27 per mile. If you plan to drive 20 miles in one day, is this deal better? Show all your work and use complete sentences to explain your reasoning.

If you plan to drive 400 miles in one day, is the special deal better? Show all your work and use complete sentences to explain.

If you plan to drive 600 miles in one day, is the special deal better? Show all your work and use complete sentences to explain.

Investigate Problem 3

5. Summarize the work that you have done so far in the table below.

	Go-Go Rentals	Wreckem Rentals	Good Rents Rentals
Quantity Name			
Unit			
Expression			

3

6. Use the bounds and intervals shown below to create graphs of all three situations on the grid.

Variable quantity	Lower bound	Upper bound	Interval
Miles driven	0	300	20
Total cost	0	150	20

Investigate Problem 3

7. Compare the three companies' prices from your Investigate Problem 3 Question 6 graph. Prepare a written report that indicates which company will cost the least and for which numbers of miles. Can you tell whether the cost will ever be the same for all three companies? If so, for which number of miles? Use complete sentences to explain.

3

3.5 Plastic Containers

Using Two-Step Equations, Part 2

Objectives

In this lesson, you will:

- Write and use two-step equations.
- Compare three problem situations.

Key Term

- two-step equation

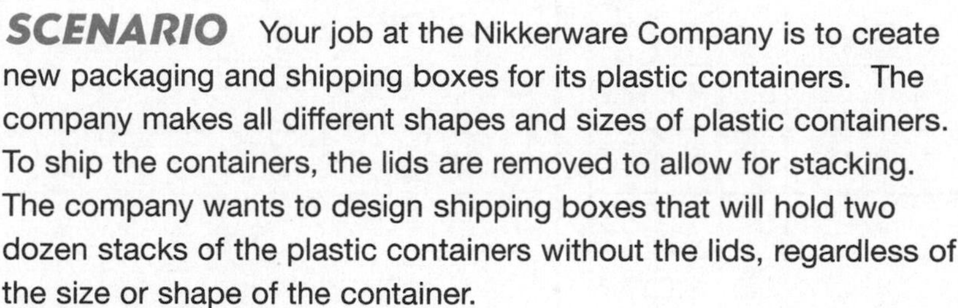

SCENARIO Your job at the Nikkerware Company is to create new packaging and shipping boxes for its plastic containers. The company makes all different shapes and sizes of plastic containers. To ship the containers, the lids are removed to allow for stacking. The company wants to design shipping boxes that will hold two dozen stacks of the plastic containers without the lids, regardless of the size or shape of the container.

Problem 1 Different Shapes and Sizes

The table below shows the data gathered from measuring the heights of different-sized stacks of the various plastic containers.

Number of containers	Stack height (centimeters)			
	Round	Square	Rectangular	
1	5.4	4.5	14.6	
2	5.9	6.2	14.9	
3	6.4	7.9	15.2	
4	6.9	9.6	15.5	
5	7.4	11.3	15.8	

If you have some stackable plastic containers in your classroom, you should add the data about them to this table.

A. What is the difference in heights between a stack of two round containers and a stack of one round container? Use a complete sentence in your answer.

B. What is the difference in heights between a stack of three round containers and a stack of two round containers? Use a complete sentence in your answer.

C. What is the difference in heights between a stack of four round containers and a stack of three round containers? Use a complete sentence in your answer.

Number of containers	Stack height (cm)		
	Round	Square	Rectangular
1	5.4	4.5	14.6
2	5.9	6.2	14.9
3	6.4	7.9	15.2
4	6.9	9.6	15.5
5	7.4	11.3	15.8

Problem 1 Different Shapes and Sizes

D. What is the difference in heights between a stack of five round containers and a stack of four round containers? Use a complete sentence in your answer.

E. How does the stack height change when one *round* container is added to a stack of *round* containers? Use a complete sentence in your answer.

F. How does the stack height change when one *square* container is added to a stack of *square* containers? Use complete sentences to explain how you found your answer.

G. How does the stack height change when one *rectangular* container is added to a stack of *rectangular* containers? Use complete sentences to explain how you found your answer.

3

Investigate Problem 1

1. What is the height of 10 *round* containers? Show all your work and use a complete sentence in your answer.

What is the height of 15 *round* containers? Show all your work and use a complete sentence in your answer.

What is the height of 20 *round* containers? Show all your work and use a complete sentence in your answer.

Use complete sentences to explain how you found your answers in Question 1.

Investigate Problem 1

2. If you use c to represent the number of containers in a stack of *round* containers, what does the expression $c - 1$ represent? Use a complete sentence to explain.

3. Let h represent the height of a stack. Write an equation that gives the height of a stack of *round* containers in terms of the number of containers c in the stack.

4. Use your equation to find the height of a stack of two dozen round containers. Show your work and use a complete sentence in your answer.

5. Let c represent the number of containers in a stack of *square* containers and let h represent the height of the stack. Write an equation that gives the height of the stack in terms of the number of containers in the stack.

6. What is the height of a stack of two dozen *square* containers? Show all your work and use a complete sentence to explain your reasoning.

7. Let c represent the number of containers in a stack of *rectangular* containers and let h represent the height of the stack. Write an equation that gives the height of the stack in terms of the number of containers in the stack.

8. What is the height of a stack of two dozen *rectangular* containers? Show all your work and use a complete sentence to explain your reasoning.

Number of containers	Stack height (cm)		
	Round	Square	Rectangular
1	5.4	4.5	14.6
2	5.9	6.2	14.9
3	6.4	7.9	15.2
4	6.9	9.6	15.5
5	7.4	11.3	15.8

3

Investigate Problem 1

9. How are the three equations you wrote similar? Why are these equations similar? Use complete sentences to explain.

10. How are the three equations you wrote different? Why are these equations different? Use complete sentences to explain.

11. In all equations, what are the variable quantities? Use a complete sentence in your answer.

What is the relationship between these quantities? In other words, which variable quantity depends on the other?

12. Does it make sense for the company to have a stack of zero containers? Why or why not? Use complete sentences to explain your reasoning.

Use your answer to explain why each of these graphs on the next page starts at 1.

13. Use the grid on the next page to create graphs for each container shape's stack height in terms of the number of containers used. Use the bounds and intervals indicated in the table. Be sure to label your graph clearly.

Variable quantity	Lower bound	Upper bound	Interval
Containers	0	75	5
Stack height	0	75	5

Investigate Problem 1

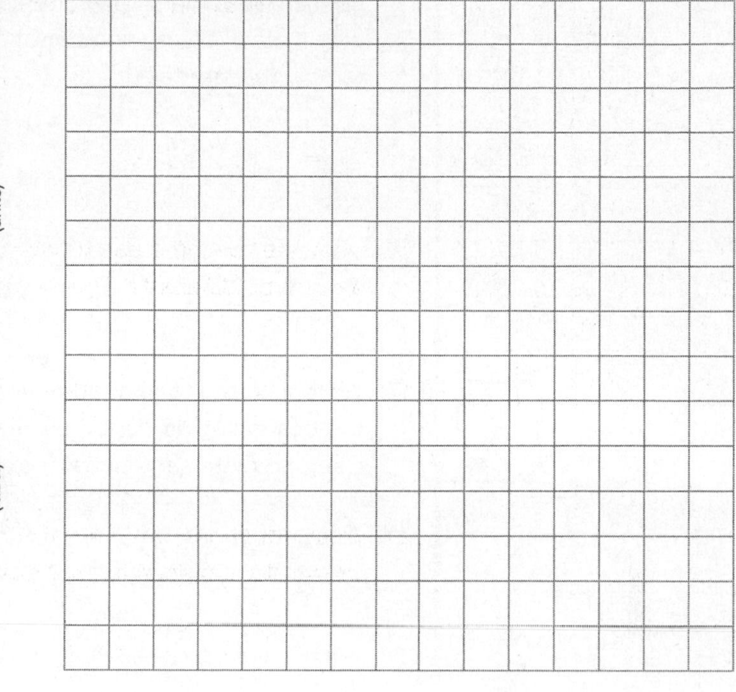

14. The square container is the shortest container. Find the number(s) of containers for which the height of a stack of square containers is the shortest. Use complete sentences to explain why the square container stack height is not always the shortest.

15. Find the number(s) of containers for which a stack of round containers is the shortest. Use complete sentences to explain why a stack of any number of round containers does not remain the shortest.

Investigate Problem 1

16. Find the number(s) of containers for which a stack of rectangular containers is the shortest. Use complete sentences to explain why a stack of any number of *rectangular* containers does not remain the shortest.

17. Write a memo to your supervisor in which you recommend the best shipping carton sizes for each type of container. Use complete sentences to explain your reasoning.

3

3.6 Brrr! It's Cold Out There!

Integers and Integer Operations

Objectives

In this lesson, you will:

- Graph integers on a number line.
- Compare integers.
- Add, subtract, multiply, and divide integers.
- Write fractions as decimals.
- Write decimals as fractions.

Key Terms

- integer
- negative integer
- positive integer
- number line
- quotient

Take Note

The symbol … is an ellipsis. It implies the continuation of a pattern. For instance, 1, 2, 3, 4, … implies that you should continue counting by 1s.

Take Note

Two integers are opposites if they are on opposite sides of 0, but are the same distance from 0. For example, 4 and –4 are opposites. You will learn more about opposites in Chapter 4.

SCENARIO You are working on a report about winter weather and you are studying the wind-chill temperature. The wind-chill temperature is a measure of how wind speed affects low temperatures and how the combination of wind and low temperature feels to a human being.

You find a table of some wind chill temperatures when the wind speed is 5 miles per hour.

Actual temperature (degrees Fahrenheit)	15	10	5	0	–5
Wind chill temperature (degrees Fahrenheit)	12	7	0	–5	–10

Problem 1 Wind Chill Temperatures

The numbers in the table are *integers*. The numbers …, –4, –3, –2, –1, 0, 1, 2, 3, 4, … are **integers.** Integers include zero, **negative integers** (integers less than zero), and **positive integers** (integers greater than zero).

A. Use a complete sentence to describe the effect that the wind has on actual temperatures.

B. One way to show the relationship between integers is to graph them on a number line. A **number line** is a line that extends in both directions forever. One point is assigned a value of zero and a given length is assigned a length of one unit. Positive integers are assigned to the units on the right of zero and negative integers are assigned to the units on the left of zero.

Use the number line below to graph each of the wind chill temperatures in the table. The first wind chill temperature is done for you.

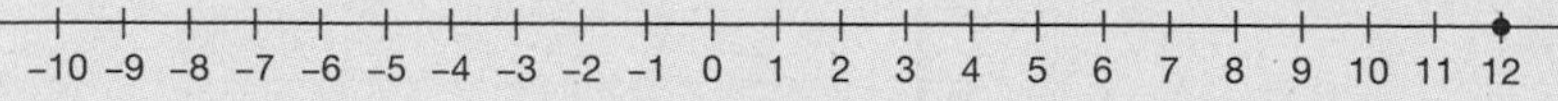

C. On the number line, the values of integers increase as you move from left to right. Write the wind chill temperatures in order from least to greatest.

Investigate Problem 1

1. When the actual temperature is 10°F and the wind speed is 15 miles per hour, the wind chill temperature is –18°F. When the wind speed is 30 miles per hour at the same actual temperature, the wind chill temperature is –33°F. Which wind chill temperature is higher? Use a complete sentence to explain.

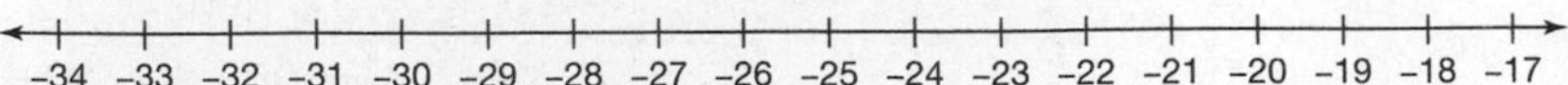

When the actual temperature is 5°F and the wind speed is 15 miles per hour, the wind chill temperature is –13°F. When the wind speed is 35 miles per hour at the same actual temperature, the wind chill temperature is –21°F. Which wind chill temperature is lower? Use a complete sentence to explain.

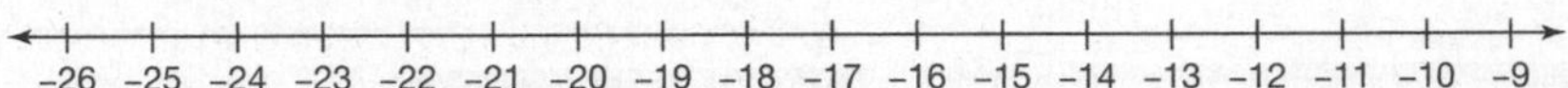

2. When the actual temperature is 25°F and the wind speed is 15 miles per hour, the wind chill temperature is 2°F. When the wind speed decreases to 10 miles per hour, the wind chill temperature increases by 8 degrees. Use a number line to find the wind chill temperature when the wind speed is 10 miles per hour. Use a complete sentence to explain.

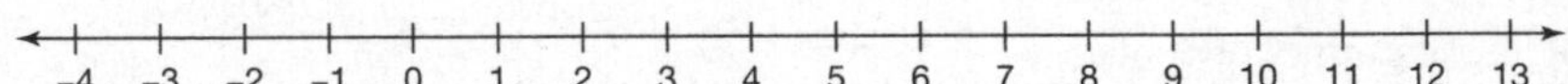

When the actual temperature is 10°F and the wind speed is 10 miles per hour, the wind chill temperature is –4°F. When the wind speed decreases to 5 miles per hour, the wind chill temperature increases by 5 degrees. Use a number line to find the wind chill temperature when the wind speed is 5 miles per hour. Use a complete sentence to explain.

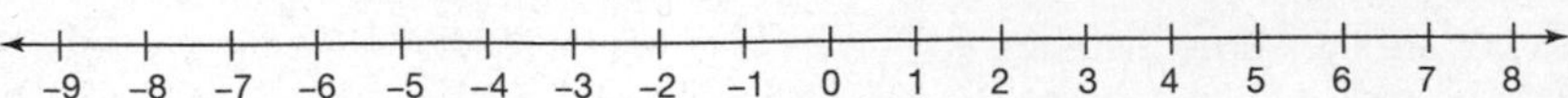

Investigate Problem 1

3. **Just the Math: Adding Negative Integers**
In Question 2, you were adding a positive integer to another integer. Complete the following instructions to add a negative integer to an integer.

To add 4 and –7, start at 4. Then move 7 units to the left. Represent this on the number line by graphing 4 on the number line and then by drawing an arrow that starts at 4 and ends 7 units to the left of 4. Where are you on the number line?

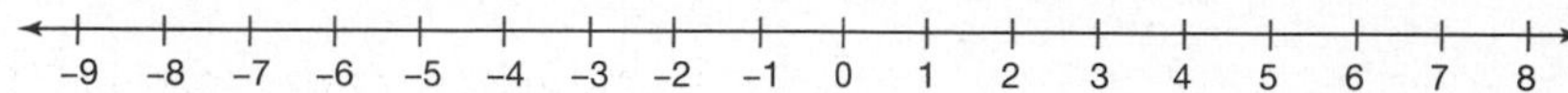

Write an integer addition equation that represents this situation.

To add –2 and –5, start at –2. Then move 5 units to the left. Represent this on the number line by graphing –2 on the number line and then by drawing an arrow that starts at –2 and ends 5 units to the left of –2. Where are you on the number line?

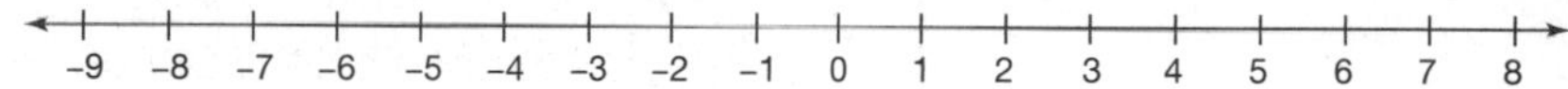

Write an integer addition equation that represents this situation.

Complete the rule below for using a number line to add two integers.

On a number line, move to the ________ when you add a positive integer, and move to the ________ when you add a negative integer.

4. When the actual temperature is 15°F and the wind speed is 10 miles per hour, the wind chill temperature is 3°F. When the wind speed increases to 20 miles per hour, the wind chill temperature decreases by 5 degrees. Use a number line to find the wind chill temperature when the wind speed is 20 miles per hour. Use complete sentences to explain how you found your answer.

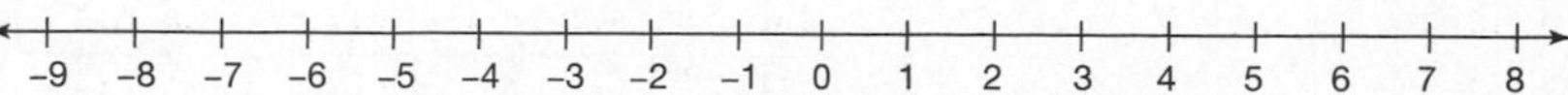

3

Investigate Problem 1

When the actual temperature is 0°F and the wind speed is 5 miles per hour, the wind chill temperature is –11°F. When the wind speed increases to 10 miles per hour, the wind chill temperature decreases by 5 degrees. Use a number line to find the wind chill temperature when the wind speed is 10 miles per hour. Use complete sentences to explain how you found your answer.

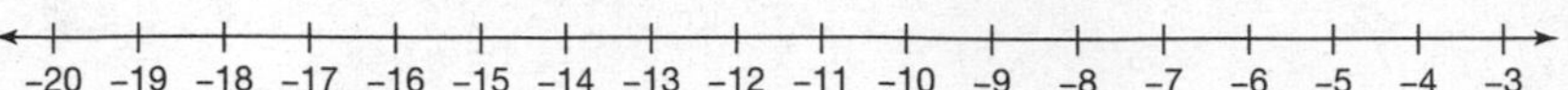

5. **Just the Math: Subtracting Negative Integers** Recall that when you add a positive integer on a number line you move to the right, when you add a negative integer on a number line, you move to the left. When you subtract a positive integer, which way do you think that you should move on a number line?

When you subtract a negative integer on a number line, which way should you move? Use complete sentences to explain your reasoning.

Complete the following instructions to subtract a negative integer from an integer.

To subtract –4 from 8, start at 8. Then subtract –4. Where are you on the number line?

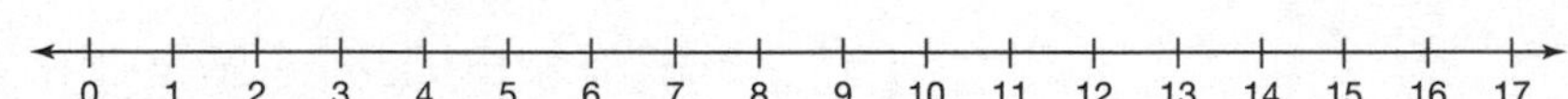

Write an integer subtraction equation that represents this situation.

To subtract –5 from –3, start at –3. Then subtract –5. Where are you on the number line?

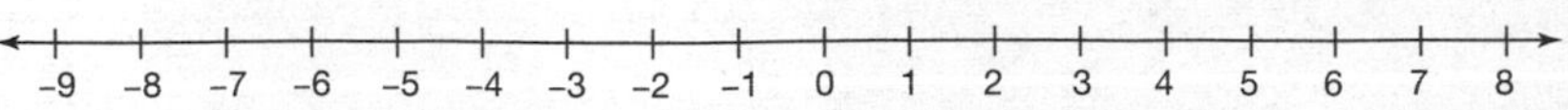

Write an integer subtraction equation that represents this situation.

Investigate Problem 1

Complete the rule below for using a number line to subtract two integers.

On a number line, move to the ________ when you subtract a positive integer, and move to the ________ when you subtract a negative integer.

6. **Just the Math: Multiplying Integers** Recall that you can think of multiplication as repeated addition. Complete each statement below.

$3(-5) = (-5) + (-5) + (-5) = \square$

$2(-1) = (-1) + (-1) = \square$

$(-1)(5) = (-1) + (-1) + (-1) + (-1) + (-1) = \square$

$4(-2) = (-2) + (-2) + (-2) + (-2) = \square$

What is the effect of multiplying a positive integer by –1? Use complete sentences in your answer.

What do you think will be the effect of multiplying a negative integer by –1?

Find each product.

$(-1)(4)$ $(-1)(4)(-1)$

What do you think is the product of –1 and –1? Use a complete sentence to explain your reasoning.

Find each product.

$3(-4) = \square$ $-3(-4) = \square$

$2(-4) = \square$ $-2(-4) = \square$

$1(-4) = \square$ $-1(-4) = \square$

$0(-4) = \square$

3

Investigate Problem 1

Complete the statements below about the product of two integers.

The product of two positive integers is a _________ integer.

The product of two negative integers is a _________ integer.

The product of a positive integer and a negative integer is a _________ integer.

The product of a negative integer and a positive integer is a _________ integer.

Take Note

Recall that the result of dividing two numbers is the **quotient.**

3

7. **Just the Math: Dividing Integers** You can find the quotient of two integers by using what you know about multiplication. For instance, if we divide 35 by 5, the result is 7 because $7 \times 5 = 35$. Find each quotient by writing a related multiplication problem.

$48 \div 6 = \square$ because $6 \times \square = 48$.

$-48 \div 6 = \square$ because $6 \times \square = -48$.

$-48 \div (-6) = \square$ because $-6 \times \square = -48$.

$48 \div (-6) = \square$ because $-6 \times \square = 48$.

Complete the statements below about the quotient of two integers.

The quotient of two positive integers is a _________ integer.

The quotient of two negative integers is a _________ integer.

The quotient of a positive integer and a negative integer is a _________ integer.

The quotient of a negative integer and a positive integer is a _________ integer.

8. Perform the indicated operations.

$7 + (-12)$	$-3 - (-4)$	$-5 + (-6)$
$4(-9)$	$(-3)^2$	$(-1)^3$
$-18 \div 3$	$-56 \div (-7)$	$14 \div (-2)$

Problem 2 Celsius Temperature Scale

As part of your report, you will also write your information about wind chill temperatures in degrees Celsius. An equation that relates a temperature C in degrees Celsius to a temperature F in degrees Fahrenheit is $F = \frac{9}{5}C + 32$.

A. Use the equation to find the temperature in degrees Celsius that corresponds to a temperature of 23°F. Show all your work and use a complete sentence in your answer.

B. Use the equation to find the temperature in degrees Fahrenheit that corresponds to a temperature of –10°C. Show all your work and use a complete sentence in your answer.

3

Investigate Problem 2

1. **Just the Math: Writing a Fraction as a Decimal** When you use the equation above to write 12°C in degrees Fahrenheit, you get $F = \frac{9}{5}(12) + 32 = \frac{268}{5}$. To write this temperature properly, we need to write it as a decimal instead of as a fraction. To write a fraction as a decimal, use long division.

$$\begin{array}{r} 53.6 \\ 5\overline{)268.0} \\ \underline{25} \\ 18 \\ \underline{15} \\ 3\,0 \end{array}$$

Use long division to write each fraction as a decimal.

$\frac{7}{2}$ $\qquad\qquad$ $\frac{4}{5}$

Take Note

Remember that the first decimal place to the right of the decimal point is tenths, the second decimal place is hundredths, and the third decimal place is thousandths.

3

Investigate Problem 2

2. Just the Math: Writing a Decimal as a Fraction
To write a decimal as a fraction, first determine the name for the last decimal place of the number that is to the right of the decimal point. Then use the name to write the decimal as the appropriate fraction.

$0.17 = \frac{17}{100}$

↑ hundredths

Write each decimal as a fraction. If possible, simplify your answer.

0.9 0.08 0.125

3. Write the temperature equation so that the fraction is a decimal. Is this equation easier to use? Use complete sentences to explain your reasoning.

4. Convert each temperature to degrees Celsius. Show all your work.

5°F –4°F

Convert each temperature to degrees Fahrenheit. Show all your work.

8°C –2°C

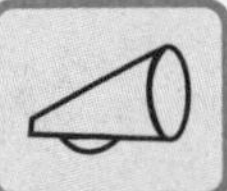

3.7 Shipwreck at the Bottom of the Sea

The Coordinate Plane

Objectives

In this lesson, you will:

- Draw a coordinate system.
- Write ordered pairs.
- Plot points in a coordinate plane.

Key Terms

- Cartesian coordinate system
- *x*-axis
- *y*-axis
- origin
- coordinate plane
- ordered pair
- *x*-coordinate
- *y*-coordinate

SCENARIO You work for a company that salvages shipwrecks. Items such as pieces of the ship and cargo from the ship are called debris. Part of your job is to examine the debris field, or the area in which items that are related to the shipwreck can be found. Once the debris field is identified, a grid is placed over the field so that the relative positions of the items can be recorded.

Problem 1 Searching the Debris Field

The figure below shows the debris field and the accompanying grid at a wreck that you are exploring.

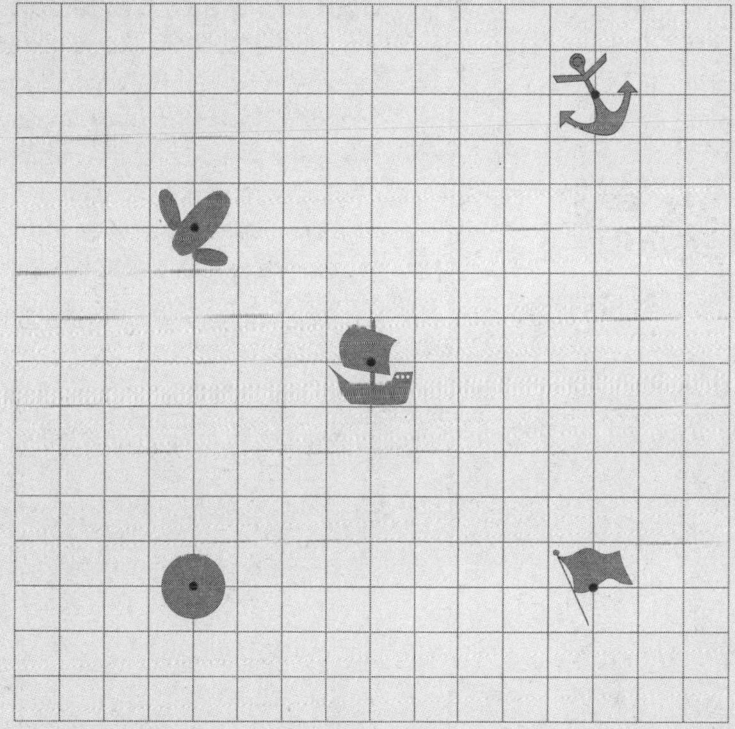

Use complete sentences to describe the location of the anchor's center in relation to the ship's center.

Use complete sentences to describe the location of the center of the gold coins in relation to the ship's center.

3

Problem 1 Searching the Debris Field

Use complete sentences to describe the location of the cannonball's center in relation to the ship's center.

Use complete sentences to describe the location of the flag's center in relation to the ship's center.

Investigate Problem 1

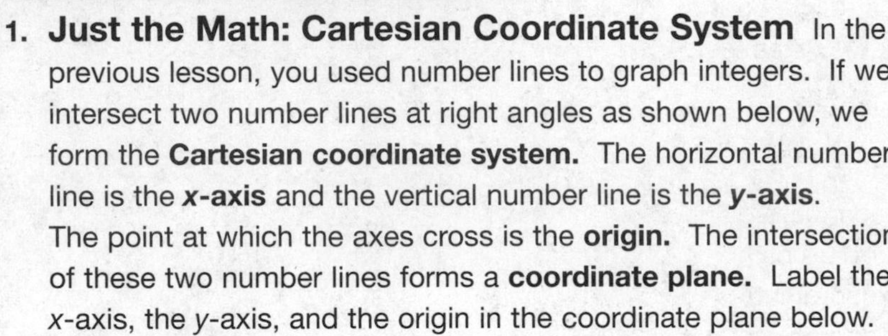

1. **Just the Math: Cartesian Coordinate System** In the previous lesson, you used number lines to graph integers. If we intersect two number lines at right angles as shown below, we form the **Cartesian coordinate system.** The horizontal number line is the ***x*-axis** and the vertical number line is the ***y*-axis**. The point at which the axes cross is the **origin.** The intersection of these two number lines forms a **coordinate plane.** Label the *x*-axis, the *y*-axis, and the origin in the coordinate plane below.

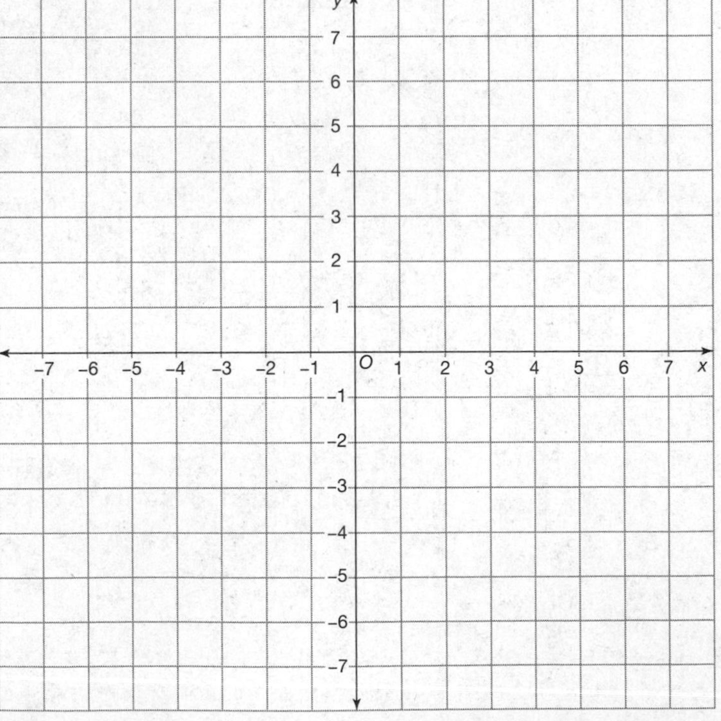

Take Note

The plural of axis is axes.

Investigate Problem 1

2. **Just the Math: Ordered Pairs** Each point on a graph can be represented by an *ordered pair.* An **ordered pair** consists of two numbers. The first number, the ***x*-coordinate,** indicates how far to the left or right the point is from the (vertical) *y*-axis. The second number, the ***y*-coordinate,** indicates how far up or down the point is from the (horizontal) *x*-axis. An ordered pair is written as (*x*-coordinate, *y*-coordinate), such as (3, –5).

For each item, write the ordered pair that represents the location of the item's center.

Draw the *x*- and *y*-axes on the grid below so that the origin is the ship's center. For each item, plot the ordered pair that represents the location of the item's center on the grid.

3

Investigate Problem 1

3. Plot and label each point in the coordinate plane.

$A(5, 2)$
$B(-3, 0)$
$C(6, -3)$
$D(1, 6)$
$E(-4, 4)$
$F(-2, -6)$

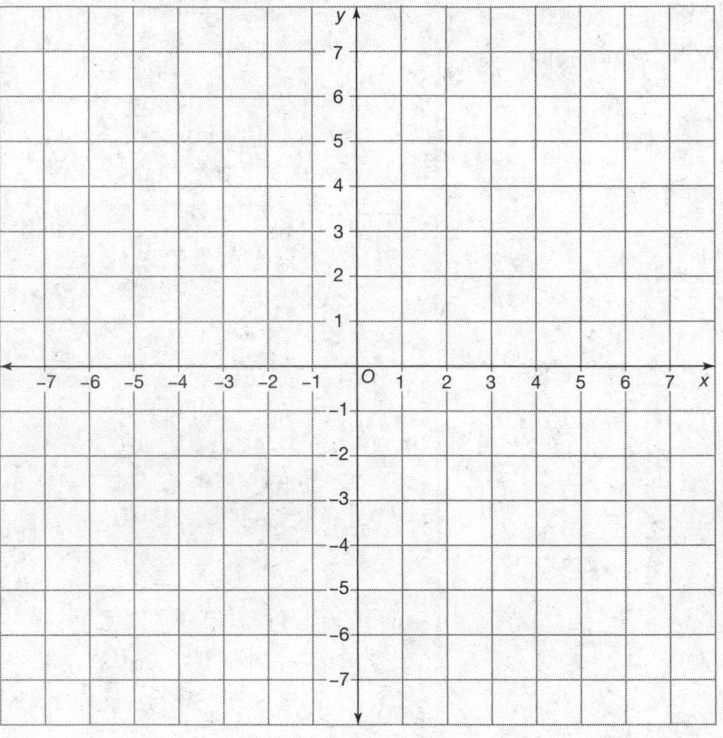

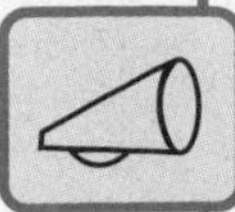

3

3.8 Engineering a Highway

Using a Graph of an Equation

Objectives

In this lesson, you will:

- Write and use a two-step equation.
- Use a graph to estimate solutions of equations.

Key Term

- estimate

SCENARIO You are a civil engineer who is overseeing a large interstate-highway construction project that will connect the cities of Pittsburgh, Pennsylvania, and Cincinnati, Ohio. Construction began several months ago, and approximately 87 miles of highway have been completed. The total length of the highway will be 267 miles. You estimate that new construction can proceed at the rate of one-fifth mile per day.

Problem 1 Construction Work

A. What are the two quantities that are changing?

B. Write an equation to model the situation.

Investigate Problem 1

1. Find the number of miles that are completed in 10 days. Show all your work and use a complete sentence in your answer.

Find the number of miles that are completed in 50 days. Show all your work and use a complete sentence in your answer.

Find the number of miles that are completed in 1 year. Show all your work and use a complete sentence in your answer.

Find the number of miles that are completed in 2 years. Show all your work and use a complete sentence in your answer.

Investigate Problem 1

Use a complete sentence to explain how you found your answers in Question 1.

2. Find the number of days it will take to complete 100 miles of highway. Show all your work and use a complete sentence in your answer.

Find the number of days it will take to complete 150 miles of highway. Show all your work and use a complete sentence in your answer.

Find the number of days it will take to complete the entire highway. Show all your work and use a complete sentence in your answer.

Investigate Problem 1

Use complete sentences to explain how you found your answers in Question 2.

Write an equation that relates the two quantities that are changing.

3. Use your equation to find the number of days it will take to complete 50 miles of highway. Show all your work and use a complete sentence to explain your reasoning.

Use complete sentences to explain the solution of the equation in terms of the problem situation.

4. How many days before new construction began was the project started? Show all your work and use complete sentences to explain your reasoning.

3

Investigate Problem 1

5. Complete the table of values that shows the relationship between the number of days and the number of miles that are completed.

Quantity Name		
Unit		
Expression		

6. Use the grid below to create a graph of the data from the table above. First, choose your bounds and intervals. Be sure to label your graph clearly.

Variable quantity	Lower bound	Upper bound	Interval

3

Take Note

When you are choosing your bounds, remember to consider when the highway was started and how many days it will take to complete the highway.

(label) (units)

(label) (units)

Investigate Problem 1

7. Use your graph to **estimate** when 30 miles of highway were completed. Use a complete sentence in your answer.

   Use your graph to estimate when 60 miles of highway were completed. Use a complete sentence in your answer.

   Use your graph to estimate when 250 miles of highway were completed. Use a complete sentence in your answer.

   Use your graph to estimate when 130 miles of highway were completed. Use a complete sentence in your answer.

   Use your graph to estimate the number of miles that were completed 50 days before new construction started. Use a complete sentence in your answer.

   Use your graph to estimate the number of miles that were completed 100 days before new construction started. Use a complete sentence in your answer.

   Use your graph to estimate the number of miles that were completed 200 days after new construction started. Use a complete sentence in your answer.

Investigate Problem 1

8. Some of the other engineers who are working on this project also responded to the question and several of them had responses that were different from yours. Use complete sentences to explain why this could occur.

9. Prepare an overview of the project that will convince the project manager that this project is on schedule and that the project is running smoothly.

Looking Ahead to Chapter 4

Focus In Chapter 4, you will learn about functions and function notation, and you will find the domain and range of a function. You will also learn about real numbers and their properties, how to solve more complicated types of equations, and how to solve absolute value equations and inequalities.

Chapter Warm-up

Answer these questions to help you review skills that you will need in Chapter 4.

Solve each equation.

1. $5x = 43$
2. $-15 + 2x = 9$
3. $8x + 13 = 19$

Read the problem scenario below.

You and your friend decide to get after-school jobs to save money for a summer vacation. You each decide to get jobs at electronics stores as salespeople. You earn a base weekly salary of \$200 plus a 5% commission on your total sales. Your friend earns an 8% commission on her total sales, but no weekly salary.

4. You and your friend each sell \$5000 worth of electronics in one week. How much money do you earn in that week? How much money does your friend earn in that week?

5. You and your friend each sell \$7500 worth of electronics in one week. How much money do you earn in that week? How much money does your friend earn in that week?

4

6. You and your friend each earn \$3200 in one week. Find your total sales. Then find your friend's total sales.

Key Terms

inequality ■ p. 154
inequality symbol ■ p. 154
compound inequality ■ p. 155
graph an inequality ■ p. 157
solve an inequality ■ p. 157
relation ■ p. 162
input ■ p. 162
output ■ p. 162
function ■ p. 162
domain ■ p. 162
range ■ p. 162
set notation ■ p. 162
independent variable ■ p. 163
dependent variable ■ p. 163
function notation ■ p. 166
evaluate the function ■ p. 166
distributive property ■ p. 169
factoring ■ p. 172
common factor ■ p. 172
greatest common factor ■ p. 172
simplify ■ p. 172
terms ■ p. 172
combine like terms ■ p. 173
like terms ■ p. 173
rational number ■ p. 175
repeating decimal ■ p. 176
irrational number ■ p. 177
real number ■ p. 177
Venn diagram ■ p. 177
real number system ■ p. 178
whole number ■ p. 178
natural number ■ p. 178
integer ■ p. 178
closure ■ p. 178
additive identity ■ p. 179
multiplicative identity ■ p. 179
additive inverse ■ p. 179
multiplicative inverse ■ p. 179
reflexive property ■ p. 181
symmetric property ■ p. 181
transitive property ■ p. 181
absolute value ■ p. 187
opposites ■ p. 189
tolerance ■ p. 189

CHAPTER

4

Linear Functions and Inequalities

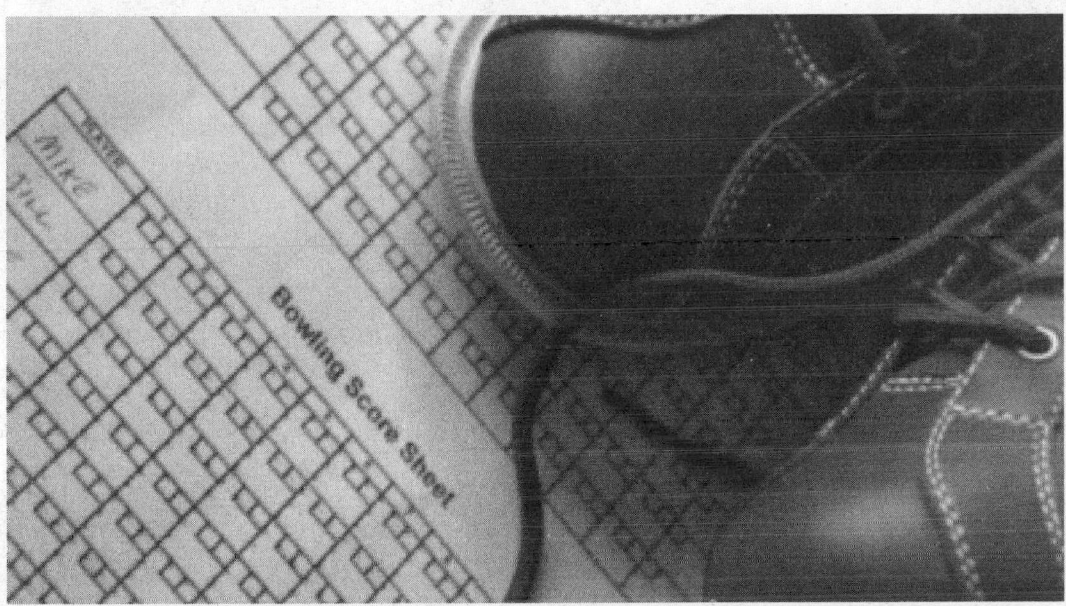

Bowling is a popular sport among people all over the world. In the United States, the most popular form of bowling is ten-pin bowling. Other forms of bowling include five-pin bowling, nine-pin skittles, and duckpin bowling, to name a few. In Lesson 4.3, you will find the cost for you and your friends to go bowling.

4

4.1 Up, Up, and Away!

Solving and Graphing Inequalities in One Variable

Objectives

In this lesson, you will:

- Write simple and compound inequalities.
- Graph inequalities.
- Solve inequalities.

Key Terms

- inequality
- inequality symbol
- compound inequality
- graph an inequality
- solve an inequality

SCENARIO You are studying Earth's atmosphere in science class. You learn that the atmosphere is made of four layers: the troposphere, the stratosphere, the mesosphere, and the thermosphere. Beyond the thermosphere is the exosphere, which extends until the atmosphere mixes with gases in space.

Problem 1 The Layers Above

In your science class, you are given the following information about these layers of the atmosphere.

Layer	Location
Troposphere	starts at Earth's surface and extends to 9 miles above Earth's surface
Stratosphere	starts just above troposphere and extends to 31 miles above Earth's surface
Mesosphere	starts just above stratosphere and extends to 53 miles above Earth's surface
Thermosphere	starts just above mesosphere and extends to 372 miles above Earth's surface
Exosphere	starts at top of thermosphere and extends upward

A. How many miles above the surface of Earth does the troposphere start? Use a complete sentence in your answer.

B. How many miles above the surface of Earth does the troposphere end? Use a complete sentence in your answer.

C. Does the stratosphere start at 9 miles above the surface of Earth? Use complete sentences to explain.

D. Does the exosphere start at 372 miles above the surface of Earth? Use complete sentences to explain.

Investigate Problem 1

1. Complete each statement below with "greater than," "less than," "greater than or equal to," or "less than or equal to."

   The height of the troposphere above Earth's surface

   is ____________________ 0 miles and

   is ____________________ 9 miles.

   The height of the stratosphere above Earth's surface

   is ____________________ 9 miles and

   is ____________________ 31 miles.

   The height of the mesosphere above Earth's surface

   is ____________________ 31 miles and

   is ____________________ 53 miles.

   The height of the thermosphere above Earth's surface

   is ____________________ 53 miles and

   is ____________________ 372 miles.

   The height of the exosphere above Earth's surface

   is ____________________ 372 miles.

2. **Just the Math: Writing Inequalities** You can use *inequalities* to represent the layers of Earth's atmosphere. An **inequality** is a statement that is formed by placing an **inequality symbol** between two expressions. Inequality symbols are $<$, $>$, $\leq$, and $\geq$.

   The symbol $<$ means "less than."

   The symbol $>$ means "greater than."

   The symbol $\leq$ means "less than or equal to."

   The symbol $\geq$ means "greater than or equal to."

   If you let x represent the number of miles above Earth's surface, you can write an inequality to represent each layer's position above Earth's surface. Complete each inequality using an inequality symbol.

   Troposphere: $x \square 0$ and $x \square 9$

   Stratosphere: $x \square 9$ and $x \square 31$

   Mesosphere: $x \square 31$ and $x \square 53$

   Thermosphere: $x \square 53$ and $x \square 372$

   Exosphere: $x \square 372$

4

Take Note

Be aware that certain words can indicate particular inequality symbols.
For instance:

- "under" indicates *less than*
- "over" indicates *greater than*
- "no more than" indicates *less than or equal to*
- "at least " indicates *greater than or equal to*

Investigate Problem 1

3. Just the Math: Writing Compound Inequalities
All but the last inequality that you wrote in Question 2 are *compound inequalities.* A **compound inequality** is formed when two inequalities are connected by the word *and* or the word *or*. If you let x represent any number, then you can write the two examples of compound inequalities below.

$1 < x \leq 5$ $\qquad\qquad$ $x \leq -3$ or $x > 6$

The first inequality is read as "all numbers greater than 1 *and* less than or equal to 5." The second inequality is read as "all numbers less than or equal to –3 *or* greater than 6."

Notice that $1 < x \leq 5$ is a compact form of the inequality $1 < x$ and $x \leq 5$. The inequality can also be written as $x > 1$ and $x \leq 5$.

Write your compound inequalities from Question 2 by using the compact form.

Troposphere: ____________

Stratosphere: ____________

Mesosphere: ____________

Thermosphere: ____________

Exosphere: ____________

4. Just the Math: Graphing Inequalities You can use a number line to represent your inequalities. The graph of an inequality in one variable is the set of all points that make the inequality true. For instance, the graph of the inequality $x \leq 4$ consists of the number 4 and all numbers smaller than 4, as shown below.

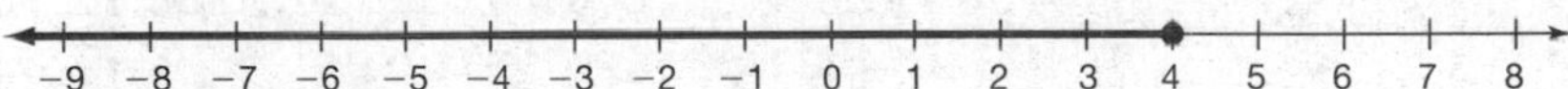

The endpoint 4 of the graph $x \leq 4$ is a solid dot because 4 is a solution of the inequality. If the endpoint of the graph is not a solution, draw an open dot for the endpoint.

Write an inequality for each graph shown.

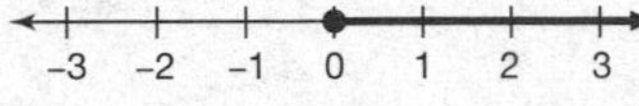

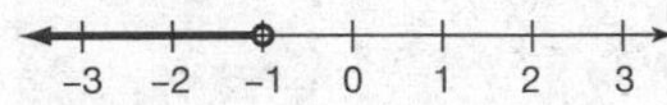

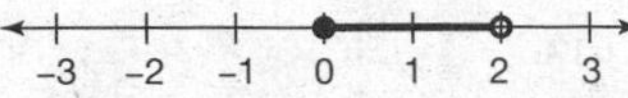

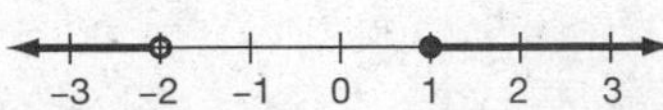

4

Investigate Problem 1

5. Graph the inequalities that you wrote in Question 3.

Troposphere:

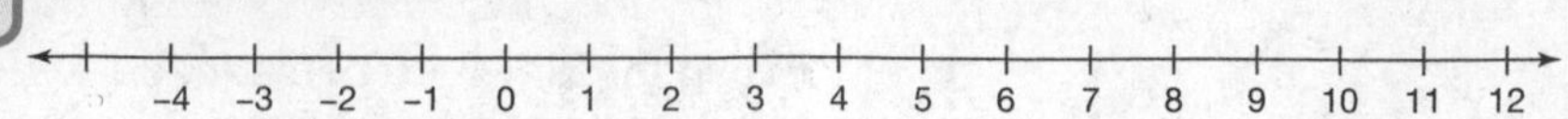

Stratosphere:

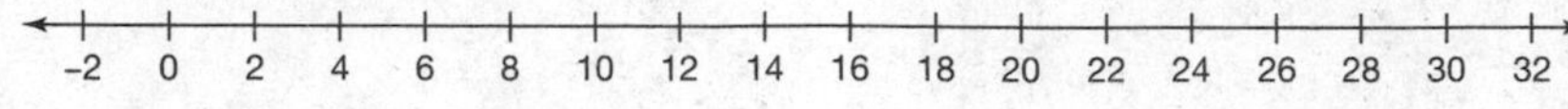

Mesosphere:

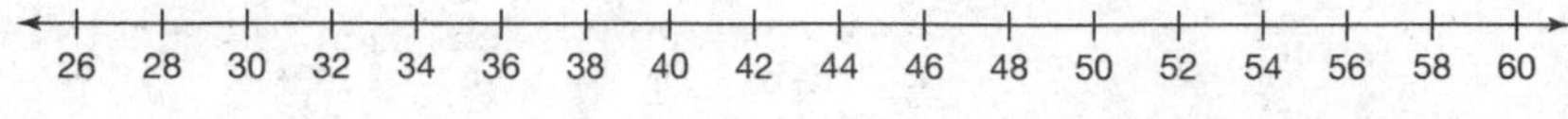

Thermosphere:

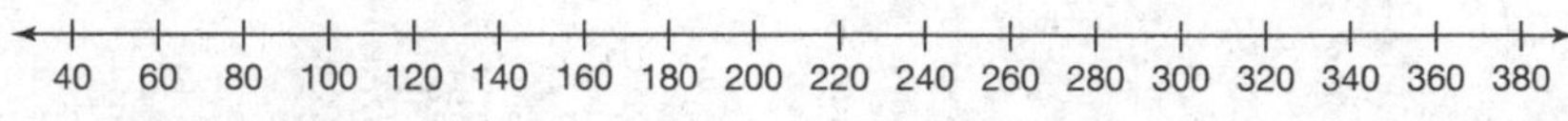

Exosphere:

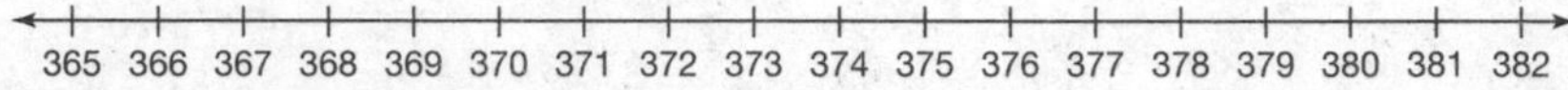

Take Note

If a point does not fall on one of the labeled units on the number line, then plot the point where you think it should be and label the point above the number line.

Problem 2 Aircraft in the Atmosphere

Different aircraft can travel in different layers of the atmosphere. Aircraft have what is called a service ceiling, or the highest altitude at which they can fly without stalling. The service ceilings of different aircraft are given in the table below.

Aircraft	Aircraft type	Approximate service ceiling (miles)
Blackhawk	Helicopter	4
Boeing 747	Commercial plane	6
Concorde	Commercial plane	11
X-15A-2	Research plane	67
X-33	Research plane	47

A. An X-33 aircraft is currently at an altitude of 15 miles. Can the X-33 climb 20 miles and stay under the service ceiling?

Can the X-33 climb 26 miles and stay under the service ceiling?

Can the X-33 climb 32 miles and stay under the service ceiling?

4

Take Note

You can indicate that two quantities are not equal by drawing a diagonal mark through the equals sign: ≠.

You can also use the diagonal mark through the less than to indicate that one quantity is not less than another quantity: ≮. This can also be done with the other three inequality symbols as ≯, ≰, and ≱.

Problem 2 Aircraft in the Atmosphere

Can the X-33 climb 35 miles and stay under the service ceiling?

B. Write and **graph an inequality** that describes the possible numbers of miles that the X-33 can climb from 15 miles and still be at or below its service ceiling. Use x to represent the number of miles that the X-33 climbs.

Investigate Problem 2

1. **Just the Math: Solving One-Variable Inequalities**
In Problem 2, you were actually writing and solving an inequality. To **solve an inequality** means to find the values of the variable that make the inequality true. The steps to solving an inequality are similar to the steps of solving an equation. That is, you want to get the variable by itself on one side of the inequality symbol by using the operations of addition, subtraction, multiplication, and division.

   What steps would you take to solve the equation $2x - 1 = 5$? Use complete sentences in your answer.

   You can use the same exact steps to solve the inequality $2x - 1 \le 5$. Solve the inequality and then graph the solution. Show all your work.

2. You can check your solution to an inequality by choosing a value that is in the solution set and substituting it into the original inequality. Choose a value in your solution of the inequality $2x - 1 \le 5$ and show that it is a solution.

3. What is the solution to the equation $2x - 1 = 5$? How do you think you should graph the solution? Explain your reasoning. Use complete sentences in your answer.

4

Investigate Problem 2

4. Whenever you *multiply* or *divide* each side of an inequality by a negative number, you have to *reverse* the inequality symbol. For instance, to solve the inequality $-2x > 14$, divide each side by –2 and reverse the inequality symbol.

$$-2x > 14$$

$$\frac{-2x}{-2} < \frac{14}{-2}$$

$$x < -7$$

Take Note

The list below shows the result of reversing the inequality symbol:

$<$ becomes $>$

$>$ becomes $<$

$\leq$ becomes $\geq$

$\geq$ becomes $\leq$

Solve each inequality and graph the solution.

$4x > 4$ $\qquad$ $\frac{x}{3} \leq -1$

$-2x < 4$ $\qquad$ $\frac{x}{-4} \geq 2$

5. Suppose that the Boeing 747 is currently at an altitude of 2 miles. Use x to represent the number of miles that the Boeing 747 climbs. Write an expression that represents the Boeing 747's altitude if it climbs x miles from its current altitude.

Now write and solve an inequality that describes the possible altitudes to which the Boeing 747 can climb and still be at or below the service ceiling. Show all your work. Use a complete sentence to summarize these altitudes.

Take Note

Whenever you see the share with the class icon, your group should prepare a short presentation to share with the class that describes how you solved the problem. Be prepared to ask questions during other groups' presentations and to answer questions during your presentation.

6. Suppose that the X-15A-2 is currently at an altitude of 28 miles. Use x to represent the number of miles that the X-15A-2 climbs. Write an expression that represents the X-15A-2's altitude if it climbs x miles from its current altitude.

Now write and solve an inequality that describes the possible altitudes to which the X-15A-2 can climb and still be at or below the service ceiling. Show all your work. Use a complete sentence to summarize these altitudes.

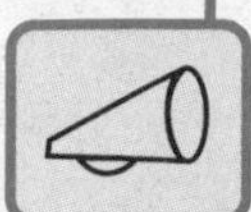

4.2 Moving a Sand Pile

Relations and Functions

Objectives

In this lesson, you will:

- Identify the inputs and outputs of relations.
- Determine whether relations are functions.
- Determine domains and ranges of functions.
- Identify independent and dependent variables.

Key Terms

- relation
- input
- output
- function
- domain
- range
- set relation
- independent variable
- dependent variable

Take Note

One cubic foot of sand is the amount of sand that would fill a container that is one foot long, one foot wide, and one foot deep.

SCENARIO You are a materials handler for a large sand and concrete company. This means that you must monitor all orders for sand, gravel, and concrete coming into and going out of the company's storage yard. Because of the large amount of material that is being moved, the storage yard is located next to a river and the material is moved on the river by barges.

Problem 1 Big Buckets of Sand

There is an enormous pile of sand, estimated to be 2500 cubic feet, which must be loaded onto a barge on the river. You have a bucket loader to transfer the sand to the barge. The bucket loader can pick up five cubic feet of sand in its bucket.

A. Find the amount of sand left in the pile after the bucket loader has transferred 50 buckets to the barge. Show all your work and use a complete sentence in your answer.

B. Find the amount of sand left in the 2500-cubic-foot-pile after the bucket loader has transferred 200 buckets to the barge. Show all your work and use a complete sentence in your answer.

C. Find the amount of sand left in the 2500-cubic-foot-pile after the bucket loader has transferred 400 buckets to the barge. Show all your work and use a complete sentence in your answer.

D. Find the amount of sand left in the 2500-cubic-foot-pile after the bucket loader has transferred 600 buckets to the barge. Show all your work and use a complete sentence in your answer.

E. Use a complete sentence to explain how you found your answers in parts (A) through (D).

Investigate Problem 1

1. You can represent the amount of sand left in the pile using the variable y and the number of buckets of sand removed from the pile using the variable x. Write an equation that represents the amount of sand left in the pile in terms of the number of buckets of sand that are removed.

Take Note

You will find that it is common to use the variables x and y when writing an equation.

2. Find the number of buckets of sand that were removed from the pile if 2000 cubic feet of sand remain in the pile. Show all your work and use a complete sentence in your answer.

   Find the number of buckets that were removed from the pile if 1550 cubic feet of sand remains in the pile. Show all your work and use a complete sentence in your answer.

   Find the number of buckets that were removed from the pile if 100 cubic feet of sand remains in the pile. Show all your work and use a complete sentence in your answer.

   Find the number of buckets that were removed from the pile if 3000 cubic feet of sand remains in the pile. Show all your work and use a complete sentence in your answer.

   Find the number of buckets that were removed from the pile if no sand remains in the pile. Show all your work and use a complete sentence in your answer.

Investigate Problem 1

Use a complete sentence to explain how you found your answers to Question 2.

Did all of your answers to Question 2 make sense? Use complete sentences to explain why or why not.

3. Complete the table of values that describes the relationship between the amount of sand in the pile and the number of buckets of sand removed.

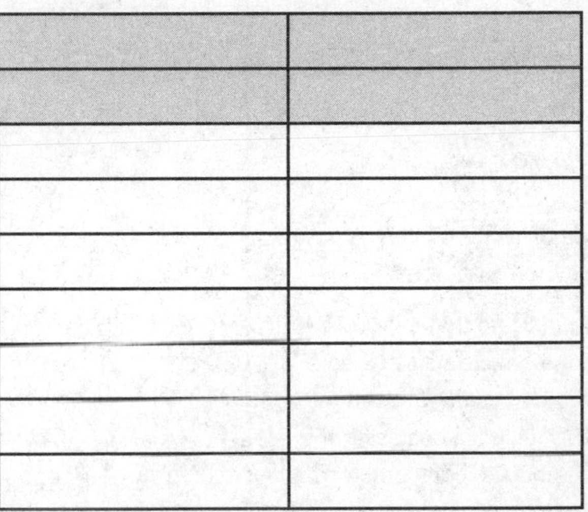

Quantity Name		
Unit		
Expression		

4. How does the amount of sand left in the pile change as the number of buckets of sand increases by one bucket? Use complete sentences to explain your reasoning.

How does the amount of sand left in the pile change as the number of buckets of sand increases by five buckets? Use complete sentences to explain your reasoning.

How does the amount of sand left in the pile change as the number of buckets of sand increases by one hundred buckets? Use complete sentences to explain your reasoning.

Investigate Problem 1

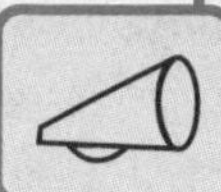

5. Write the ordered pairs given by the values in the table in Question 3.

6. Just the Math: Relations The ordered pairs that you wrote in Question 5 form a *relation*. A **relation** is any set of ordered pairs. The first coordinate of an ordered pair in a relation is the **input** and the second coordinate is the **output.** Identify the inputs and outputs of the relation given by the ordered pairs in Question 5. Use complete sentences in your answer.

7. Just the Math: Functions, Domain, and Range
A relation is a **function** if for each input there is exactly one output. Determine whether the relation below is a function. Use a complete sentence to explain your answer.

Relation: (2, 6), (3, 9), (4, 12), (5, 15), (6, 18)

Take Note

To indicate that a group of numbers are part of a set, you can use **set notation.** This includes enclosing the numbers in curly braces: { }. For instance, to indicate that the numbers 0, 1, and 2 belong to a set, use the notation {0, 1, 2}.

The set of all input values of a function is the **domain** of the function, and the set of all output values is the **range** of the function. The domain of the function above is {2, 3, 4, 5, 6} and the range is {6, 9, 12, 15, 18}.

Decide whether each relation is a function. If the relation is a function, identify the domain and range. If the relation is not a function, explain why. Use complete sentences in your answer.

Relation: (–3, 2), (–1, 5), (1, 8), (3, 11), (5, 14)

Relation: (–2, 4), (–1, 1), (0, 0), (1, 1), (2, 4)

Relation: (1, 4), (3, 6), (4, 8), (4, 2), (5, 10)

Do the set of ordered pairs from Question 5 represent a function? If so, identify the domain and range. Use a complete sentence in your answer.

Investigate Problem 1

8. **Just the Math: Independent and Dependent Variables** In Lesson 1.7, we first discussed independent and dependent variables. In a function, the **independent variable** represents the input values of the function and the **dependent variable** represents the output values. What are the independent and dependent variables in the problem situation? Use a complete sentence in your answer.

9. Use the grid below to create a graph of the data from the table in Question 3. First, choose your bounds and intervals. Be sure to label your graph clearly.

Variable quantity	Lower bound	Upper bound	Interval

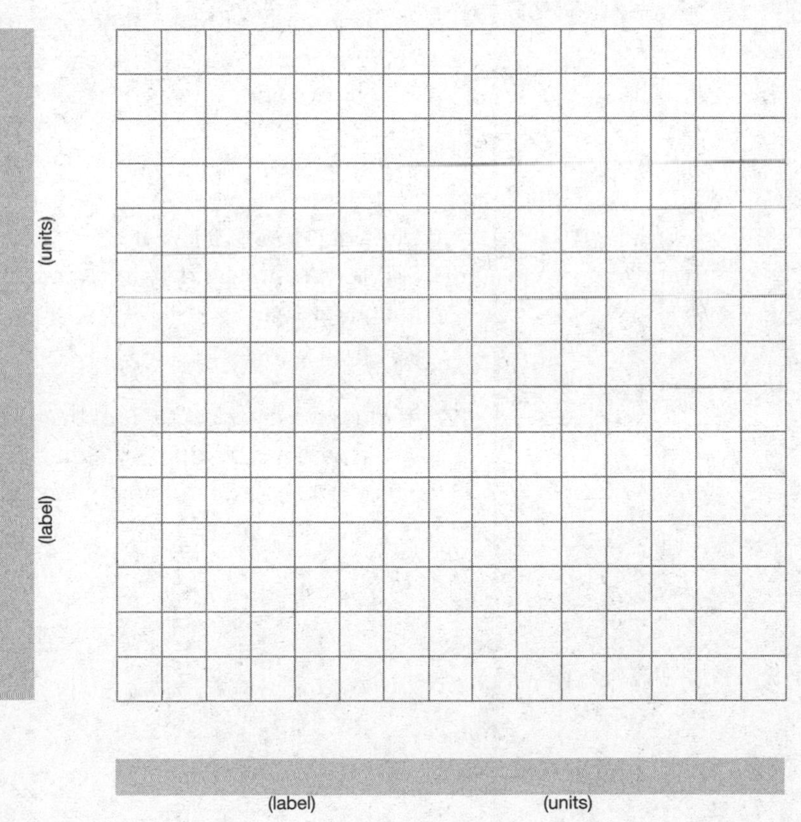

Investigate Problem 1

10. Use your graph to find the number of buckets of sand that were removed from the pile if 1000 cubic feet of sand remain. Use a complete sentence in your answer.

Use your graph to find the number of buckets of sand that were removed from the pile if 500 cubic feet of sand remain. Use a complete sentence in your answer.

Use your graph to find the number of buckets of sand that were removed from the pile if 2200 cubic feet of sand remain. Use a complete sentence in your answer.

11. Use your graph to find the amount of sand left in the pile if 100 buckets of sand were removed. Use a complete sentence in your answer.

Use your graph to find the amount of sand left in the pile if 250 buckets of sand were removed. Use a complete sentence in your answer.

Use your graph to find the amount of sand left in the pile if 350 buckets of sand were removed. Use a complete sentence in your answer.

12. If you were given a graph of this problem situation, how would you create a table and write an equation for the problem situation? Use complete sentences in your explanation.

4.3 Let's Bowl!

Evaluating Functions, Function Notation, Domain, and Range

Objectives

In this lesson, you will:

- Write and evaluate functions.
- Write and use function notation.
- Determine the domain and range of functions.

Key Terms

- function
- function notation
- evaluate a function
- domain
- range

SCENARIO You and your friends decide to go bowling on a Friday evening. It costs $2.25 to rent a pair of shoes and $2.75 to bowl one game. Neither you nor your friends have shoes, so you all must rent them.

Problem 1 The Cost of Bowling

A. Find the total cost of bowling if you bowl two games. Show all your work and use a complete sentence in your answer.

B. Find the total cost of bowling if you bowl four games. Show all your work and use a complete sentence in your answer.

C. Find the total cost of bowling if you bowl six games. Show all your work and use a complete sentence in your answer.

D. Write an equation that represents the total cost y in dollars in terms of the number of games bowled x.

4

Investigate Problem 1

1. The equation that you wrote in part (D) above is a compact way to represent a set of ordered pairs. In other words, you can use the equation to generate ordered pairs. What ordered pair can you generate if you find the total cost of bowling 3 games? Show all your work.

Does your equation represent a relation? Use a complete sentence to explain your answer.

Investigate Problem 1

2. **Just the Math: Function** A function relates two quantities. One way to express a function is to use a rule written as an equation that describes how the two quantities (the input and the output) relate. Remember that for a function there is only one output for each input. Is your equation from part (D) a function? Use complete sentences to explain.

3. **Just the Math: Function Notation** As you will see later, not every equation represents a function. For this reason, it is often helpful to use **function notation** to indicate that an equation is also a function. In function notation, a letter is used as the name of a function. For instance, consider the function given by the equation $y = 2x - 9$. Let's name the function f and replace y by the notation $f(x)$, where $f(x)$ means "the value of f at x." So, using function notation, the equation becomes $f(x) = 2x - 9$.

   Let f be the name of your function that gives the total cost of bowling in terms of the number of games bowled. Use function notation to write the equation.

Take Note

Common function names are f, g, and h. All other letters except for e, i, l, I and O can be used as function names. The letters x and y are usually avoided because they are typically used as variables.

4. **Just the Math: Evaluating a Function** Suppose that you were asked to find the total cost of bowling 7 games. Use complete sentences to explain how you would find the total cost.

   What you were actually doing above was **evaluating the function** f at the value $x = 7$. In function notation, you were finding $f(7)$ by replacing x with the value 7.

   $f(x) = 2.25 + 2.75x$

   $f(7) = 2.25 + 2.75(7)$

   $= 21.50$

   Use complete sentences to describe what it means to evaluate a function at a particular value.

5. Evaluate each function at the specified value. Show your work.

   $f(x) = x - 5$ at $x = 12$

   $g(x) = 4x$ at $x = 5$

   $h(x) = 6x + 7$ at $x = -2$

   $f(x) = 8 - 3x$ at $x = 4$

4

Take Note

The domain of a function is all possible numbers that x can be so that either $f(x)$ is a number or $f(x)$ makes sense in the real-life problem situation.

Investigate Problem 1

6. When you use a function to describe a real-life situation, you will discover that the domain of the function in terms of the real-life situation may be different from the domain of the function without considering the real-life situation. For instance, consider your bowling cost function. Describe the values of x that are in the domain of the function, taking the problem situation into account. In other words, describe the values of x that make sense to use in the problem situation. Explain your reasoning. Use complete sentences in your answer.

Now consider your bowling function again, this time without considering the problem situation. What numbers could you use for x and get a number for $f(x)$?

In the case that the domain of x includes any number, we say that the domain is "all real numbers." You can write the domain using set notation as {all real numbers}.

What is the domain of the bowling function if you do not consider the problem situation? Use a complete sentence in your answer.

Now suppose that you know that you only have four hours to bowl and it takes about one half hour to bowl one game. What is the domain of the bowling function now? Use a complete sentence in your answer.

7. For each domain in Question 6, find the corresponding range of the function.

Domain: {1, 2, 3, 4, ...} Range: ____________________

Domain: {any real number} Range: ____________________

Domain: {1, 2, 3, 4, 5, 6, 7, 8} Range: ____________________

4

4.4 Math Magic

The Distributive Property

Objectives

In this lesson, you will:

- Write and use distributive properties.
- Use distributive properties to factor expressions.
- Use distributive properties to simplify expressions.

Key Terms

- distributive property
- factoring
- common factor
- greatest common factor
- simplify
- terms
- combine like terms
- like terms

SCENARIO Your friend claims that she has a foolproof method for multiplying numbers in her head. You give her two different multiplication problems to solve and she quickly and correctly does the multiplication in her head. How did she do it?

Problem 1 Fast Math

You first ask your friend to find the product of 8 and 240. Find this product. Show all your work.

Your friend gives you the correct answer in less than 3 seconds. She explains her method to you: first multiply 8 and 200 to get 1600. Then multiply 8 and 40 to get 320. Then add 1600 and 320 to get 1920. Write an expression that shows the mathematical steps that your friend did to find the answer.

Investigate Problem 1

1. **Just the Math: Distributive Property of Multiplication over Addition** Your friend actually used a property of mathematics called the *distributive property of multiplication over addition* to quickly find the product. There are four different forms of the distributive property. Using words, the distributive property of multiplication over addition states that "the product of a number and a sum is equal to the sum of the products of the number with each addend." Using symbols, this property can be written as, "If a, b, and c are any numbers, then $a \cdot (b + c) = a \cdot b + a \cdot c$."

   Write an equation that shows how your friend found the product of 8 and 240.

   Find the product of 9 and 47 by using the distributive property of multiplication over addition. Show all your work.

4

Investigate Problem 1

2. **Just the Math: Distributive Property of Multiplication over Subtraction** Next, your friend quickly finds that the product of 4 and 149 is 596. She again explains her method to you: first multiply 4 and 150 to get 600. Then multiply 4 and 1 to get 4. Finally subtract 4 from 600 to get 596. Your friend has demonstrated the Distributive Property of Multiplication over Subtraction. Write an equation that shows how your friend found the product.

   Now write the property using symbols.

3. **Just the Math: Distributive Property of Division over Addition** The distributive property of division over addition states that if *a*, *b*, and *c* are any numbers and $c \neq 0$, then $\frac{a+b}{c} = \frac{a}{c} + \frac{b}{c}$. Choose three numbers and use them to show that this property is true. Then use complete sentences to write the property in words using the words *sum* and *quotient*.

4. **Just the Math: Distributive Property of Division over Subtraction** The distributive property of division over subtraction states that if *a*, *b*, and *c* are any numbers and $c \neq 0$, then $\frac{a-b}{c} = \frac{a}{c} - \frac{b}{c}$. Choose three numbers and use them to show that this property is true. Then use complete sentences to write the property in words using the words *difference* and *quotient*.

4

Investigate Problem 1

5. Use a distributive property to simplify each expression. Show all your work.

$6(10 + 9)$

$7(15 - 3)$

$\frac{15 + 9}{3}$

$\frac{24 - 32}{4}$

$7(3x + 4)$

$\frac{12 - 3x}{3}$

4

Problem 2 Math Magician

Your friend now claims that she can do even more complicated calculations in her head. You give her the problem $8(17) + 8(23)$ and she quickly gives you the correct result, 320. She tells you that you can just add 17 and 23 to get 40 and then multiply the result by 8. Write an expression that shows the initial mathematical steps that your friend took. Then set this expression equal to the original problem.

Take Note

To find a **common factor** of two numbers, you can write each number as the product of its prime factors. For instance, 12 = 2(2)(3) and 30 = 2(3)(5). So 2, 3, and 2(3) = 6 are common factors of 12 and 30. The **greatest common factor** of 12 and 30 is 6.

Investigate Problem 2

1. **Just the Math: Factoring Out the Greatest Common Factor** Your friend was using the distributive property in reverse to find the answer. Using the distributive property in reverse is called **factoring.** Because 8 is a common factor of 8(17) and 8(23), you can use the distributive property to factor the 8 from each product. This is because 8(17) + 8(23) = 8(17 + 23) is the same as 8(17 + 23) = 8(17) + 8(23). In other words, equality works in both directions, which you will see in the next lesson.

   Use the distributive property to factor the *greatest common factor* from each expression. Then **simplify** the expression. Show all your work.

   4(13) − 4(8)   13(7) + 13(3)

2. The distributive properties also hold true for algebraic expressions, which means that you can also use them in reverse to factor an *algebraic expression*. For instance, the expression $2x + 10$ can be written as $2(x) + 2(5)$. According to the distributive property of multiplication over addition, $2(x) + 2(5) = 2(x + 5)$. Use the distributive property in reverse to rewrite each algebraic expression. Show all your work.

   $6x + 12$ $8x - 4$

3. **Just the Math: Combining Like Terms** You can also use the distributive properties to *simplify* algebraic expressions. For instance, consider the expression $3x + 10x$. What factors do the addends have in common?

   You can use a distributive property to rewrite each sum.

   $3x + 10x = x(\square + \square)$ Use a distributive property.

   $= x(\square)$

   $= \square$

   $5ab + 16ab = ab(\square + \square)$ Use a distributive property.

   $= ab(\square)$

   $= \square$

Take Note

The **terms** of an expression are the parts that are added together or subtracted from each other.

Investigate Problem 2

4. You have just **combined like terms.** The terms $3x$ and $10x$ are called **like terms** because their variable portions are the same.

Use a distributive property to simplify the algebraic expression. Show all your work.

$8x + 24x$ $21x - 7x$

$12x - 30x$ $36x + 15x$

Use complete sentences to write a simple rule that you can use to add or subtract like terms.

4

5. **Just the Math: Using an Area Model** You know some math magic of your own that you want to show to your friend. You draw and label the rectangle below.

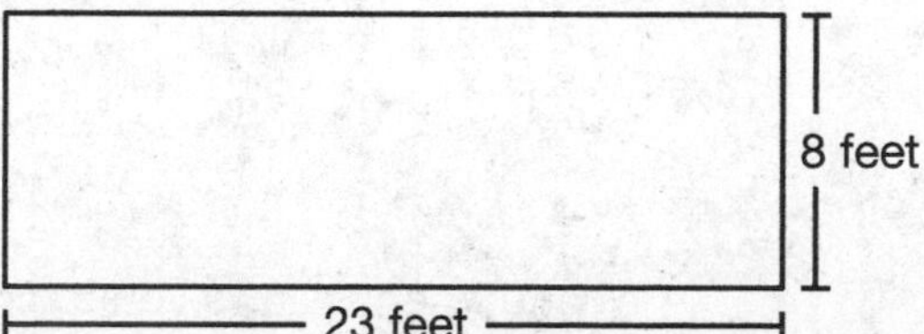

You then show your friend that you can find the area of the rectangle in two ways. You can find the area by finding the product of the rectangle's width and length.

Area = (8 feet)(23 feet)

Investigate Problem 2

You can also divide the rectangle and find the area of two rectangles, as shown below, and then find the area of each rectangle and add to get the total.

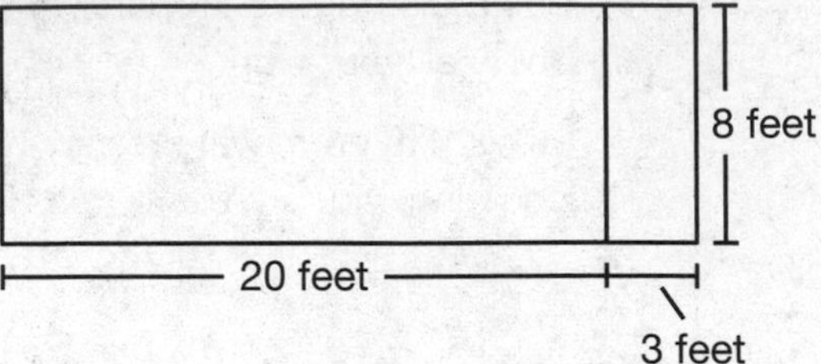

Area = (8 feet)(20 feet) + (8 feet)(3 feet)

Find both areas. Which area is easier to find? Use a complete sentence to explain your reasoning.

Write two expressions for the total area of the two rectangles below. Then find the total area. Show all your work.

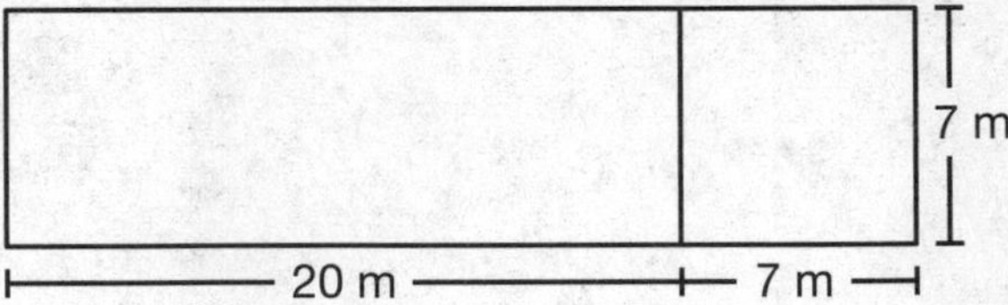

What property allows you to find the total area of the rectangles in two different ways? Write your answer using a complete sentence.

4

4.5 Numbers in Your Everyday Life

Real Numbers and Their Properties

Objectives

In this lesson, you will:

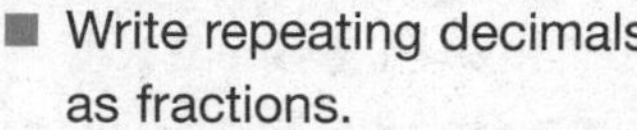

- Write repeating decimals as fractions.
- Compare real numbers.
- Classify real numbers.
- Understand the properties of real numbers.

Key Terms

- rational number
- repeating decimal
- irrational number
- real number
- Venn diagram
- real number system
- whole number
- natural number
- integer
- closure
- additive identity
- multiplicative identity
- additive inverse
- multiplicative inverse

SCENARIO Every day, you use different kinds of numbers. Whether you are paying for an item at a store, taking a measurement, or counting, you are using numbers from the *real number system.*

Problem 1 Where Are All the Numbers?

A. Give examples of as many different kinds of numbers that you use as you can. Then use complete sentences to describe how these numbers are different from one another.

In Lesson 3.6, you studied integers. When you form a quotient of two integers so that the denominator is not zero, you form a **rational number.**

B. Use a complete sentence to describe a real-life situation in which you would use a rational number with a numerator that is less than the denominator.

C. Use a complete sentence to describe a real-life situation in which you would use a rational number with a numerator that is greater than the denominator.

D. Use a complete sentence to describe a real-life situation in which you would use a rational number with a numerator that is equal to the denominator.

E. Do you think that every integer is a rational number? Use complete sentences to explain your reasoning.

Investigate Problem 1

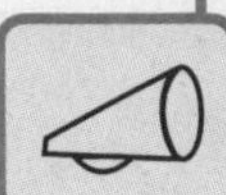

1. In Lesson 3.6, you wrote decimals as fractions. How would you classify these kinds of decimals? Use a complete sentence to explain your reasoning.

2. **Just the Math: Repeating Decimals** Consider the decimal 0.333... . This decimal is made up of 3s that repeat forever. Is this kind of decimal, called a **repeating decimal,** a rational number?

Take Note

Another way to write a repeating decimal is to write a bar over the digit or digits that repeat. For instance, $0.333... = 0.\overline{3}$ and $0.151515... = 0.\overline{15}$.

You can write the decimal 0.333... as a rational number. Let w represent this rational number. So,

$w = 0.333...$.

Because this is an equation, you can multiply each side by 10.

$10w = 3.333...$ $\quad\quad$ $10(0.333...) = 3.333...$

Now subtract the first equation from the second equation.

$$\begin{array}{r} 10w = 3.333... \\ -w = 0.333... \\ \hline 9w = 3 \end{array}$$

Solve the equation $9w = 3$. What have you shown? Use a complete sentence in your answer.

4

3. Use the method shown in Question 2 to write each repeating decimal as a rational number. Show all your work.

0.444... $\quad\quad$ 0.0808...

Take Note

When the repeating portion of the decimal is one digit, you multiply each side of your equation by 10. When the repeating portion is two digits, you multiply each side by 100. You can continue this idea for different numbers of repeating digits.

Investigate Problem 1

4. **Just the Math: Irrational Numbers** From the work you have done so far, what can you conclude about the decimal representation of a rational number? Use a complete sentence in your answer.

Just as there are rational numbers, there are numbers that cannot be written as the quotient of two integers. These numbers are called **irrational numbers.** What do you think is true about the decimal representation of an irrational number? Use a complete sentence in your answer.

The most famous irrational number is the number π. This number is the ratio of a circle's circumference to its diameter. Supercomputers have been used to try to find as many digits of π as possible. If you use a calculator, you will see that $\pi \approx 3.14159265\ldots$.

Although the digits of π have been computed to more than 200 million digits, no repeating pattern exists.

5. Graph all of the numbers below on the same number line. Then list the numbers from least to greatest.

$-\frac{2}{3}$, 4.4, -0.25, $\frac{11}{10}$, $0.\overline{5}$, 1.12345..., $\frac{1}{2}$, π

6. **Just the Math: Real Numbers** The rational numbers and the irrational numbers together form the **real numbers.** You can use a **Venn diagram** to represent all real numbers. The Venn diagram on the next page describes the relationships among the sets of numbers within the set of real numbers.

4

Take Note

The **whole numbers** are the set {0, 1, 2, 3, 4, ...} and the **natural numbers** are the set {1, 2, 3, 4, ...}.

Investigate Problem 1

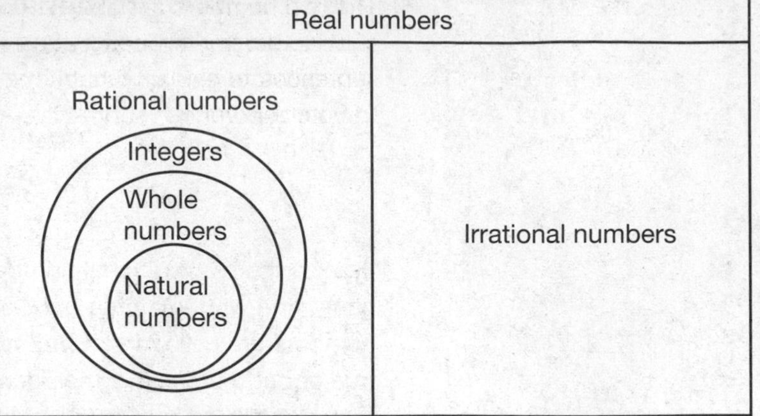

Use the Venn diagram to answer the following questions.

If a real number is a rational number, can it be an irrational number? Use complete sentences to explain.

Is every whole number an integer? If not, give an example that supports your reasoning.

Is every rational number a natural number? If not, give an example that supports your reasoning.

4

Problem 2 The Real Number System

The real numbers, together with their properties and operations, form the **real number system.** You have already been using some of the properties in previous lessons. We will formally state these properties below. Note that the distributive properties also apply to real numbers.

A. Closure A set of numbers is **closed** under an operation if the result of the operation on two numbers in the set is a number in the set.

Is the set of real numbers closed under addition? That is, if a and b are any real numbers, then is $a + b$ a real number? Use an example to support your answer.

Problem 2 The Real Number System

The real numbers are also closed under the operations of subtraction, multiplication, and division. Use complete sentences to explain what it means for the set of real numbers to be closed under subtraction, multiplication, and division.

Consider the set of integers. Is the set of integers closed under the operations of addition, subtraction, multiplication, and division? Use examples to support your answers.

B. Additive Identity An **additive identity** is a number such that when you add it to a second number, the sum is the second number.

In other words, let a be the additive identity and let b be any real number. Then $a + b = b$. What is the value of a? Use complete sentences in your answer.

C. Multiplicative Identity A **multiplicative identity** is a number such that when you multiply it by a second number, the product is the second number.

In other words, let a be the multipicative identity and let b be any real number. Then $a \cdot b = b$. What is the value of a? Use complete sentences in your answer.

D. Additive Inverse Two numbers are **additive inverses** of each other if their sum is the additive identity.

Use symbols to complete the representation of the property.

Let a be any real number. Then $a + \boxed{} = 0$.

Check your representation by using a real number for a. Show your work.

E. Multiplicative Inverse Two numbers are **multiplicative inverses** of each other if their product is the multiplicative identity.

Problem 2 The Real Number System

Use symbols to complete the representation of the property.

Let a be any real number. Then $a \cdot \square = 1$.

Check your representation by using a real number for a. Show your work.

F. **Commutative Property of Addition** The order in which you add two or more numbers does not affect the sum.

Use symbols to complete the representation of the property.

Let a and b be any real numbers. Then $a + b = \square$.

Check your representation by using real numbers for a and b. Show your work.

G. **Commutative Property of Multiplication** The order in which you multiply two or more numbers does not affect the product.

Use symbols to complete the representation of the property.

Let a and b be any real numbers. Then $a \cdot b = \square$.

Check your representation by using real numbers for a and b. Show your work.

H. **Associative Property of Addition** If you are adding three numbers, the sum is not affected by the way in which you group two of the three numbers.

Use symbols to complete the representation of the property.

Let a, b, and c be any real numbers.
Then $(a + b) + c = \square + (\square)$.

Check your representation by using real numbers for a, b, and c. Show your work.

I. **Associative Property of Multiplication** If you are multiplying three numbers, the product is not affected by the way in which you group two of the three numbers.

Use symbols to complete the representation of the property.

Let a, b, and c be any real numbers.
Then $(a \cdot b) \cdot c = \square \cdot (\square)$.

4

Problem 2 The Real Number System

Check your representation by using real numbers for a, b, and c. Show your work.

J. Properties of Equality

Reflexive Property For any real number a, $a = a$.

Use a real number to demonstrate this property.

Symmetric Property For any real numbers a and b, if $a = b$, then $b = a$.

Use real numbers to demonstrate this property.

Transitive Property For any real numbers a, b, and c, if $a = b$ and $b = c$, then $a = c$.

Use real numbers to demonstrate this property.

4

Investigate Problem 2

1. For each equation, identify the property that is used in each step. The first equation is done as an example.

$6(5 + 3) - 40 = 7(2 - 5) + 29$	Given problem
$30 + 18 - 40 = 7(2 - 5) + 29$	Distributive Property of Multiplication Over Addition
$30 + 18 - 40 = 14 - 35 + 29$	Distributive Property of Multiplication Over Subtraction
$(30 + 18) - 40 = (14 - 35) + 29$	Associative Property of Addition
$48 - 40 = -21 + 29$	Add and subtract.
$8 = 8$	Reflexive Property of Equality

Investigate Problem 2

$4(3x + 20) = \frac{140 + 80}{5}$ Given problem

$12x + 80 = \frac{140 + 80}{5}$ ______

$12x + 80 = \frac{140}{5} + \frac{80}{5}$ ______

$12x + 80 = 28 + 16$ ______

$12x + 80 = 44$ ______

$12x + 80 - 80 = 44 - 80$ ______

$12x = -36$ ______

$\frac{12x}{12} = \frac{-36}{12}$ ______

$x = -3$ ______

$30 + (x + 8) + 4 = 2(10 + 5) + 3$ Given problem

$30 + x + (8 + 4) = 2(10 + 5) + 3$ ______

$30 + x + 12 = 2(10 + 5) + 3$ ______

$x + (30 + 12) = 2(10 + 5) + 3$ ______

$x + 42 = 2(10 + 5) + 3$ ______

$x + 42 = 2(10) + 2(5) + 3$ ______

$x + 42 = 20 + 10 + 3$ ______

$x + 42 = (20 + 10) + 3$ ______

$x + 42 = 30 + 3$ ______

$x + 42 = 33$ ______

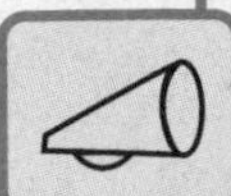

$x + 42 - 42 = 33 - 42$ ______

$x = -9$ ______

4.6 Technology Reporter

Solving More Complicated Equations

Objectives

In this lesson, you will:

- Solve equations with variables on both sides.

Key Terms

- solve
- simplify

SCENARIO You are a technology reporter for a local newspaper. One of your duties is to review and compare technology equipment, services, and software for consumers. You are currently comparing different high-speed Internet services.

Problem 1 Comparing DSL

A. You have been comparing the DSL (digital subscriber line) services of two different companies. One company, Colossal Communications, charges \$200 for the modem and other equipment plus \$30 per month for the service. Write an expression that represents the total cost of the service, using x to represent the number of months that you have the service.

B. The other company that you are studying, Lightning Bolt Internet Services, charges nothing for the modem and other equipment and charges \$40 per month for the service. Write an expression that represents the total cost of the service, using x to represent the number of months that you have the service.

C. As part of your consumer report, you want to determine the number of months after which the cost of using either service is the same. Use a complete sentence to explain how you can use the expressions from part (A) and part (B) to write an equation to find the number of months.

Are the costs the same for 1 month of service? Show all your work and use a complete sentence in your answer.

Are the costs the same for 6 months of service? Show all your work and use a complete sentence in your answer.

4

Investigate Problem 1

1. You solved equations in Chapter 3. How is this equation different from the equations you solved in Chapter 3? Use a complete sentence in your answer.

2. The process of solving this equation is no different than the process of solving the equations from Chapter 3. First, move the variables to one side of the equation. Do this by subtracting 30x from each side of the equation. Complete this step.

$$200 + 30x = 40x$$

$200 + 30x$ [ ] $= 40x$ [ ]

Now you need to simplify each side of the equation. What real number property must you use to do this?

Simplify each side of the equation by combining like terms.

Finally, how do you isolate the variable? Use a complete sentence in your answer.

Finish solving the equation. What does the solution mean in the context of the problem situation? Use complete sentences in your answer.

When the services costs are the same, what is the cost? Show all your work and use a complete sentence in your answer.

3. Suppose that Lightning Bolt Communications changes its pricing policy and decides to start charging \$50 for the modem and other equipment. Write a new equation that you can use to determine the number of months it takes for the total costs to be the same.

Take Note

Remember that when you are performing operations on an equation, you have to preserve the *property of equality.* For instance, when you subtract the expression 30x from one side of the equation, you must also subtract it from the other side.

4

Investigate Problem 1

4. How do you think you should solve this equation? Use a complete sentence in your answer.

Complete the steps to solve the equation.

$$200 + 30x = 50 + 40x$$

$$200 + 30x - 30x = 50 + 40x - \square$$

$$\square = 50 + \square$$

$$200 - \square = 50 + 10x - \square$$

$$\square = \square$$

$$\frac{150}{\square} = \frac{10x}{\square}$$

$$\square = x$$

After how many months are the service costs the same? What is the cost? Use complete sentences in your answer.

Problem 2 Cellular Phone Question

A. At the newspaper office, you receive a letter from a reader who would like you to recommend the best "pay as you go" cellular phone plan. The reader has two teenaged children and wants to choose the best plan. The first plan has a flat charge of \$.40 each day plus \$.08 per minute of phone calls. Write an expression for the daily cost of one phone, letting x represent the number of minutes of phone calls used in one day.

The expression below shows the total cost for two phones. Complete the expression.

2(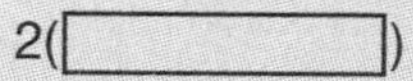)

The second plan charges \$.25 per minute of phone calls with no additional daily charge. Write an expression for the daily cost of two phones, letting x represent the number of minutes of phone calls used in one day.

B. Write the equation you would use to find the number of minutes of phone calls it takes for the costs to be the same.

4

Investigate Problem 2

1. Before you begin to solve an equation, it is a good idea to first look at each side of the equation to determine whether you can first simplify each side separately and then isolate the variable. Simplify each side of your equation in part (B). Show all your work.

   Now solve the equation.

2. Write a complete sentence to interpret your solution in terms of the problem situation.

3. Solve each equation. Show all your work. Be sure to check your answer in the original equation.

   $4x = 3x + 20$ $\qquad$ $9x + 2 = 14x - 13$

   $6(x - 4) = 30$ $\qquad$ $5(x + 2) = 3x - 4$

   $5x + 8 = 2(3x + 1)$ $\qquad$ $4(3x - 1) = 2(x + 3)$

4

4.7

Rules of Sports

Solving Absolute Value Equations and Inequalities

Objectives

In this lesson, you will:

- Find the absolute value of a number.
- Evaluate absolute value expressions.
- Solve absolute value equations.
- Solve and graph absolute value inequalities.

Key Terms

- absolute value
- opposites
- tolerance

SCENARIO In most sports, not only are there rules for how to play the game, but there are also specifications for any equipment that is used to play the game. For instance, in professional baseball, there are specifications for the size, weight, and positioning of the bases.

Problem 1 The Weight of a Baseball

A baseball manufacturer must check the weights of its baseballs to ensure that they meet the weight specified in the official rules for professional baseball. The manufacturer watches for a certain number of balls to fail to meet the specifications. This usually indicates that the machines that create the balls need to be serviced.

The table below shows five baseballs that failed to meet specifications and the number of grams that the baseballs were above or below specifications. A negative number indicates a weight that is below specifications and a positive number indicates a weight that is above specifications.

Baseball	A	B	C	D	E
Difference (grams)	–2	–5	–1	2	3

A. In order to determine which baseballs are the farthest from the specifications, you can write the *absolute value* of each number in the table. The **absolute value** of a number is the distance between the number and 0 on the number line.

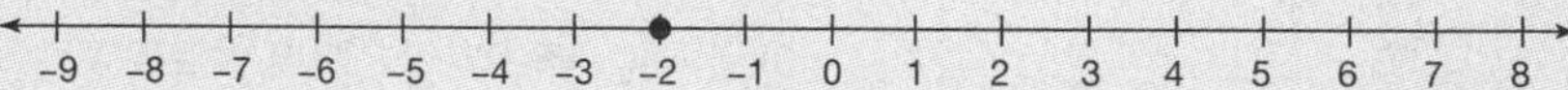

The distance between –2 and 0 is 2 units, so the absolute value of –2 is 2. The symbol for absolute value is | |. We indicate the absolute value of –2 by writing $|-2| = 2$. Graph the other values in the table on the number line above. Then find the absolute value of each difference.

B. Which baseball is the farthest from the specifications?

C. Can an absolute value ever be negative? Use complete sentences to explain your reasoning.

4

4

Investigate Problem 1

1. **Just the Math: Absolute Value, Addition, and Subtraction** A *conjecture* is a possible explanation that can be tested by further investigation. Suggest a possible conjecture that explains how to find the value of absolute value expressions that involve addition or subtraction, such as $|-4 + 7|$ and $|-4| + |7|$.

   Write two other examples, similar to the expressions above, that use addition of absolute values to test your conjecture. Then write two examples that use subtraction of absolute values to test your conjecture. Show all your work.

   Evaluate each expression. Show all your work.

   $|3 + 8|$ $|-3 + 8|$

   $|3 - 8|$ $|3| + |8|$

   $|-3| + |8|$ $|3| - |8|$

2. **Just the Math: Absolute Value, Multiplication, and Division** Evaluate each expression. Show all your work. Then use complete sentences to describe how you should evaluate absolute value expressions that involve multiplication or division.

   $|4(5)|$ $|(-4)(5)|$

   $|-4| \cdot |5|$ $|4| \cdot |5|$

   $\left|\frac{12}{-3}\right|$ $\frac{|12|}{|-3|}$

Investigate Problem 1

3. You can also use absolute value to find the distance, or the number of units between two numbers. Distance is always expressed as a positive number and can be found by taking the absolute value of the difference of the two numbers. Find the distance between the numbers by writing an absolute value expression.

Distance between 2 and 7

Distance between –2 and –7

Distance between 2 and –7

4. On a number line, when two numbers are the same distance from 0 but are on opposite sides of 0, the numbers are **opposites.** Graph the numbers –6, 8, –1, 0, and 4 on the number line. Then graph the opposite of each number.

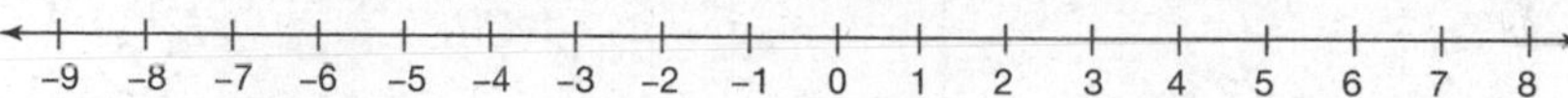

Complete the following statement: *Two numbers are opposites if they have the same* ________________ *but different signs.*

Problem 2 Possible Baseball Weights

The official rules state that a range of weights for a baseball are acceptable. One way that the ranges of weights are stated is by stating the *tolerances.* A **tolerance** is the amount by which a quantity is allowed to vary from the normal or target quantity. Suppose that the baseball manufacturer has set the target weight as 145.045 grams on its machines and is allowing a tolerance of 3.295 grams. So, the manufactured baseball's weight can be 3.295 grams above or below the target weight.

A. Write an expression that represents the difference between a manufactured baseball's weight and the target weight. Use x to represent a manufactured baseball's weight.

B. Suppose that the manufactured baseball weighs more than the target weight. Write an equation that represents the largest acceptable difference in the weights. Then solve the equation to determine the heaviest acceptable baseball's weight.

Problem 2 Possible Baseball Weights

C. Suppose that the manufactured baseball weighs less than the target weight. Solve the equation below that represents the largest acceptable difference in the weights. This solution represents the baseball's lightest acceptable weight.

$x - 145.045 = -3.295$

Investigate Problem 2

1. Just the Math: Solving Absolute Value Equations When you solved the two equations in Problem 2, you were actually solving the *absolute value equation* $|x - 145.045| = 3.295$. When we solve an absolute value equation, we use the fact that the expression inside the absolute value symbol can be positive or negative. For instance, consider the equation $|x| = 3$. The absolute values of what two numbers are equal to 3? Use a complete sentence in your answer.

So, to solve the equation $|x| = 3$, set the expression inside the absolute value symbol equal to –3 and 3 to write two equations:

$x = 3$ or $x = -3$

Now consider the equation $|x - 1| = 6$. To solve this equation, you need to set the expression inside the absolute value symbol equal to two numbers. What are the numbers? Use a complete sentence in your answer. Then write the two equations.

Now solve each equation. Show all your work.

Finally, check your answer by substituting your solutions into the original equation. Show all your work.

Note that whenever you solve an absolute value equation, you first must isolate the absolute value expression on one side of the equation. For instance, to isolate the absolute value expression in $|x| - 4 = 2$, add four to each side to get $|x| = 6$.

4

Investigate Problem 2

2. Solve the absolute value equation. Show all your work and check your solutions.

$|x - 1| = 4$

$|x + 6| = 0$

$|3x + 1| = 8$

$|x + 4| - 1 = 5$

Problem 3 The Final Ruling on a Baseball's Weight

In Problem 2, we considered the heaviest and lightest a baseball could be and still fall within the specifications. Remember that the tolerance is the amount that the weight can vary. So, to determine *all* of the acceptable weights that the manufactured baseball could be, we could use the *absolute value inequality* $|x - 145.045| \leq 3.295$, where x is the manufactured baseball's weight in grams.

A. A manufactured baseball weighs 147 grams. Is this baseball acceptable? Show all your work and use a complete sentence in your answer.

B. A manufactured baseball weighs 140.8 grams. Is this baseball acceptable? Show all your work and use a complete sentence in your answer.

4

Problem 3 The Final Ruling on a Baseball's Weight

C. A manufactured baseball weighs 148.34 grams. Is this baseball acceptable? Show all your work and use a complete sentence in your answer.

D. A manufactured baseball weighs 141.75 grams. Is this baseball acceptable? Show all your work and use a complete sentence in your answer.

E. A manufactured baseball weighs 149 grams. Is this baseball acceptable? Show all your work and use a complete sentence in your answer.

F. What is the heaviest acceptable weight? What is the lightest acceptable weight? Use a complete sentence in your answer.

G. Complete the inequality that describes all the acceptable weights, where x is the baseball's weight.

$\square \le x \le \square$

4

Investigate Problem 3

1. Consider the inequality $|x| < 4$. The solution of this inequality is every value of x whose absolute value is less than 4. Use the number line to determine the solutions of this inequality. Write your answer as an inequality.

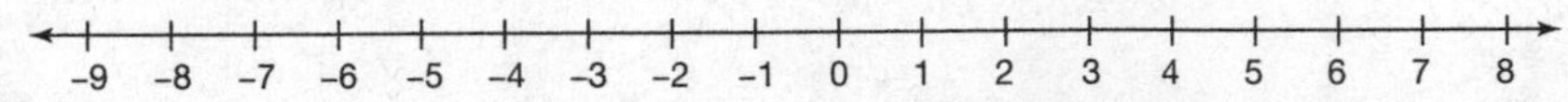

Consider the inequality $|x| > 4$. The solution of this inequality is every value of x whose absolute value is greater than 4. Use the number line to determine the solutions of this inequality. Write your answer as an inequality.

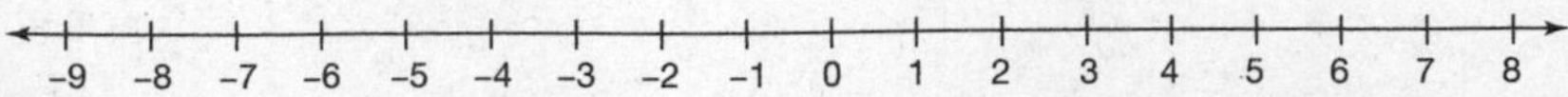

Investigate Problem 3

What kind of inequalities are the solutions to the absolute value inequalities? Use a complete sentence in your answer.

2. **Just the Math: Solving Absolute Value Inequalities**
Absolute value inequalities can take four different forms, shown below. To solve an absolute value inequality, you must first write it in a simpler form. The equivalent (simpler) forms of each kind of inequality are also shown below.

Absolute Value Inequality	Equivalent Inequality
$\lvert ax + b \rvert < c$	$-c < ax + b < c$
$\lvert ax + b \rvert \le c$	$-c \le ax + b \le c$
$\lvert ax + b \rvert > c$	$ax + b < -c$ or $ax + b > c$
$\lvert ax + b \rvert \ge c$	$ax + b \le -c$ or $ax + b \ge c$

Solve the absolute value inequality and graph your solution on a number line.

$\lvert x + 3 \rvert < 4$

$\lvert x - 5 \rvert > 2$

$\lvert 2x - 4 \rvert \ge 6$

$\lvert 2x + 1 \rvert < 5$

$\lvert x \rvert - 4 > 5$

$\lvert x \rvert + 6 < 10$

4

Looking Ahead to Chapter 5

Focus In Chapter 5, you will learn how to write linear equations in a variety of forms. You will learn what the different pieces of a linear equation represent, and how they apply to real-life situations.

Chapter Warm-up

Answer these questions to help you review skills that you will need in Chapter 5.

Evaluate the equation $y = 3x - 17$ for each value of x.

1. $x = 3$

2. $x = 0$

3. $x = -8$

Evaluate the equation $y = -7x + 24$ for each value of x.

4. $x = -4$

5. $x = 14$

6. $x = -9$

Solve each inequality.

7. $3x - 5 < 19$

8. $8x + 20 \geq 36$

9. $15 < 4 - 7x$

Read the problem scenario below.

In order to entice people to work for them, a local used car lot advertises that it will pay a commission to its employees in the amount of 12% of the employee's total sales for each month.

10. How much in total sales would an employee have to sell in one month to earn $2700 in commission?

11. How much would an employee earn in commission if they sold $76,000 worth of used cars in one month?

5

Key Terms

CHAPTER 5

Writing and Graphing Linear Equations

One of the most frequently performed full-length plays by high schools in the United States is William Shakespeare's *A Midsummer Night's Dream*. In Lesson 5.7, you will determine the costs to produce flyers to advertise a school play.

5.1 Widgets, Dumbbells, and Dumpsters

Multiple Representations of Linear Functions

Objective

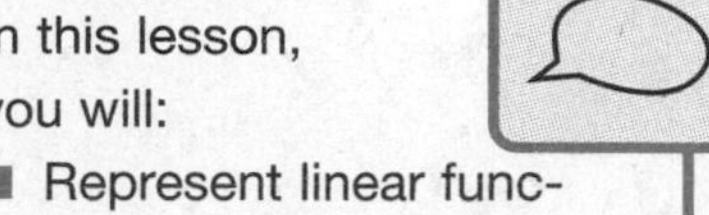

In this lesson, you will:

- Represent linear functions using equations, tables, and graphs.

Key Terms

- linear equation
- linear function
- function notation

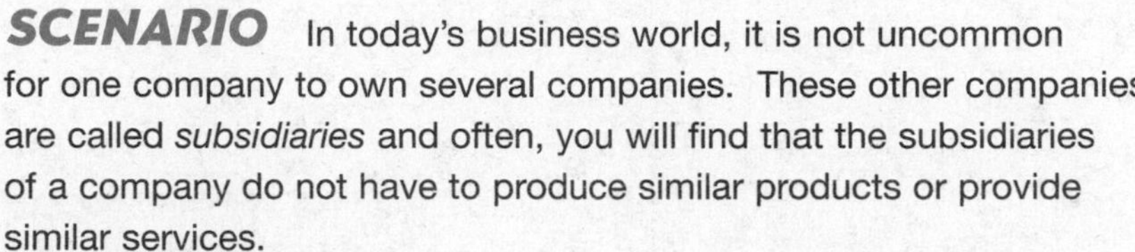

SCENARIO In today's business world, it is not uncommon for one company to own several companies. These other companies are called *subsidiaries* and often, you will find that the subsidiaries of a company do not have to produce similar products or provide similar services.

Problem 1 Making and Selling Widgets

One subsidiary of a company makes and sells widgets. The subsidiary sells the widgets for $4 each and adds a $9 shipping charge to the cost of an order.

A. Use complete sentences to describe how you would find the total cost of an order of 12 widgets.

B. Use complete sentences to describe how you would find the total cost of an order of 257 widgets.

C. Use complete sentences to describe how you would find the total cost of an order of any number of widgets.

Investigate Problem 1

1. Write an equation that gives the total cost of an order in terms of the number of widgets. Use x to represent the number of ordered widgets and use y to represent the total cost in dollars.

2. Use your equation to find the total cost of an order of 12 widgets. Show all your work and use a complete sentence in your answer.

Use your equation to find the total cost of an order of 257 widgets. Show all your work and use a complete sentence in your answer.

Investigate Problem 1

3. Use your equation to find the number of widgets that can be ordered for $89. Show all your work and use a complete sentence in your answer.

Use your equation to find the number of widgets that can be ordered for $2069. Show all your work and use a complete sentence in your answer.

Use your equation to find the number of widgets that can be ordered for $7789. Show all your work and use a complete sentence in your answer.

Use complete sentences to describe how you found your answers in Question 3.

4. Complete the table of values that shows the relationship between the total cost and the number of widgets ordered.

Quantity Name	Widgets ordered	Total cost
Unit		
Expression		
	12	
		89
		2069

5

Investigate Problem 1

5. Use the grid below to create a graph of the data from the table on the previous page. First, choose your bounds and intervals. Be sure to label your graph clearly.

Variable quantity	Lower bound	Upper bound	Interval

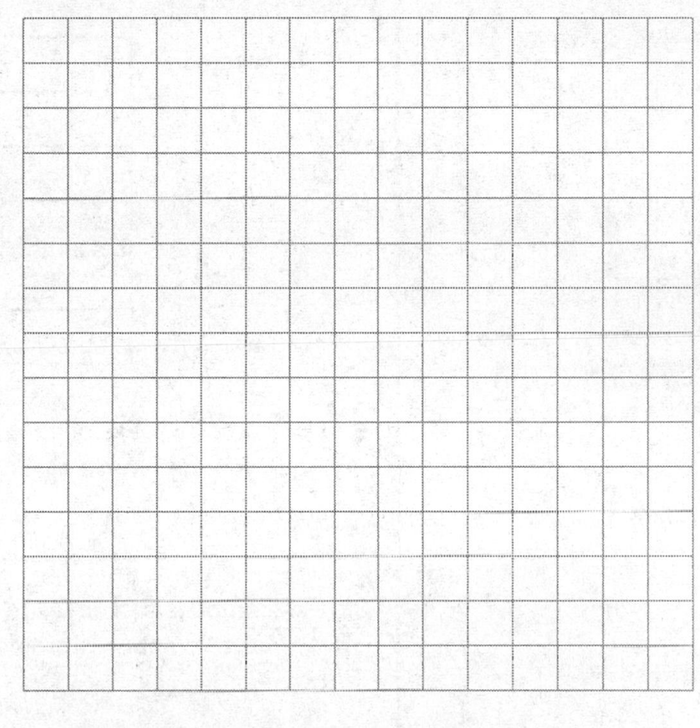

6. Use your graph to approximate the total cost of ordering 900 widgets. Then explain how you found your answer, using complete sentences.

Use your graph to approximate the number of widgets that can be ordered for $6000. Then explain how you found your answer, using complete sentences.

5

Problem 2 Making and Selling Dumbbells

Another subsidiary of the company makes and sells dumbbells. The subsidiary sells the dumbbells by the pound for $.50 per pound. Because dumbbells are heavy, the subsidiary adds an $18 shipping-and-handling charge to the cost of an order.

A. Complete the table of values that shows the relationship between the total cost and the number of pounds of dumbbells ordered.

Quantity Name	**Dumbbells ordered**	**Total cost**
Unit		
Expression		
	120	
		89
	300	

B. Use complete sentences to describe how to find the total cost when you are given the number of pounds of dumbbells ordered.

C. Use complete sentences to describe how to find the number of pounds of dumbbells ordered when you are given the total cost of the order.

Investigate Problem 2

1. Use the grid on the next page to create a graph of the data from the table above. First, choose your bounds and intervals. Be sure to label your graph clearly.

Variable quantity	Lower bound	Upper bound	Interval

Investigate Problem 2

2. Use your graph to determine whether the total cost of an order of 220 pounds of dumbbells should be $115. Use complete sentences to explain.

Use your graph to determine whether the total cost of an order of 260 pounds of dumbbells should be $155. Use complete sentences to explain.

Use your graph to determine whether the total cost of an order of 200 pounds of dumbbells should be $118. Use complete sentences to explain.

3. Describe a different way in which you could determine whether the ordered weights and corresponding total costs are correct. Use complete sentences in your answer.

Problem 3 Dumpster Rentals

Yet another subsidiary of the company is a company that provides a dumpster rental service. The company will deliver a dumpster to a customer's site for a one-time fee of $150. The company also charges a fee each day that the dumpster is rented. The table below shows the cost per week (7 days) without the delivery charge. You will complete the last column of the table in part (B).

Length of rental	Cost	Cost per day
weeks	dollars	dollars per day
1	192.50	
2	385.00	
3	577.50	
4	770.00	
5	962.50	

A. You want to create a new table that shows the rental cost for different numbers of days. What information do you need to create this table? Use a complete sentence in your answer.

B. How can you determine the cost of a rental for one day by using the rows in the table above? Use a complete sentence in your answer. Then complete the last column of the table.

C. Complete the table of values below that shows the cost of a rental for 1 to 7 days. Include the one-time cost of dumpster delivery.

Quantity Name	Duration of rental	
Unit	days	
	1	
	2	
	3	
	4	
	5	
	6	
	7	

5

Investigate Problem 3

1. Write an equation that you can use to find the total cost in terms of the number of days of the rental. Identify your variables and use a complete sentence in your answer.

2. Use the grid below to create a graph of the data from the table on the previous page. First, choose your bounds and intervals. Be sure to label your graph clearly.

Variable quantity	Lower bound	Upper bound	Interval

(label) (units)

(label) (units)

3. Use your graph to approximate the number of days that a dumpster can be rented for $680. Use complete sentences to explain how you got your answer.

5

Investigate Problem 3

Use your graph to approximate the total cost of renting a dumpster for 20 days. Use complete sentences to explain how you found your answer.

4. Is your graph in Question 2 the graph of a function? Use complete sentences to explain your reasoning.

5. If a graph is a straight non-vertical line, is it the graph of a function? Use complete sentences to explain your reasoning.

6. **Just the Math: Linear Equations and Linear Functions** When the graph of an equation is a straight line, then the equation is a *linear equation*. A **linear equation** in two variables is an equation in which each of the variables is raised to the first power (such as x, rather than x^2) and each variable appears at most once. All linear equations, except those in the form $x = a$ (where a is any number), are also **linear functions.** However, not every equation is a function. You will discover this later in this text.

   Is the equation that you wrote for Investigate Problem 1, Question 1 a linear function? Use complete sentences to explain your reasoning.

   Is the graph for Investigate Problem 2, Question 1 the graph of a linear function? Use complete sentences to explain your reasoning.

   If the graph in Investigate Problem 2, Question 1 is that of a linear function, write the equation using function notation.

7. Look at the three equations that you have written so far in this lesson. What do you think is a general form of a linear equation? Use a complete sentence in your answer.

5.2 Selling Balloons

Finding Intercepts of a Graph

Objectives

In this lesson, you will:

- Interpret the meaning of intercepts in a problem situation.

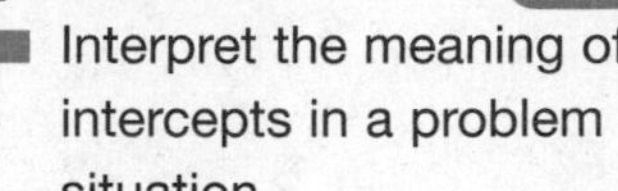

- Find intercepts graphically.
- Find intercepts algebraically.

Key Terms

- *x*-intercept
- *y*-intercept

Take Note

Recall from Lesson 1.2 that the *profit* is the amount of money that you have left after you subtract the costs from the amount of money that you make.

SCENARIO Your local community group wants to raise money to fix one of the playgrounds in your area. Your group decides to sell balloons because they are popular with young children.

Problem 1 Making a Difference

Your group buys a box of Mylar balloons with zoo animals printed on them for $10 and decides to sell the balloons for $2 each.

A. What is your profit if your group sells 30 balloons? Show all your work and use a complete sentence in your answer.

B. What is your profit if your group sells 5 balloons? Show all your work and use a complete sentence in your answer.

C. What is your profit if your group sells 3 balloons? Show all your work and use a complete sentence in your answer.

D. What does your answer to part (C) mean in terms of the problem situation? Use complete sentences in your answer.

E. Write an equation for the problem situation. Use x to represent the number of balloons sold. Use y to represent the profit in dollars.

Investigate Problem 1

1. Use your equation to find the value of y when x is 7. Show all your work and use a complete sentence in your answer.

Use your equation to find the value of y when x is –9. Show all your work and use a complete sentence in your answer.

5

Investigate Problem 1

Does an x-value of –9 make sense in the problem situation? Use complete sentences to explain.

Use your equation to find the value of y when x is 25. Show all your work and use a complete sentence in your answer.

2. Use your equation to find the value of x when y is 10. Show all your work and use a complete sentence in your answer.

Use your equation to find the value of x when y is –16. Show all your work and use a complete sentence in your answer.

Use your equation to find the value of x when y is –10. Show all your work and use a complete sentence in your answer.

3. Write the ordered pairs that you created in Question 2.

4. Write three more sets of ordered pairs that satisfy your equation.

5. Use the grid on the next page to graph the ordered pairs in Questions 3 and 4. Then create a graph of your equation. Use the bounds and intervals given below. Be sure to label your graph clearly.

Variable quantity	Lower bound	Upper bound	Interval
Balloons sold	–5	10	1
Profit	–16	14	2

Investigate Problem 1

6. Use complete sentences to explain which point on your graph represents in the problem situation.

7. Name the point where your graph crosses the *x*-axis. What does this point tell you about the relationship between the profit and the number of balloons sold? Use complete sentences in your answer.

Name the point where your graph crosses the *y*-axis. What does this point tell you about the relationship between the profit and the number of balloons sold? Use complete sentences in your answer.

5

Investigate Problem 1

8. Just the Math: Intercepts In Question 7, you found the *intercepts* of the graph. The **x-intercept** of a graph is the *x*-coordinate of the point where the graph crosses the *x*-axis. The **y-intercept** of a graph is the *y*-coordinate of the point where the graph crosses the *y*-axis. Name the *x*- and *y*-intercepts of the graph in Question 5. Use a complete sentence in your answer.

Find the *x*- and *y*-intercepts of each graph below.

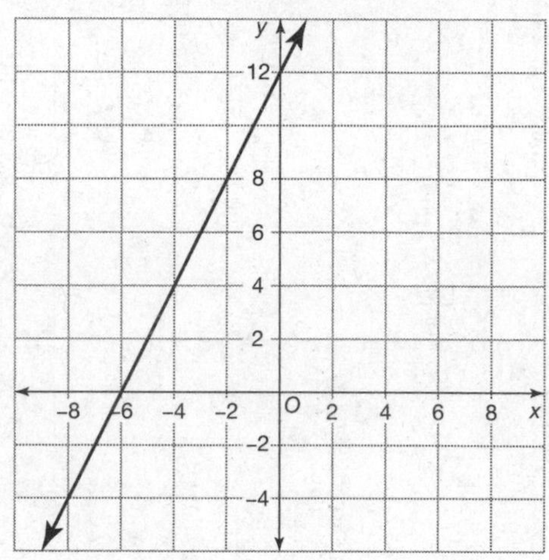

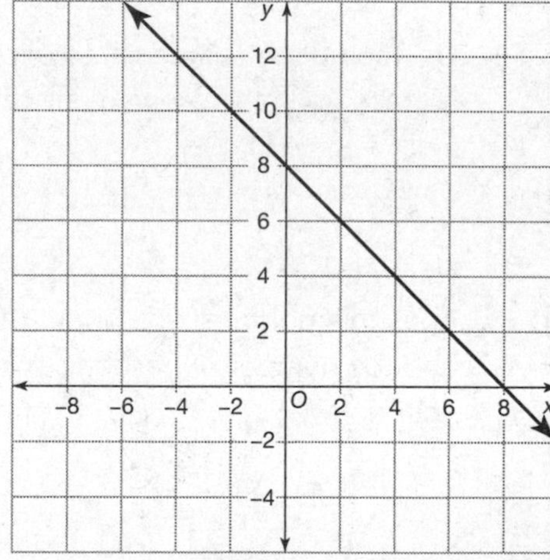

9. What do you notice about a point that contains the *x*-intercept? What do you notice about a point that contains the *y*-intercept? Use complete sentences in your answer.

5

Investigate Problem 1

10. **Just the Math: Finding Intercepts Algebraically** If you know the equation of a graph, you can *algebraically* find the intercepts. To *algebraically* find the x-intercept, find the value of x when y is 0. For instance, the x-intercept of the graph of $y = 2x + 4$ is –2 because:

$0 = 2x + 4$	Substitute 0 for y.
$-4 = 2x$	Subtract 4 from each side.
$-2 = x$	Divide each side by 2.

To *algebraically* find the y-intercept, find the value of y when x is 0. For instance, the y-intercept of the graph of $y = 2x + 4$ is 4 because:

$y = 2(0) + 4$	Substitute 0 for x.
$= 0 + 4$	Multiply.
$= 4$	Add.

Algebraically find the intercepts of the graph of the equation. Show all your work. Then graph the equation to check your answer.

$y = 3x - 9$

5

Investigate Problem 1

$y = -4x + 8$

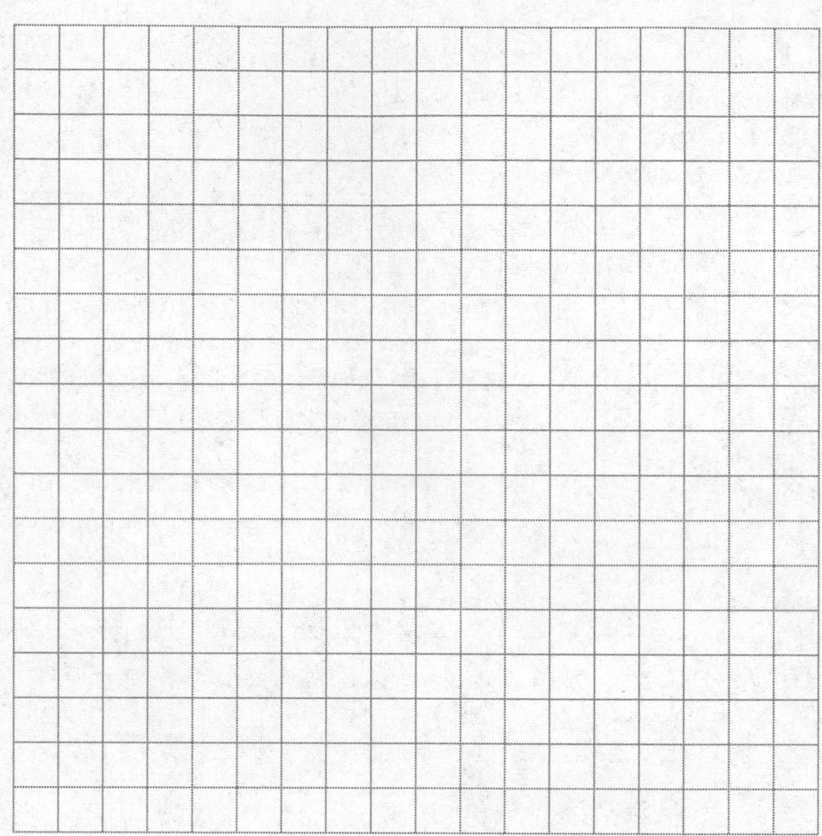

11. Use what you know about *x*-intercepts and *y*-intercepts to complete each statement.

In the ordered pair (6, 0) the _____ is the *x*-intercept.

In the ordered pair (0, –5) the _____ is the *y*-intercept.

A vertical line that does not lie on an axis has one ___________________ and no ___________________.

A horizontal line that does not lie on an axis has one ___________________ and no ___________________.

A straight line that is neither vertical nor horizontal has ________ *x*-intercept(s) and ________ *y*-intercept(s).

5.3 Recycling and Saving

Finding the Slope of a Line

Objectives

In this lesson, you will:

- Find unit rates.
- Describe slopes of lines.
- Find rates of change.
- Find slopes of lines through two points.

Key Terms

- unit rate
- slope
- vertical change
- horizontal change
- rate of change

Glass recycled
Lower Bound: 0
Upper Bound: 15
Interval: 1

Earnings
Lower Bound: 0
Upper Bound: 0.75
Interval: 0.05

SCENARIO Your class is raising money for a new wheelchair ramp at a community center. Your class plans to collect and recycle materials such as aluminum and glass to earn money.

Problem 1 Recycling Glass

The scrap yard where you recycle the materials pays \$.05 per pound of glass.

A. Write an equation that relates the weight of the recycled glass in pounds to the amount of money in dollars earned from recycling. Use x to represent the weight of the recycled glass and use y to represent the amount of money earned.

B. Write a sentence that predicts what the graph of the equation will look like. Then use the grid below to create a graph of your equation. In your graph, use the bounds and intervals given at the left. Be sure to label your graph clearly.

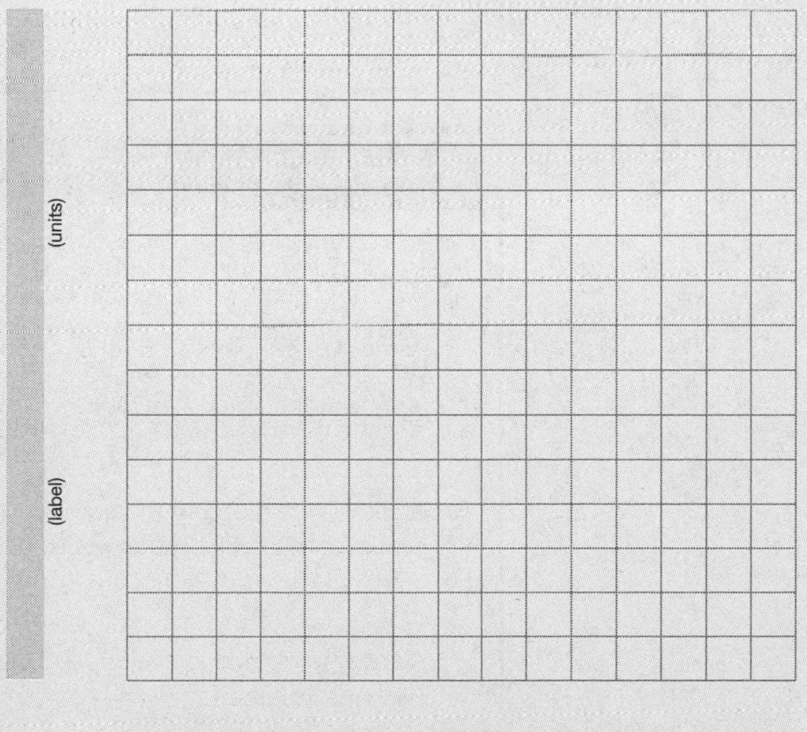

5

Take Note

Recall that a *unit rate* is a rate per one given unit.

Investigate Problem 1

1. Use your graph to find the increase in earnings when the amount of recycled glass increases by 1 pound. Use a complete sentence in your answer. Then write a unit rate that compares the increase in earnings to the increase in the amount of recycled glass.

2. Use your graph to find the increase in earnings when the amount of recycled glass increases by 5 pounds. Use a complete sentence in your answer. Then write a unit rate that compares the increase in earnings to the increase in the amount of recycled glass.

3. Use your graph to find the increase in earnings when the amount of recycled glass increases by 10 pounds. Use a complete sentence in your answer. Then write a unit rate that compares the increase in earnings to the increase in the amount of recycled glass.

4. Explain how you found your answers in Questions 1 through 3. What do you notice about the unit rates? Use complete sentences in your answer.

Problem 2 Recycling Plastic

The scrap yard pays $.40 for each pound of plastic that you recycle.

A. Write an equation that relates the weight of the recycled plastic in pounds to the amount of money in dollars earned from recycling. Use x to represent the weight of the recycled plastic and use y to represent the amount of money earned.

B. What will the graph of the equation look like? Use a complete sentence to explain your reasoning.

5

Problem 2 Recycling Plastic

Plastic recycled
Lower Bound: 0
Upper Bound: 15
Interval: 1

Earnings
Lower Bound: 0
Upper Bound: 6
Interval: 0.40

C. Use the grid below to create a graph of your equation. Use the bounds and intervals given at the left. Be sure to label your graph clearly.

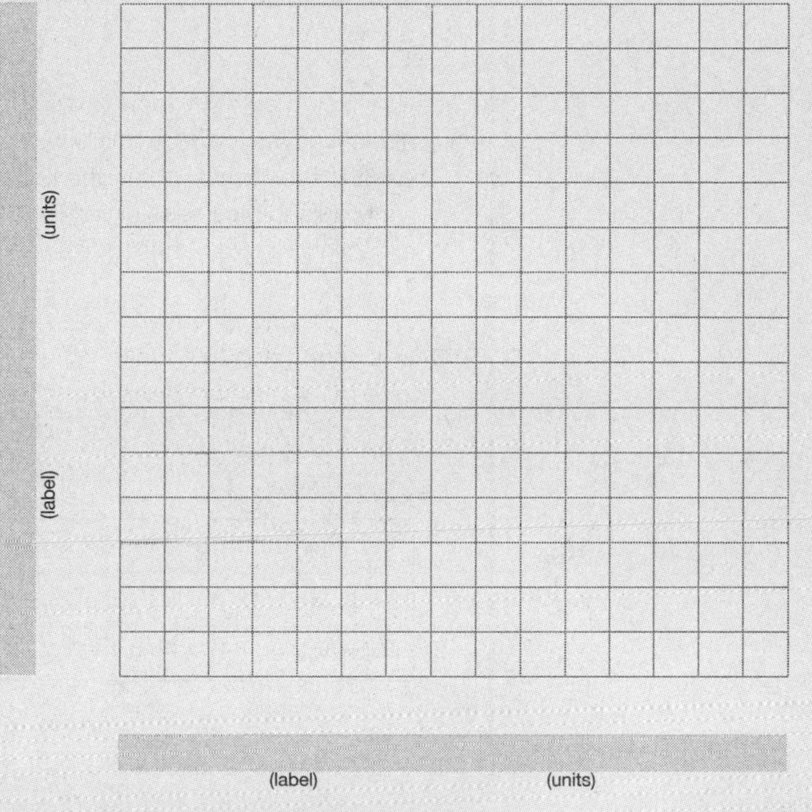

Investigate Problem 2

1. Use your graph to find the increase in earnings when the amount of recycled plastic increases by 1 pound. Use a complete sentence in your answer. Then write a unit rate that compares the increase in earnings to the increase in the amount of recycled plastic.

2. Use your graph to find the increase in earnings when the amount of recycled plastic increases by 5 pounds. Use a complete sentence in your answer. Then write a unit rate that compares the increase in earnings to the increase in the amount of recycled plastic.

5

Investigate Problem 2

3. Use your graph to find the increase in earnings when the amount of recycled plastic increases by 10 pounds. Use a complete sentence in your answer. Then write a unit rate that compares the increase in earnings to the increase in the amount of recycled plastic.

4. Explain how you found your answers in Questions 1 through 3. What do you notice about the unit rates? Use complete sentences in your answer.

5. Use the grid below to graph both equations together. Use the bounds and intervals given below. Be sure to label your graph clearly.

Variable quantity	Lower bound	Upper bound	Interval
Material recycled	0	15	1
Earnings	0	6	0.40

5

Investigate Problem 2

6. How are the graphs for glass and plastic recyclables similar? How are they different? Use complete sentences to explain your reasoning.

7. Just the Math: Slope as a Rate of Change
In Problems 1 and 2, you were using your graphs to determine the change in earnings given the change in the amount of recycled material. The change in earnings was represented by a vertical change in the graph, and the change in the amount of recycled material was represented by a horizontal change in the graph. The **slope** of a line is the ratio of the vertical change to the horizontal change.

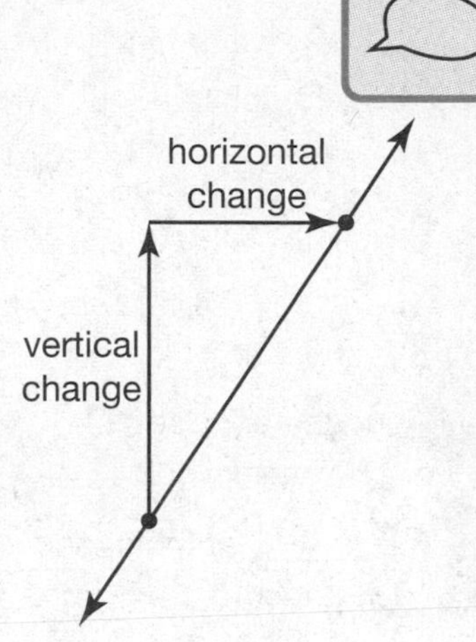

$$\text{Slope} = \frac{\text{vertical change}}{\text{horizontal change}}$$

When the slope is used to describe a rate of increase (or decrease) in a real-life situation, the slope represents a **rate of change.** You found rates of change in Investigate Problem 1, Questions 1 through 3 and Investigate Problem 2, Questions 1 through 3.

What is the slope of your graph in Problem 1? Write your answer as a unit rate.

What is the slope of your first graph in Problem 2? Write your answer as a unit rate.

8. Just the Math: Slope as a Ratio Slope can also be used to represent the ratio a vertical distance to horizontal distance. Suppose that the wheelchair ramp for the community center will have a slope of $\frac{1}{20}$. Draw a picture of the ramp and label the vertical and horizontal distances. Be sure to include units.

5

Investigate Problem 2

9. The slope of a line is either *positive*, *negative*, *zero*, or *undefined*. Determine whether the slope of the line in each graph is positive, negative, zero, or undefined. Complete each sentence to explain.

Take Note

Ratios of the form $\frac{?}{0}$ or $\frac{0}{0}$ are considered to be *undefined* because you cannot divide a number by 0.

The vertical change of the line is a ______________ number, and the horizontal change is a ______________ number.

So, the slope, the ratio of the vertical change to the horizontal change, is ______________.

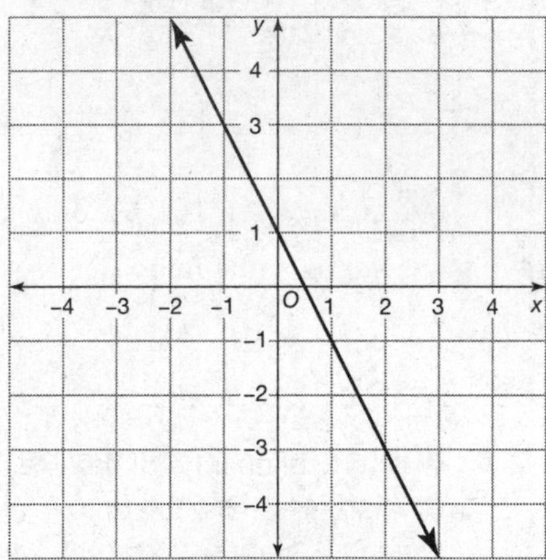

The vertical change of the line is a ______________ number, and the horizontal change is a ______________ number.

So, the slope, the ratio of the vertical change to the horizontal change, is ______________.

5

Investigate Problem 2

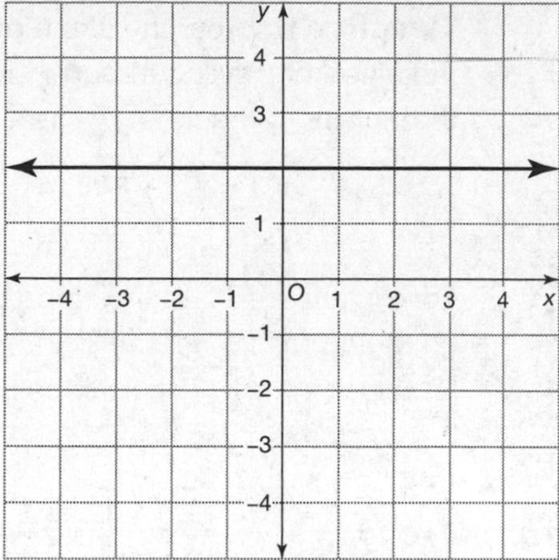

The vertical change of the line is _______________, and the horizontal change is a _______________ number.

So, the slope, the ratio of the vertical change to the horizontal change, is _______________.

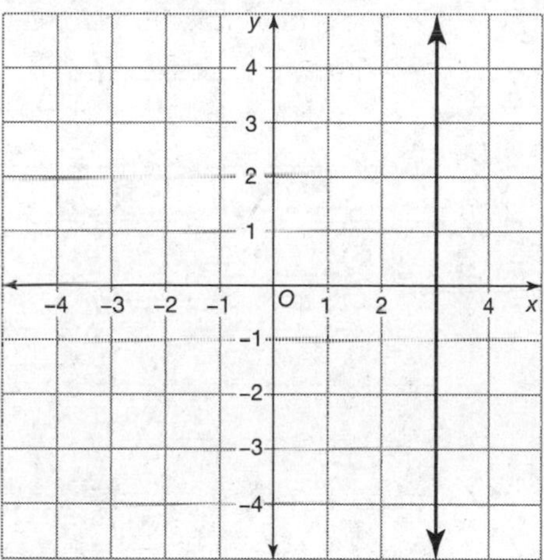

The vertical change of the line is a _______________ number, and the horizontal change is _______________.

So, the slope, the ratio of the vertical change to the horizontal change, is _______________.

10. Use complete sentences to describe lines that have positive slope, negative slope, zero slope, or undefined slope.

5

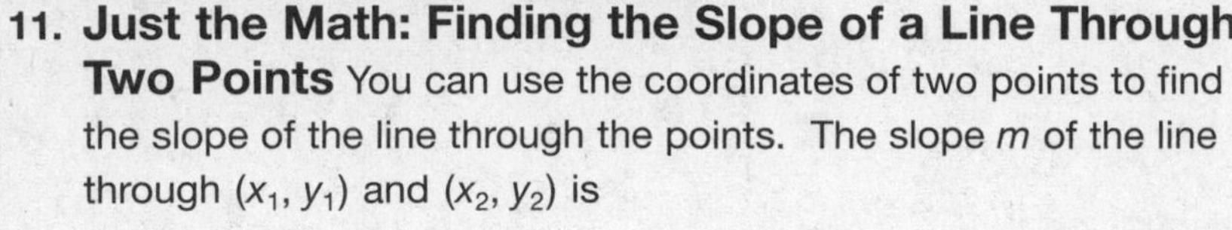

11. Just the Math: Finding the Slope of a Line Through Two Points You can use the coordinates of two points to find the slope of the line through the points. The slope m of the line through (x_1, y_1) and (x_2, y_2) is

$$m = \frac{y_2 - y_1}{x_2 - x_1}.$$

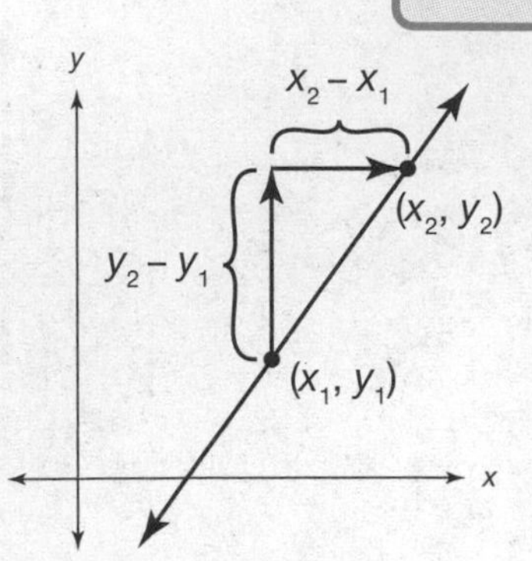

For instance, to find the slope of the line through the points (2, 6) and (5, 10), let the point (x_1, y_1) be the point (2, 6) and let the point (x_2, y_2) be the point (5, 10). Complete the ratio below to find the slope of the line through the points.

$$m = \frac{y_2 - y_1}{x_2 - x_1} = \frac{\square - \square}{\square - \square} = \frac{\square}{\square}$$

Take Note

Because the letter m is commonly used to represent the slope of a line, you should avoid using this letter as a variable.

12. Use the coordinates of the points to find the slope of each line. Show all your work.

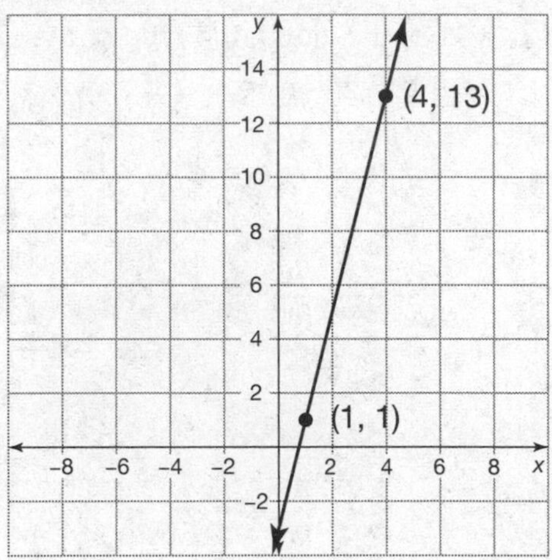

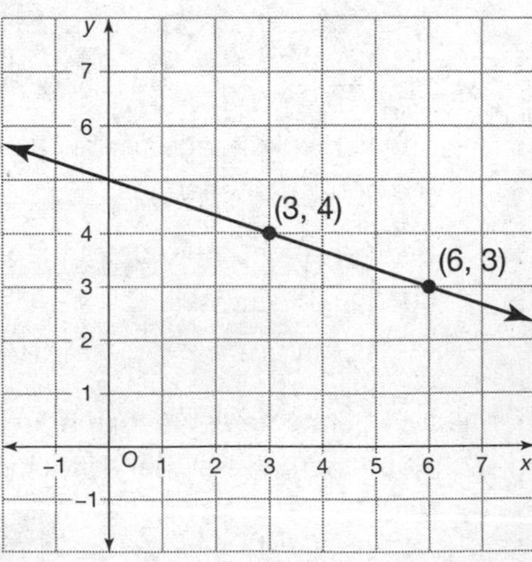

5.4 Running in a Marathon

Slope-Intercept Form

Objectives

In this lesson, you will:

- Compare slopes and y-intercepts of lines.
- Identify slopes and y-intercepts from equations.
- Write equations in slope-intercept form.
- Graph equations in slope-intercept form.

Key Term

- slope-intercept form

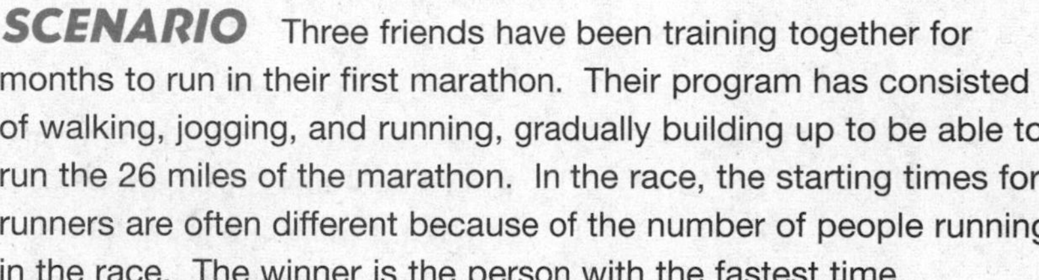

SCENARIO Three friends have been training together for months to run in their first marathon. Their program has consisted of walking, jogging, and running, gradually building up to be able to run the 26 miles of the marathon. In the race, the starting times for runners are often different because of the number of people running in the race. The winner is the person with the fastest time.

Problem 1 Going the Distance

The marathon has started, and the first friend is now 8 miles into the race and is currently running at a constant rate of 4.5 miles per hour.

A. How far will the first friend be into the race one hour after the first eight miles are completed? Show all your work and use a complete sentence in your answer.

B. How far will the first friend be into the race two hours after the first eight miles are completed? Show all your work and use a complete sentence in your answer.

C. How far will the first friend be into the race thirty minutes after the first eight miles are completed? Show all your work and use a complete sentence in your answer.

D. Use complete sentences to explain how to find the distance the friend has run for any amount of time after the first eight miles are completed.

Investigate Problem 1

1. Write an equation that gives the total distance that the first friend has run in terms of the number of hours that have passed after the first eight miles were completed. Use x to represent the number of hours that have passed and y to represent the total distance run in miles.

Investigate Problem 1

2. Use your equation to find the number of miles into the race that the first friend will be in 2.5 hours after the first eight miles are completed. Show all your work and use a complete sentence in your answer.

Use your equation to find the number of hours that it will take for the first friend to complete 21.5 miles of the race after the first eight miles are completed. Show all your work and use a complete sentence in your answer.

Problem 2 Where's the Finish Line?

The second friend has completed 6 miles of the marathon and is currently running at a constant rate of 2.5 miles in 0.5 hour.

A. How many miles is the second friend now running in one hour? Show all your work.

B. How far will the second friend be into the race 1.5 hours after the first 6 miles are completed? Show all your work and use a complete sentence in your answer.

C. How far will the second friend be into the race 120 minutes after the first 6 miles are completed? Show all your work and use a complete sentence in your answer.

D. How far will the second friend be into the race 45 minutes after the first 6 miles are completed? Show all your work and use a complete sentence in your answer.

E. Write an equation that gives the total distance that the second friend has run in terms of the number of hours that have passed after the first 6 miles were completed. Use x to represent the number of hours that have passed and y to represent the total distance run in miles.

Investigate Problem 2

1. The third friend has completed 5 miles and is currently running at a constant rate of 12 miles in 3 hours. Write an equation that gives the total distance in terms of the number of hours that have passed after the first 5 miles were completed. Use x to represent the number of hours that have passed and y to represent the total distance run in miles. Show all your work and use complete sentences to explain.

2. How are the three equations that you have written the same? How are they different? Use complete sentences in your answer.

3. Use the grid below to create graphs of all three equations. First, choose your bounds and intervals. Be sure that you can see the y-intercepts and the results at the end of the race. Label your graph clearly.

Variable quantity	Lower bound	Upper bound	Interval

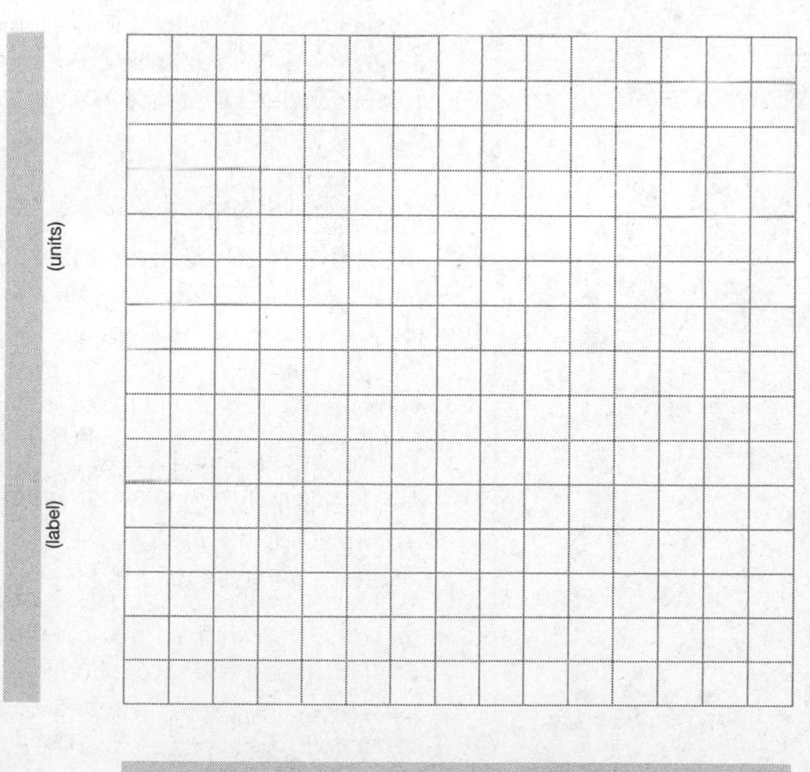

Investigate Problem 2

4. For each line, identify the slope and y-intercept. Show all your work.

First friend: slope: ________ y-intercept: ________

Second friend: slope: ________ y-intercept: ________

Third friend: slope: ________ y-intercept: ________

5. Compare your equation for the first friend to the slope and intercepts of the equation's graph. What do you notice? Use a complete sentence in your answer.

Compare your equation for the second friend to the slope and intercepts of the equation's graph. What do you notice? Use a complete sentence in your answer.

Compare your equation for the third friend to the slope and intercepts of the equation's graph. What do you notice? Use a complete sentence in your answer.

6. Just the Math: Slope-Intercept Form The linear equations you have been writing so far have been in *slope-intercept form.* A linear equation in **slope-intercept form** is $y = mx + b$ where m is the slope of the line and b is the y-intercept.

Write each equation in slope-intercept form, if necessary. Then identify the slope and y-intercept.

$y = 3x + 2$ $y = -0.8x + 1.4$

$y = 6x - 10$ $y = 4(x + 3)$

5

Investigate Problem 2

7. Once you can identify the slope-intercept form of a linear equation, you can quickly draw a graph of the equation. For instance, to graph the equation $y = -3x + 1$, begin by plotting the point that contains the y-intercept, (0, 1). Then write the slope –3 as $\frac{-3}{1}$, which tells you to move down three units for every one unit you move to the right. You can use this slope to plot another point on the line, (1, –2). Then draw a straight line through the points.

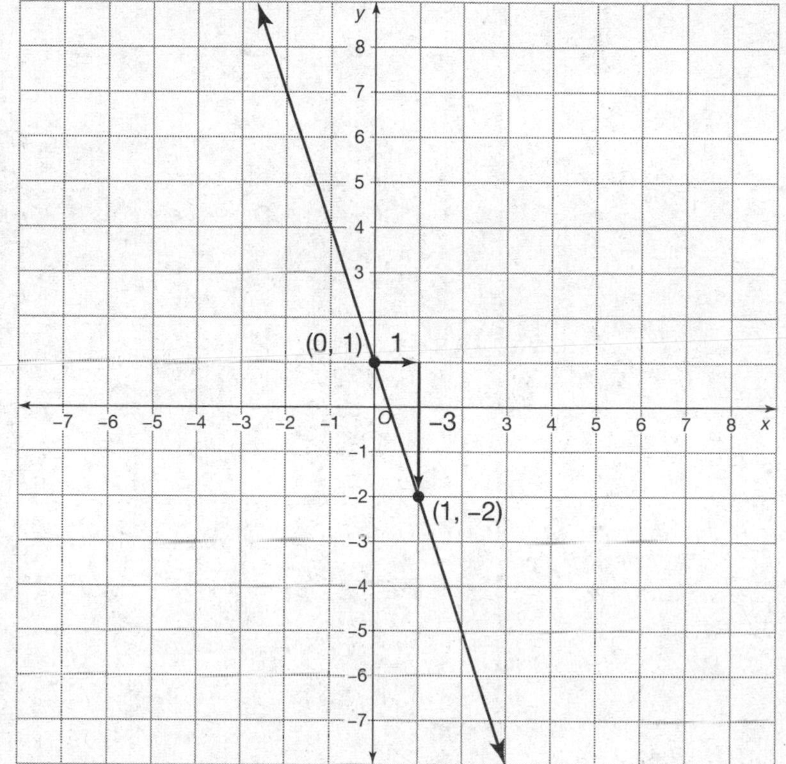

Suppose we had interpreted the slope –3 as $\frac{3}{-1}$. What would be the second point on the line?

Show that the point (1, –2) and the point you found above are both solutions of the equation $y = -3x + 1$. What does this tell you about the slope of the line? Use complete sentences in your answer.

5

Investigate Problem 2

8. Draw a graph of each equation by using the slope and y-intercept of the equation.

$y = -2x + 3$

$y = \frac{2}{3}x - 1$

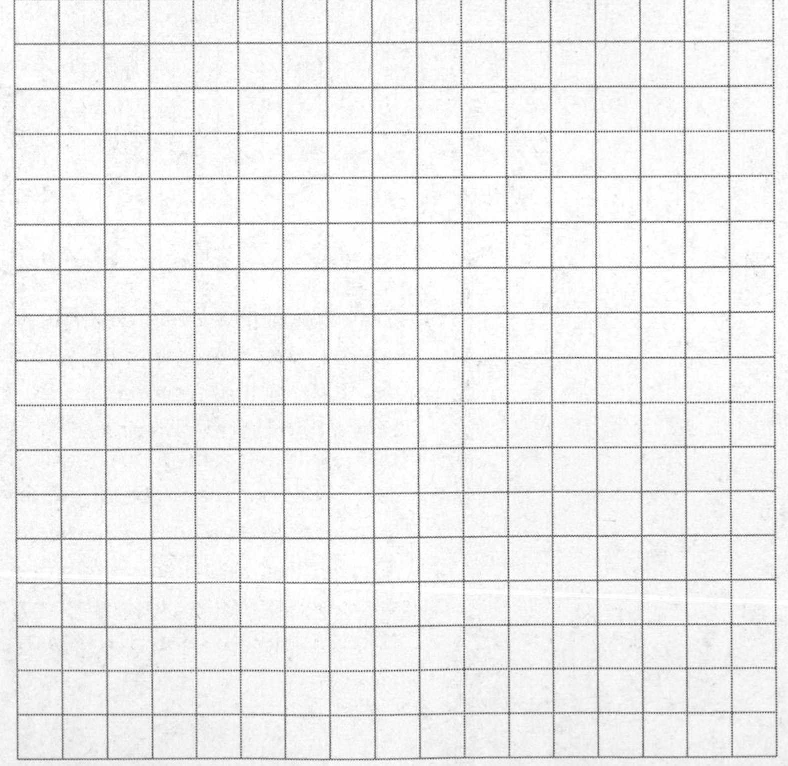

5

Investigate Problem 2

9. Write the equation of the line from its graph.

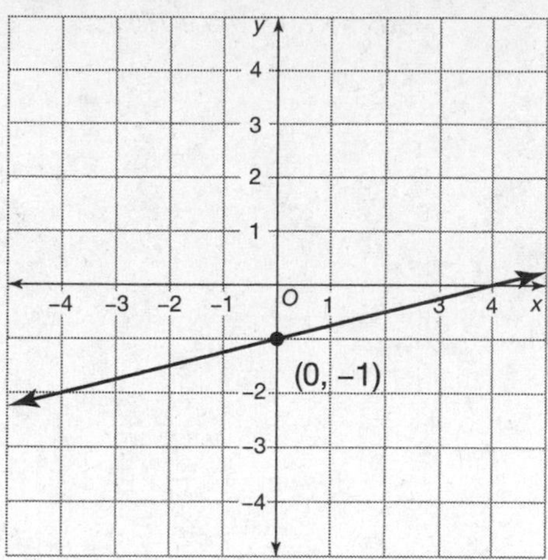

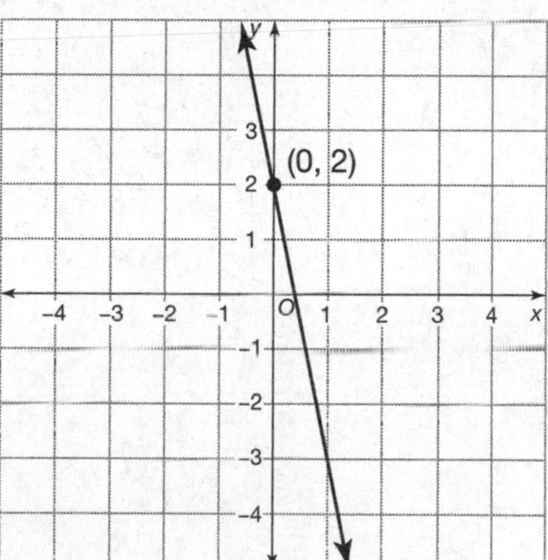

10. Consider all lines with a positive slope. How does the number that represents the slope of a steep line compare to the number that represents the slope of a line that is less steep? Use a complete sentence to explain.

Consider all lines with a negative slope. How does the number that represents the slope of a steep line compare to the number that represents the slope of a line that is less steep? Use a complete sentence to explain.

5

5.5

Saving Money

Writing Equations of Lines

Objectives

In this lesson, you will:

- Use a point and a slope to write an equation of a line in point-slope form.
- Use a point and a slope to write an equation of a line in slope-intercept form.
- Use two points to write an equation of a line in point-slope form and in slope-intercept form.

Key Terms

- slope-intercept form
- point-slope form

SCENARIO Your local community center recently offered a class to young adults about saving money. You took the class and applied what you learned in the class by saving money regularly.

Problem 1 Saving for the Future

You started saving money regularly 6 months ago, and you have $410 in the account today. You have been meeting your goal of saving an additional $15 each week.

A. How much money had you saved one week ago? Show your work and use a complete sentence in your answer.

B. How much money had you saved one month ago? (Assume 4 weeks in a month.) Show your work and use a complete sentence in your answer.

C. How much money had you saved two months ago? Show your work and use a complete sentence in your answer.

D. Complete the table below that shows the amount of money that you have saved for different numbers of weeks.

Time since money started to be saved regularly	Amount saved
weeks	dollars
0	
4	
8	
12	
16	
20	
22	
23	
24	

5

Investigate Problem 1

1. Use the grid below to create a graph of the table in part (D). First, choose your bounds and intervals. Be sure to label your graph clearly.

Variable quantity	Lower bound	Upper bound	Interval

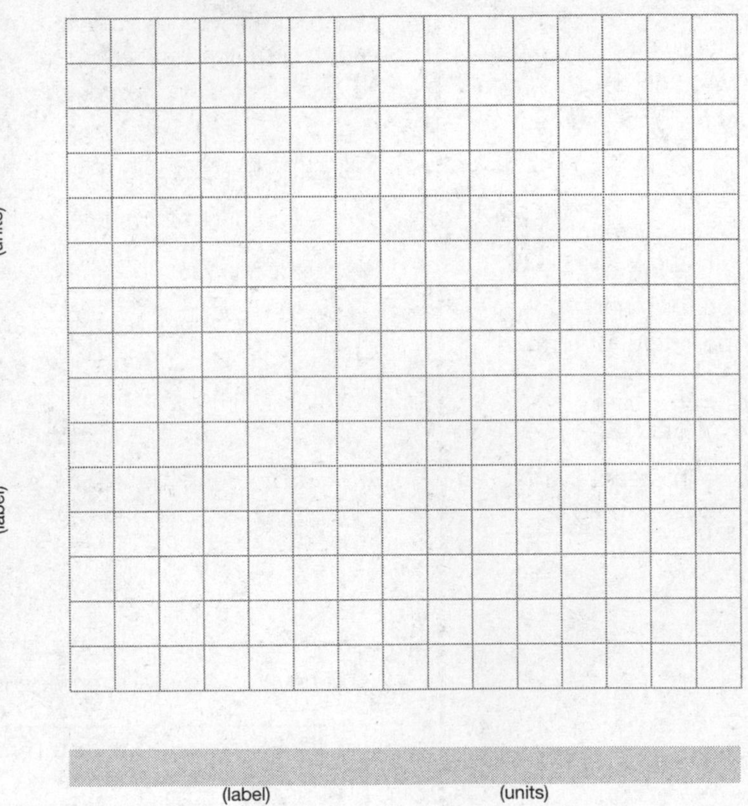

(label) (units)

2. What is the slope of the line in your graph? Did you have to use the graph to determine the slope? Use complete sentences to explain your reasoning.

3. What is the y-intercept of your graph? Did you have to use the graph to determine the y-intercept? Use complete sentences to explain your reasoning.

4. Write an equation that gives the savings in terms of time. Use x to represent the time in weeks since you started saving money regularly and use y to represent your savings in dollars.

5

Investigate Problem 1

5. If you look at the original problem again, what information about the graph were you given? Use a complete sentence in your answer.

6. **Just the Math: Point-Slope Form** Instead of creating a table and a graph of the situation to use to write the equation, you can write the equation directly by using the **point-slope form** of a linear equation. The point-slope form of an equation of the line that passes through the point (x_1, y_1) and has slope m is

   $y - y_1 = m(x - x_1)$.

   What point were you given in the problem statement?

   What slope were you given in the problem statement?

   Write the point-slope form of the equation.

   Now write the equation in slope-intercept form. Show all your work.

   What do you notice? Use a complete sentence in your answer.

7. What does the y-intercept mean in terms of the problem situation?

8. What are the advantages of each method of finding the equation? What are the disadvantages of each method? Use complete sentences in your answer.

5

Investigate Problem 1

9. Write the equation of a line that passes through the given point and has the given slope. Then write the equation in slope-intercept form. Show all your work.

Passes through (–5, 6) and has slope of 3

Passes through (4, 0) and has slope of $\frac{1}{2}$

Passes through (3, –2) and has slope of –4

Take Note

You can check your answer by first checking that the given slope and the slope in your equation are the same. Then substitute the ordered pair into your equation and show that it is a solution.

Problem 2 Everybody's Saving!

A friend of yours also took the class and also started saving money regularly. She excitedly tells you that, after only 6 weeks she had \$132 saved, and after 12 weeks she had \$240 saved. She told you that she has been saving the same amount each week.

A. Do you think that you can generalize this problem situation by using a linear equation? Use complete sentences to explain your reasoning.

B. Use the grid on the next page to create a graph with the information you have so far. First, choose your bounds and intervals. Be sure to label your graph clearly.

Variable quantity	Lower bound	Upper bound	Interval

5

Problem 2 Everybody's Saving!

C. How does this problem differ from the previous problem? Use complete sentences to explain.

D. What information do you need in order to write an equation that generalizes the problem situation? Use a complete sentence in your answer.

Investigate Problem 2

1. Find the slope of the line that you graphed in part (B). Show all your work.

5

Investigate Problem 2

2. Find an equation of the line in slope-intercept form. Show all your work.

3. Could you have used either point to find the equation of the line? Use complete sentences to explain your reasoning.

Take Note

You can check your answer by substituting each ordered pair into your equation. Both ordered pairs should be solutions of your equation.

4. Find an equation of the line in slope-intercept form that passes through each given set of points. Show all your work.

(–2, 2) and (1, 5)

(1, 7) and (3, 2)

(–3, 1) and (8, 1)

5

Summary Writing an Equation of a Line

To write the equation of a line, you need to know at least two pieces of information:

- The slope and the y-intercept,
- The slope and another point on the line, or
- Two points on the line.

Then, use the slope-intercept form of the equation of a line, $y = mx + b$, to write the equation of the line.

5.6 Spending Money

Linear and Piecewise Functions

Objectives

In this lesson, you will:

- Find the domain and range of a linear function.
- Graph a piecewise function.
- Write the equations for a piecewise function.

Key Terms

- domain
- range
- linear function
- piecewise function

SCENARIO As part of the class you took about saving money, you also learned about how to monitor your spending.

Problem 1 I Won?

You won $48 in a ping-pong tournament. You figure that you will spend an average of $3 of your winnings each day.

A. How much money will you have left after three days? Show your work and use a complete sentence in your answer.

B. How much money will you have left after five days? Show your work and use a complete sentence in your answer.

C. How much money will you have left after ten days? Show your work and use a complete sentence in your answer.

D. Complete the table below that shows the amount of money you have left for different numbers of days.

Time since you won	Amount of winnings left
days	dollars
0	
1	
2	
3	
4	
5	

5

Investigate Problem 1

1. Write an equation that gives the amount of money you have left in terms of the number of days since you started spending your winnings. Be sure to tell what each variable in your equation represents.

Investigate Problem 1

2. Use the grid below to create a graph of your equation. First, choose your bounds and intervals. Be sure to label your graph clearly.

Variable quantity	Lower bound	Upper bound	Interval

(label) (units)

(label) (units)

3. Find the *x* and *y* intercepts of the graph. Use complete sentences to explain what they mean in terms of the problem situation.

4. Is the slope of your line positive or negative? Does this make sense in terms of the problem situation? Use complete sentences to explain your reasoning.

5

Take Note

Remember that every linear equation, except those in the form $x = a$, is a linear function.

Take Note

Recall that the set of all possible input values of a function is the *domain* of the function and the set of all possible output values is the *range* of the function.

Investigate Problem 1

5. Consider your linear function without considering the problem situation. You can determine the domain of your linear function by using your graph. The *x*-axis gives you the potential *x*-values in the domain. For which *x*-values will you have only one *y*-value? What is the domain of the function? Use complete sentences to explain.

You can also determine the range by using your graph. The *y*-axis gives you the potential *y*-values for the given *x*-values in the domain. Which *y*-values are given by *x*-values from the domain? Use a complete sentence in your answer.

6. What do you think are the domain and range of any linear function of the form $f(x) = mx + b$? Use complete sentences to explain your reasoning.

7. Now consider your linear function again in terms of the problem situation. What is the domain of the linear function in the problem situation? Use complete sentences to explain your reasoning.

What is the range of the linear function in the problem situation? Use complete sentences to explain your reasoning.

5

Problem 2 Controlling Your Spending

Suppose that you did not spend the $48 by spending $3 each day. Instead, after five days of spending $3 each day, you do not spend anything for five days. Then you reduce your spending to $1.50 each day.

A. Complete the table below that shows the amount of money you have left for different numbers of days.

Time since money was won	Amount left
days	dollars
0	
1	
2	
3	
4	
5	
6	
7	
8	
9	
10	
11	
12	
13	

B. Use the grid on the next page to create a graph of the table in part (A). First, choose your bounds and intervals. Be sure that you are able to see the number of days when you have no money left. Label your graph clearly.

Variable quantity	Lower bound	Upper bound	Interval

5

Problem 2 Controlling Your Spending

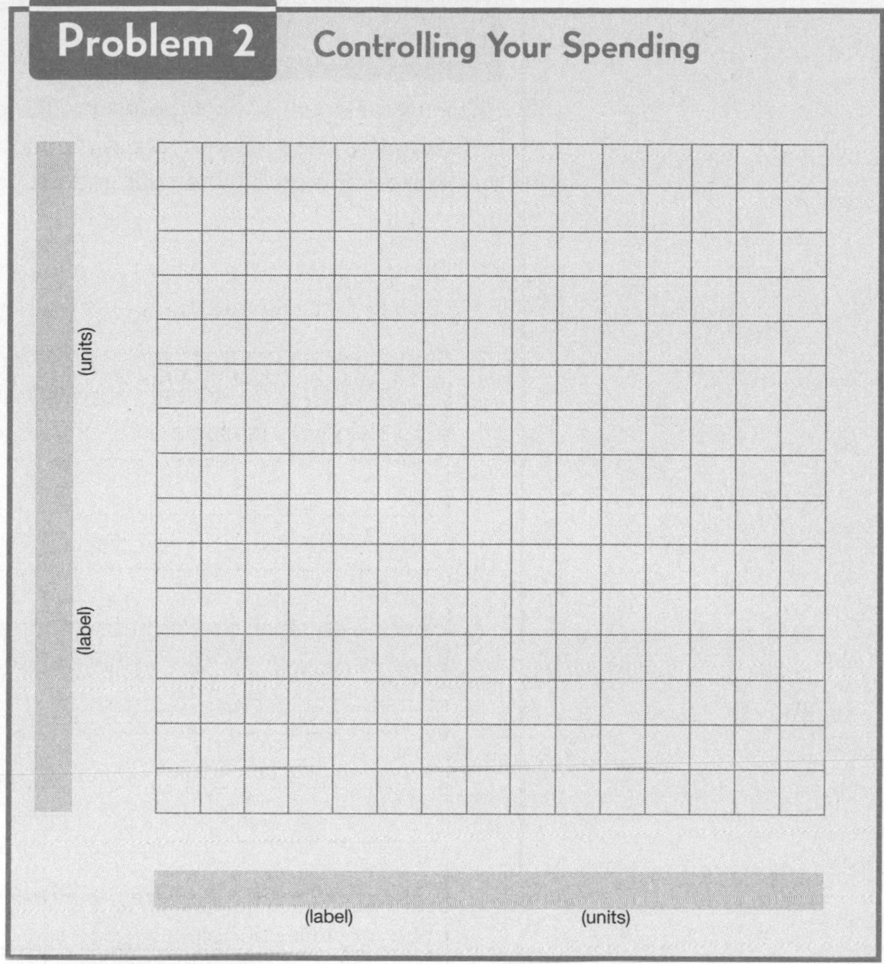

Take Note

The function represented by the graph above can be called a piecewise *linear* function because each piece can be represented by a linear equation.

Investigate Problem 2

1. **Just the Math: Piecewise Function** The graph that you created in part (B) above represents a *piecewise function*. A **piecewise function** is a function that can be represented by more than one function, each of which corresponds to a part of the domain.

   What is the domain of this function in the problem situation?

   How many pieces make up this function? In other words, how many different equations are needed to describe this function? Use a complete sentence in your answer.

   What is the domain of each piece?

Investigate Problem 2

2. Find the equation that represents the piece of the function from 0 days to 5 days. Show your work and use complete sentences to explain how you found your answer.

3. Find the equation that represents the piece of the function from 6 days to 10 days. Show your work and use complete sentences to explain your reasoning.

4. Find the equation that represents the piece of the function from 11 days to 32 days. Show your work and use complete sentences to explain your reasoning.

5. **Just the Math: Writing a Piecewise Function** You can write your piecewise function in the following way. Use x to represent a number from the domain of your function f. Complete the definition of f below. For each piece of the domain, write the equation you found in Questions 2, 3, or 4.

$$f(x) = \begin{cases} \boxed{}, & 0 \le x \le 5 \\ \boxed{}, & 5 < x \le 10 \\ \boxed{}, & 10 < x \le 32 \end{cases}$$

6. Which piece should you use to find the x-intercept? Which piece should you use to find the y-intercept? Use complete sentences in your answer.

5

7. Find the intercepts of the graph. Show all your work.

8. When will you run out of money? How does this compare to the number of days it took you to run out of money in Problem 1?

5.7 The School Play

Standard Form of a Linear Equation

Objectives

In this lesson, you will:

- Write a linear equation in standard form.
- Convert an equation in slope-intercept form to standard form.
- Convert an equation in standard form to slope-intercept form.

SCENARIO Your theater group at school is putting on a play next month. They want to advertise, so they have designed a flyer to distribute around the school and in local stores.

Problem 1 Sending Out the Flyers

One member of the group has found an office supply store that sells plain white paper for $6 per ream (a package of 500 sheets) and blue paper for $10 per ream. The group agrees that it would be good to get both white and blue paper.

A. Write an expression that represents the total cost of the paper if the group buys x reams of white paper and y reams of blue paper.

Key Terms

- slope-intercept form
- standard form
- point-slope form

B. The theater group has a budget of $30 for the paper. Complete the equation in terms of x and y that represents the amount that the group will spend if they spend the entire budgeted amount.

________ = 30

C. Using the equation, write the intercepts of the equation's graph. Show all your work.

What do the intercepts mean in terms of the problem situation? Use complete sentences in your answer.

5

Investigate Problem 1

1. Use the grid below to create a graph of the equation in part (B). First, choose your bounds and intervals. Be sure to label your graph clearly.

Variable quantity	Lower bound	Upper bound	Interval

(label) (units)

(label) (units)

2. How many reams of white paper can you buy if you buy two reams of blue paper? Show your work and explain your reasoning. Use complete sentences in your answer.

3. How many reams of blue paper can you buy if you buy one ream of white paper? Show your work and explain your reasoning. Use completes sentences in your answer.

5

Investigate Problem 1

4. **Just the Math: Standard Form** In part (B), you wrote a linear equation in *standard form*. A linear equation is in **standard form** if it is written as $Ax + By = C$, where A, B, and C are constants and A and B are not both zero. Identify A, B, and C in your equation in part (B).

5. Are there any benefits in using an equation in standard form rather than using an equation in slope-intercept form?

Problem 2 Another Possibility

Another member of the group has found a different source for the paper, an art supply store. This member tells the group that the total cost and the number of reams of each kind of paper bought are related by the equation $y = -\frac{6}{9}x + \frac{30}{9}$, where x is the number of reams of white paper and y is the number of reams of blue paper.

A. How many reams of white paper can you buy if you buy two reams of blue paper? Show all your work. Use a complete sentence in your answer.

B. How many reams of blue paper can you buy if you buy three reams of white paper? Explain your reasoning. Use complete sentences in your answer.

5

Problem 2 Another Possibility

C. Find both intercepts of the equation's graph by using the equation. Show all your work.

What do the intercepts mean in terms of the problem situation? Use complete sentences in your answer.

5

Investigate Problem 2

1. Use the grid on the next page to create a graph of the given equation. First, choose your bounds and intervals. Be sure to label your graph.

Variable quantity	Lower bound	Upper bound	Interval

Investigate Problem 2

2. Can you tell the cost of one ream of each kind of paper from the information you have so far?

3. You can determine the cost of one ream of each kind of paper by writing your equation in standard form. To write $y = -\frac{6}{9}x + \frac{30}{9}$ in standard form, first clear the terms of fractional coefficients by multiplying each side of the equation by 9. Complete the steps below.

$9y = 9\left(-\frac{6}{9}x + \frac{30}{9}\right)$

$9y = 9(\square) + 9(\square)$ Use the distributive property.

$9y = \square + \square$ Multiply.

The final step is to get both variable expressions on one side of the equation. Write the final equation below.

Take Note

Recall that the coefficient of an expression is the number that is multiplied by a variable. For instance, in the expression $7x$, 7 is the coefficient of x.

5

Investigate Problem 2

How much does one ream of each kind of paper cost? Use complete sentences to explain how you found your answer.

4. From which store should the group buy their paper? Use complete sentences to explain your reasoning.

5. Write each equation in standard form. Be sure to clear the terms of fractional coefficients. Show all your work.

$y = -6x + 4$ $\qquad\qquad$ $y = \frac{1}{2}x + 5$

$y = \frac{3}{8}x - \frac{1}{8}$ $\qquad\qquad$ $y = -\frac{1}{2}x + \frac{3}{4}$

6. Write each equation in slope-intercept form. Show all your work.

$6x + 3y = 12$ $\qquad\qquad$ $4x - 2y = 1$

$-3x + 5y = 10$ $\qquad\qquad$ $8x - 10y = 15$

Summary

Linear Equations

In this chapter, you have learned three different forms of a linear equation:

- Slope-intercept form: $y = mx + b$, where m is the slope and b is the y-intercept
- Point-slope form: $y - y_1 = m(x - x_1)$, where m is the slope and (x_1, y_1) is a point on the line
- Standard form: $Ax + By = C$, where A, B, and C are constants and A and B are not both zero

5.8 Earning Interest

Solving Literal Equations

Objective

In this lesson, you will:

- Solve an equation for a specified variable.

Key Terms

- interest
- principal
- simple interest
- interest rate
- literal equation

Take Note

Recall that to write a percent as a decimal, you divide the number in front of the percent symbol by 100.

SCENARIO In Lesson 5.5, we talked about saving money. If you put your money into a savings account, the bank pays you money, called **interest,** for being able to use your money.

Problem 1 How Interesting!

The amount of money that you deposit into the account is called the **principal.** **Simple interest** is interest that is paid only as a percent of the principal. The formula for simple interest is $I = Prt$, where I is the amount of interest that you earn in dollars, P is the principal in dollars, r is the **interest rate** (the percent) in decimal form, and t is the amount of time in years that the money is in the account.

A. Use a complete sentence to write the simple interest formula in words.

B. Find the amount of interest earned in one year by depositing \$100 into an account that earns 2% interest for 1 year. Show all your work and use complete sentences to explain how you found your answer.

C. Find the amount of time it will take to earn \$10 in simple interest if you deposit \$100 into an account that earns 2% interest. Show all your work and use complete sentences to explain how you found your answer.

5

Problem 1 How Interesting!

D. Suppose that you have \$200 to put into a savings account and your bank offers a 2.5% annual interest rate. Write a simple interest equation that represents this situation. Then simplify the equation.

If you want to easily determine how long you have to keep your money in the account to earn different amounts of interest, solve your equation for *t*. What is your new equation?

E. How long does the money need to be in the account if you want to earn \$10 in interest? Show your work and use a complete sentence in your answer.

How long does the money need to be in the account if you want to earn \$25 in interest? Show your work and use a complete sentence in your answer.

F. Is your equation a function? Use a complete sentence to explain.

G. Identify the independent variable and the dependent variable in your equation.

Investigate Problem 1

1. **Just the Math: Literal Equations** The equation for simple interest, $I = Prt$, contains two or more variables to represent known quantities, so it is a **literal equation.** The formula for the area of a rectangle, $A = \ell w$, is also a literal equation. From the equation, upon what two quantities does the area of a rectangle depend? Write your answer using a complete sentence.

   Suppose that you know that the area of a rectangle is 39 square feet and the length of the rectangle is 13 square feet. Use the formula for the area of a rectangle, $A = \ell w$, to find the width. Use a complete sentence to explain your reasoning.

5

Investigate Problem 1

In the same way that you solved the equation for w after you substituted the values, you can solve the equation $A = \ell w$ for w before you substitute. Solve the formula for the area of a rectangle, $A = \ell w$, for w. Show all your work.

Use a complete sentence to express the width of the rectangle in terms of the area and the length.

2. The formula to find the distance that you travel when you know the rate at which you are traveling and the time you spent traveling is $D = rt$, where D is the distance, r is the rate, and t is the time. Solve the equation for r. Show all your work. Then use a complete sentence to explain how you can find the rate when you know the distance and the time.

3. The formula that you can use to convert a temperature in degrees Celsius to degrees Fahrenheit is $F = \frac{9}{5}C + 32$. Solve the equation for C. Show all your work.

4. The formula that you can use to find the area of a trapezoid is $A = \frac{1}{2}h(b_1 + b_2)$ where h is the height of the trapezoid and b_1 and b_2 are the lengths of the two bases of the trapezoid. Solve the equation for b_2. Show all your work.

5

Looking Ahead to Chapter 6

Focus In Chapter 6, you will plot data from experiments and other sources in scatter plots. From these scatter plots you will learn how to fit a line that best describes the data. You will also use technology to help determine the line that best fits the data.

Chapter Warm-up

Answer these questions to help you review skills that you will need in Chapter 6.

In each equation, find the slope and the *y*-intercept.

1. $y = 3x + 12$

2. $y = -\frac{4}{7}x - 1$

3. $6x + 3y = -8$

Write the equation of the line that passes through the given points in point-slope form.

4. (4, 1) and (9, –5)

5. (–1, –1) and (3, 8)

6. (6.5, –3) and (4, 2.5)

Read the problem scenario below.

You are given the responsibility of providing drinks for the weekly math club meetings. You have decided to bring juice boxes. Each grape juice box costs $2 and each pineapple-orange juice box costs $3.50. This week you have $28 to spend on juice. Let *x* represent the number of grape juice boxes that you purchase and let *y* represent the number of pineapple-orange juice boxes that you purchase.

7. Write an equation that represents the number of pineapple-orange juice boxes and the number of grape juice boxes you can purchase this week.

8. What is the *x*-intercept of this equation? What does the *x*-intercept represent?

9. What is the *y*-intercept of this equation? What does the *y*-intercept represent?

Key Terms

CHAPTER

6

Lines of Best Fit

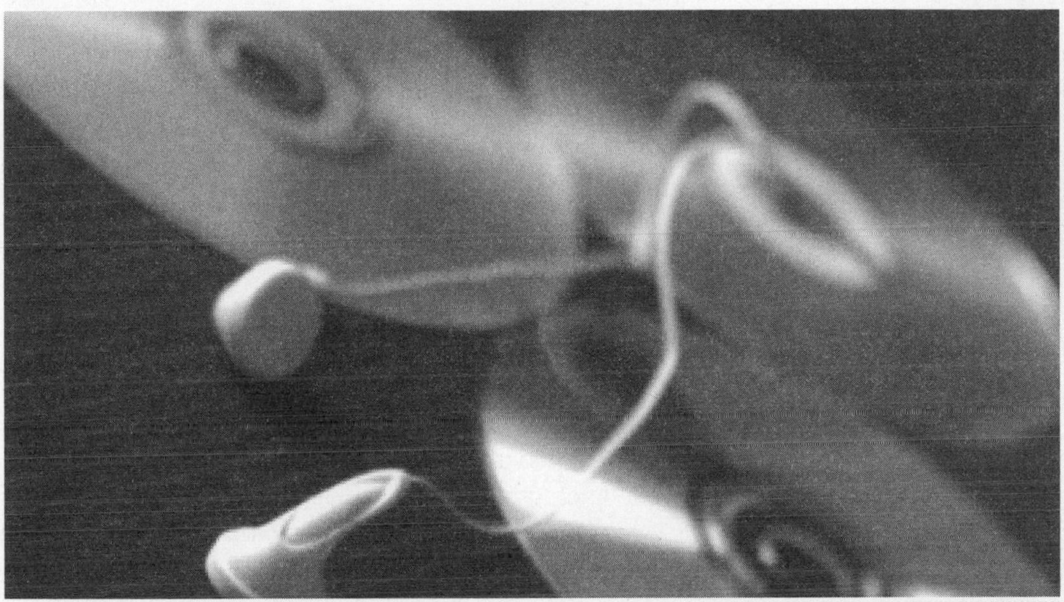

Popular music can be played using vinyl records, CDs, and MP3s. In Lesson 6.2, you will conduct a survey to determine where people purchase most of their music.

6.1 Mia's Growing Like a Weed

Drawing the Line of Best Fit

Objectives

In this lesson, you will:

- Create a scatter plot.
- Draw a line of best fit.
- Find an equation of a line of best fit.
- Use a line of best fit to make predictions.

Key Terms

- scatter plot
- line of best fit
- model

SCENARIO Your cousin Mia was born a healthy, happy baby girl. At each doctor's visit, Mia's height and weight were recorded. Mia's records from birth until she was 18 months old are shown in the table below.

Age	Weight	Height
months	**pounds**	**inches**
0.0	6.1	17.9
1.0	8.1	20.5
1.8	10.0	21.0
2.3	10.3	21.8
4.0	13.7	25.0
6.0	17.0	25.8
8.0	21.0	27.0
10.0	22.0	27.0
12.0	23.0	29.3
15.0	23.0	30.5
18.0	25.1	32.5

Problem 1 How Does Mia's Weight Change?

A. Consider the relationship between Mia's age and her weight. What happens to Mia's weight as she gets older? Use a complete sentence in your answer.

B. Write a unit rate that compares Mia's change in weight to her change in age from age four months to age six months. Show all your work and use a complete sentence in your answer.

C. Write a unit rate that compares Mia's change in weight to her change in age from age six months to age eight months. Show all your work and use a complete sentence in your answer.

6

Age	Weight	Height
months	pounds	inches
0.0	6.1	17.9
1.0	8.1	20.5
1.8	10.0	21.0
2.3	10.3	21.8
4.0	13.7	25.0
6.0	17.0	25.8
8.0	21.0	27.0
10.0	22.0	27.0
12.0	23.0	29.3
15.0	23.0	30.5
18.0	25.1	32.5

Problem 1 How Does Mia's Weight Change?

D. Is Mia gaining weight faster from age four months to age six months or from age six months to age eight months? Use complete sentences to explain.

Investigate Problem 1

1. Write ordered pairs from the table that show Mia's weight as a function of her age.

2. **Just the Math: Scatter Plot** A **scatter plot** is a graph of data points. Create a scatter plot of the ordered pairs on the grid below. First, choose your bounds and intervals. Be sure to label your graph clearly.

Variable quantity	Lower bound	Upper bound	Interval

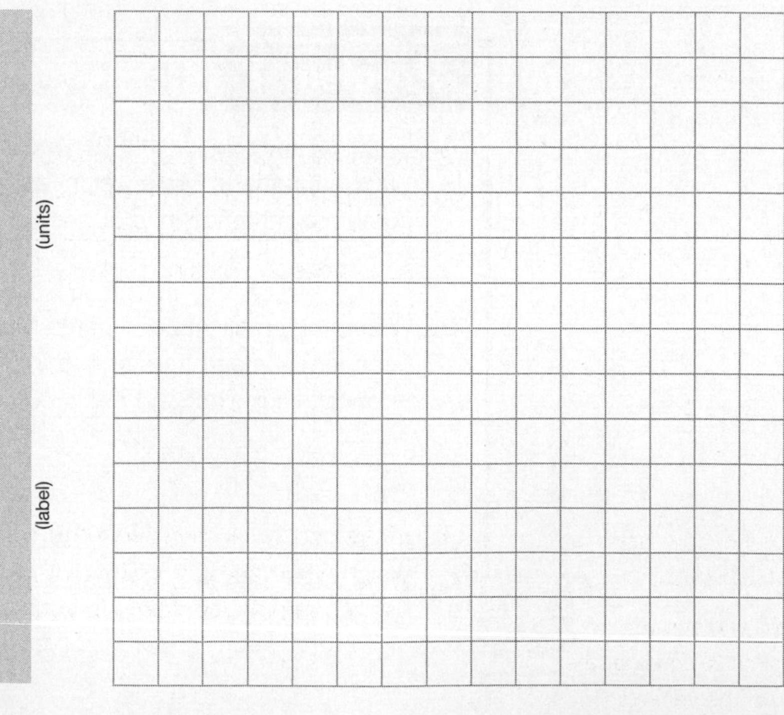

6

Investigate Problem 1

3. Do all the points in your scatter plot lie on the same line? What does this tell you about Mia's weight change as time changes? Use complete sentences to explain your reasoning.

4. **Just the Math: Line of Best Fit** Although a straight line will not pass through all of the points in your scatter plot, you can use a line to approximate the data as closely as possible. This kind of line is called a **line of best fit.** A line of best fit is as close to as many points as possible, but doesn't have to go through all the points. Use a ruler to draw the line that best fits the data on your graph in part (C).

Take Note

When you use a line of best fit, the line and its equation are often referred to as a **model** of the data.

5. Write the equation of your line. Show your work. Be sure to define your variables and include the units.

Take Note

When you find the equation for your line of best fit, you may need to round the values of the slope and *y*-intercept.

6. According to your line, approximately how many pounds did Mia gain each month from the time she was born until she was 18 months old? How did you find your answer? Use complete sentences to explain.

7. If Mia continues to grow at this rate, how much will she weigh when she is 2 years old? Show all your work and use a complete sentence in your answer.

Take Note

Before you answer Question 7, consider the units of the variables in your equation.

6

Age	Weight	Height
months	pounds	inches
0.0	6.1	17.9
1.0	8.1	20.5
1.8	10.0	21.0
2.3	10.3	21.8
4.0	13.7	25.0
6.0	17.0	25.8
8.0	21.0	27.0
10.0	22.0	27.0
12.0	23.0	29.3
15.0	23.0	30.5
18.0	25.1	32.5

Investigate Problem 1

If Mia continues to grow at this rate, how much will she weigh when she is 5 years old? Show all your work and use a complete sentence in your answer.

If Mia continues to grow at this rate, how much will she weigh when she is 18 years old? Show all your work and use a complete sentence in your answer.

8. Do all your answers to Question 7 make sense? Use a complete sentence in your answer. Compare your answers for Questions 4 through 8 with your group.

9. What can you conclude about the accuracy of your model? Use a complete sentence in your answer.

Problem 2 How Does Mia's Height Change?

A. Consider the relationship between Mia's age and her height. What happens to Mia's height as she gets older? Use a complete sentence in your answer.

B. Write the ordered pairs from the table that show Mia's height as a function of her age.

C. Create a scatter plot of the ordered pairs on the grid on the next page. First, choose your bounds and intervals. Be sure to label your graph clearly.

Variable quantity	Lower bound	Upper bound	Interval

Problem 2 How Does Mia's Height Change?

D. Can these data be exactly represented by a linear equation? Use a complete sentence to explain your reasoning.

Investigate Problem 2

1. Use a ruler to draw the line that best fits your data on your graph in part (C). Then write the equation of your line. Be sure to define your variables and include the units.

2. According to your line, approximately how many inches did Mia grow each month from the time she was born until she was 18 months old? How did you find your answer? Use complete sentences in your answer.

6

Investigate Problem 2

3. If Mia continues to grow at this rate, how tall will she be when she is 2 years old? Show all your work and use a complete sentence in your answer.

   If Mia continues to grow at this rate, how tall will she be when she is 5 years old? Show all your work and use a complete sentence in your answer.

   If Mia continues to grow at this rate, how tall will she be when she is 18 years old? Show all your work and use a complete sentence in your answer.

4. Do all of your answers to Question 3 make sense? Use complete sentences in your answer.

5. What can you conclude about the accuracy of your model? Use a complete sentence in your answer.

Problem 3 More Data for Mia

The table below shows Mia's growth from age 2 (24 months) to age $5\frac{1}{2}$ (66 months).

Age	Weight	Height
years	pounds	inches
2.0	27.3	34.5
2.5	30.0	35.8
3.0	32.0	36.6
3.5	33.0	38.0
4.5	39.0	42.0
5.5	44.0	45.0

A. Before you can add the values from the table to your scatter plots, what do you need to do first? Use a complete sentence in your answer.

Problem 3 More Data for Mia

Complete the table below by converting each age from years to months.

Age	Age	Weight	Height
years	months	pounds	inches
2.0		27.3	34.5
2.5		30.0	35.8
3.0		32.0	36.6
3.5		33.0	38.0
4.5		39.0	42.0
5.5		44.0	45.0

B. The initial scatter plot that relates Mia's age to her weight is shown below. Include the new data from the table on the scatter plot.

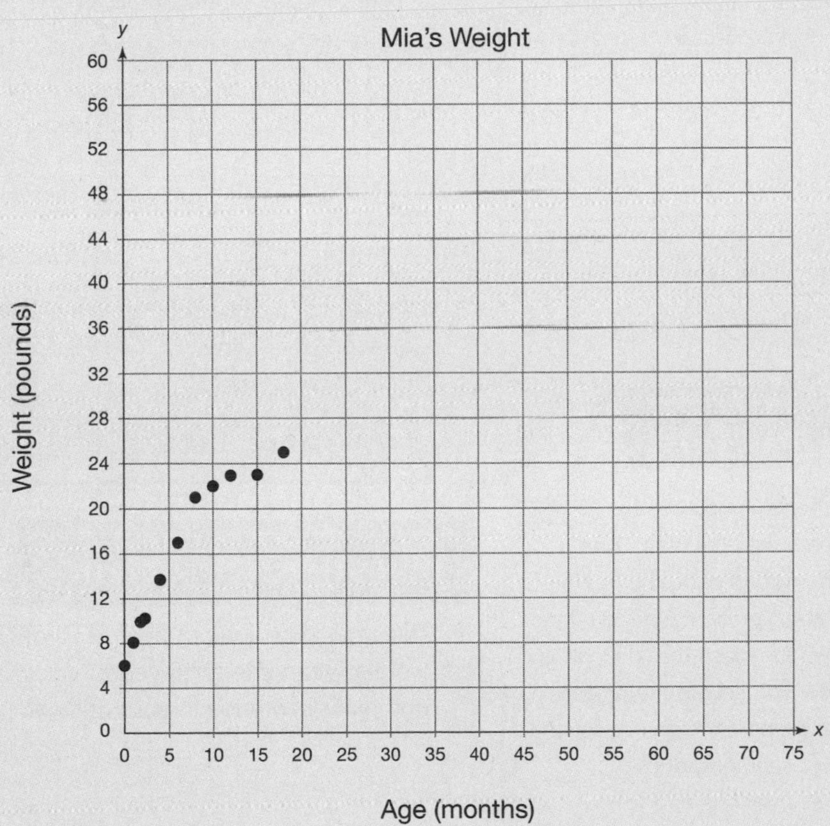

C. Draw the line of best fit on the plot in part (B). Then find the equation of the line.

Age	Weight	Height
months	pounds	inches
24	27.3	34.5
30	30.0	35.8
36	32.0	36.6
42	33.0	38.0
54	39.0	42.0
66	44.0	45.0

Problem 3 More Data for Mia

D. The initial scatter plot that relates Mia's age to her height is shown below. Include the new data from the table on the scatter plot.

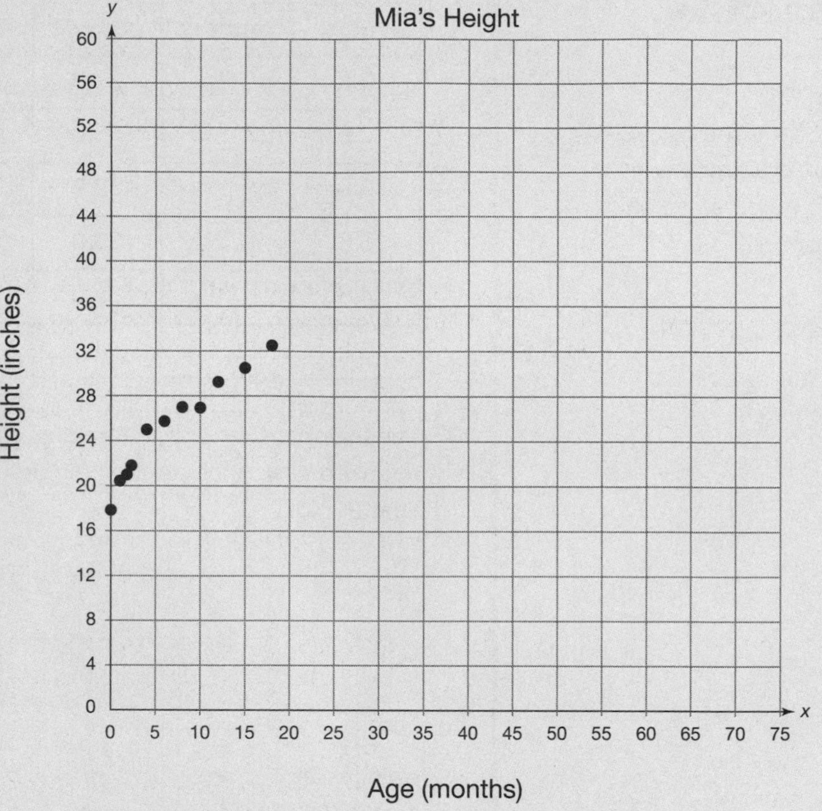

E. Draw the line of best fit on the plot in part (D). Then find the equation of the line.

Take Note

Whenever you see the share with the class icon, your group should prepare a short presentation to share with the class that describes how you solved the problem. Be prepared to ask questions during other groups' presentations and to answer questions during your presentation.

Investigate Problem 3

1. Use your new lines of best fit to determine Mia's height and weight when she is 18 years old. Show all your work and use a complete sentence in your answer.

2. How do these predictions compare to the predictions in Problems 1 and 2? Are these predictions reasonable? Use complete sentences to explain your reasoning.

6

6.2 Where Do You Buy Your Music?

Using Lines of Best Fit

Objectives

In this lesson, you will:

- Use a line of best fit to make predictions.
- Compare two lines of best fit.

Key Terms

- line of best fit
- model

SCENARIO You can purchase music from a variety of different sources: a music store, a department store, the Internet, a music club, and so on. The source for purchasing music changes as the available formats (CDs, MP3s) for music change.

Problem 1 Purchasing from a Music Store

The table below shows the percent of all recorded music sales that came from music stores for the years 1998 through 2004.

Year	1998	1999	2000	2001	2002	2003	2004
Percent of total sales	50.8	44.5	42.4	42.5	36.8	33.2	32.5

A. Write the ordered pairs from the table that show the percent of total sales as a function of the year.

B. Because the points are close together and are far from the origin, it would be difficult to draw an accurate line of best fit for these points. Why? Use complete sentences to explain.

C. Because the *x*-coordinates represent time, we can define time as the number of years since 1998. So, 1998 would become 0. What number would you use for 1999? Use a complete sentence to explain your reasoning.

What number would you use for 2000?

What number would you use for 2001?

6

Investigate Problem 1

1. Now write the ordered pairs that show the percent of total sales as a function of the number of years since 1998.

2. Create a scatter plot of the ordered pairs on the grid below. First, choose your bounds and intervals. Label your graph clearly.

Variable quantity	Lower bound	Upper bound	Interval

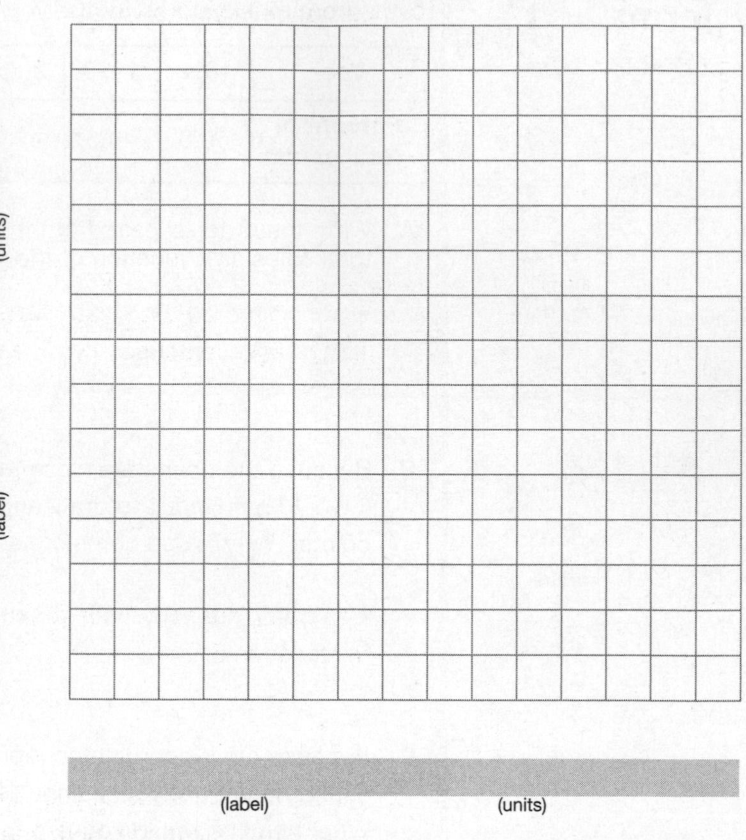

3. Use a ruler to draw the line that best fits your data on the graph above. Then write the equation of the line. Define your variables and include the units.

4. Use your equation to predict the percent of total sales for music stores in 2005. Show all your work and use a complete sentence in your answer.

Take Note

When you use 0 to indicate a particular year, such as 1998, you should indicate this on your graph with the appropriate axis label. One way to do this is to use a double arrow: $0 \leftrightarrow 1998$. You can think of the double arrow as meaning "is the same as."

6

Investigate Problem 1

Use your equation to predict the percent of total sales for music stores in 2007. Show all your work and use a complete sentence in your answer.

Use complete sentences to explain how you found your answers in Question 4.

5. Use your equation to predict the year in which music store sales were 60% of total sales. Show all your work and use a complete sentence in your answer.

   Use your equation to predict the year in which music store sales will be 20% of total sales. Show all your work and use a complete sentence in your answer.

   Use complete sentences to explain how you found your answers in Question 5.

6. What does the slope of your line represent in this problem situation? Use a complete sentence in your answer.

7. What does the *y*-intercept represent in this problem situation? Use a complete sentence in your answer.

8. Use your equation to determine the percent of total sales for music stores in 2000. Show all your work and use a complete sentence in your answer.

6

Investigate Problem 1

How close is this answer to the actual data? Use a complete sentence in your answer.

9. Do you think that your model provides reasonable answers to the questions? Use complete sentences to explain your reasoning.

Problem 2 Purchasing from Non-Music Stores

The table below shows the percent of all recorded music sales that came from non-music stores for the years 1998 through 2004.

Year	1998	1999	2000	2001	2002	2003	2004
Percent of total sales	34.4	38.3	40.8	42.4	50.7	52.8	53.8

A. Write the ordered pairs from the table that show the percent of total sales as a function of the year.

B. Because the points are close together and far from the origin, it would be difficult to draw an accurate line of best fit for these points. Why? Use complete sentences to explain.

C. Because the *x*-coordinates represent time, we can define time as the number of years since 1998. So, 1998 would become 0. What number would you use for 1999? Use a complete sentence to explain your reasoning.

What number would you use for 2000?

What number would you use for 2001?

D. Now write the ordered pairs that show the percent of total sales as a function of the number of years since 1998.

Investigate Problem 2

1. Create a scatter plot of the ordered pairs on the grid below. First, choose your bounds and intervals. Be sure to label your graph clearly.

Variable quantity	Lower bound	Upper bound	Interval

Take Note

When you use 0 to indicate a particular year, such as 1998, you should indicate this on your graph with the appropriate axis label. One way to do this is to use a double arrow: 0 ↔ 1998. You can think of the double arrow as meaning "is the same as."

2. Use a ruler to draw the line that best fits your data on the graph above. Then write the equation of the line. Define your variables and include the units.

3. Use your equation to predict the percent of total sales for non-music stores in 2005. Show all your work and use a complete sentence in your answer.

   Use your equation to predict the percent of total sales for non-music stores in 2007. Show all your work and use a complete sentence in your answer.

6

Investigate Problem 2

Use complete sentences to explain how you found your answers in Question 3.

4. Use your equation to predict the year in which non-music store sales will be 60% of total sales. Show all your work and use a complete sentence in your answer.

Use your equation to predict the year in which non-music store sales were 20% of total sales. Show all your work and use a complete sentence in your answer.

Use complete sentences to explain how you found your answers in Question 4.

5. What does the slope of your line represent in this problem situation? Use a complete sentence in your answer.

6. What does the *y*-intercept represent in this problem situation? Use a complete sentence in your answer.

How close is the value of the *y*-intercept to the actual value? Use a complete sentence in your answer.

7. Use your equation to predict the percent of total sales for non-music stores in 2000. Show all your work and use a complete sentence in your answer.

Investigate Problem 2

How close is this answer to the actual data? Use a complete sentence in your answer.

8. Do you think that your model provides reasonable answers to the questions? Use complete sentences to explain your reasoning.

Problem 3 Comparing Music Store and Non-Music Store Sales

A. Do you think that the data from Problems 1 and 2 are related? Use complete sentences in your answer.

B. For which kind of stores, music stores or non-music stores, is the percent of all sales changing faster? Show all your work and use complete sentences to explain your reasoning.

C. Which equation from Problem 1 and Problem 2 models its data better? Show all your work and use complete sentences to explain your reasoning.

6

6

6.3 Stroop Test

Performing an Experiment

Objectives

In this lesson, you will:

- Perform an experiment.
- Find and use the equations of lines of best fit.
- Compare results of an experiment.

Key Terms

- Stroop Test
- matching list
- non-matching list

SCENARIO The purpose of cognitive psychology is to understand and explain how the human brain works. One way to study how the human brain works is to perform experiments on human subjects. The Stroop Test is one such experiment.

Problem 1 Running the Stroop Test

The **Stroop Test** studies a person's perception of words and colors by using lists of color words (red, green, black, and blue) that are written in one of the four colors. A person that participates in the Stroop Test will receive one of two lists, a *matching list* or a *non-matching list* with a varying number of words. In a **matching list**, the color of the ink matches the color of the word. In a **non-matching list**, the color of the ink does not match the color of the word.

The experiment is performed by giving the person either kind of list. The person says aloud the color of the *ink* in which each word is written. The time it takes for the person to say the color of the ink for the list and the number of words in the list are recorded. The experiment is repeatedly performed with different people until enough data are collected to make a conclusion about the experiment.

A. If you were to perform this experiment, what results would you expect to see for either the matching lists or non-matching lists? Use a complete sentence in your answer.

B. How do you think the results for the matching and non-matching lists would compare? Use a complete sentence in your answer.

C. What are the two quantities that vary in the experiment? Use a complete sentence in your answer.

D. Which quantity depends on the other? Use a complete sentence in your answer.

6

Investigate Problem 1

1. Perform the experiment and record your data in the tables below. Be sure to record the matching or non-matching list's data in the correct table. You will complete the last column of the table in Question 2.

Matching Lists				
List length (words)	Time 1 (seconds)	Time 2 (seconds)	Time 3 (seconds)	

Non-matching Lists				
List length (words)	Time 1 (seconds)	Time 2 (seconds)	Time 3 (seconds)	

Investigate Problem 1

2. In the fifth column of each table, record the average time in seconds for each list. Round your answers to the nearest hundredth.

3. Write the ordered pairs from the matching lists table that show the time as a function of the length of the list.

Take Note

Remember that to find the average of a list of numbers, first find the sum of the numbers. Then divide the result by the number of numbers in the list.

4. Create a scatter plot of the ordered pairs on the grid below. First, choose your bounds and intervals. Be sure to label your graph clearly.

Variable quantity	Lower bound	Upper bound	Interval

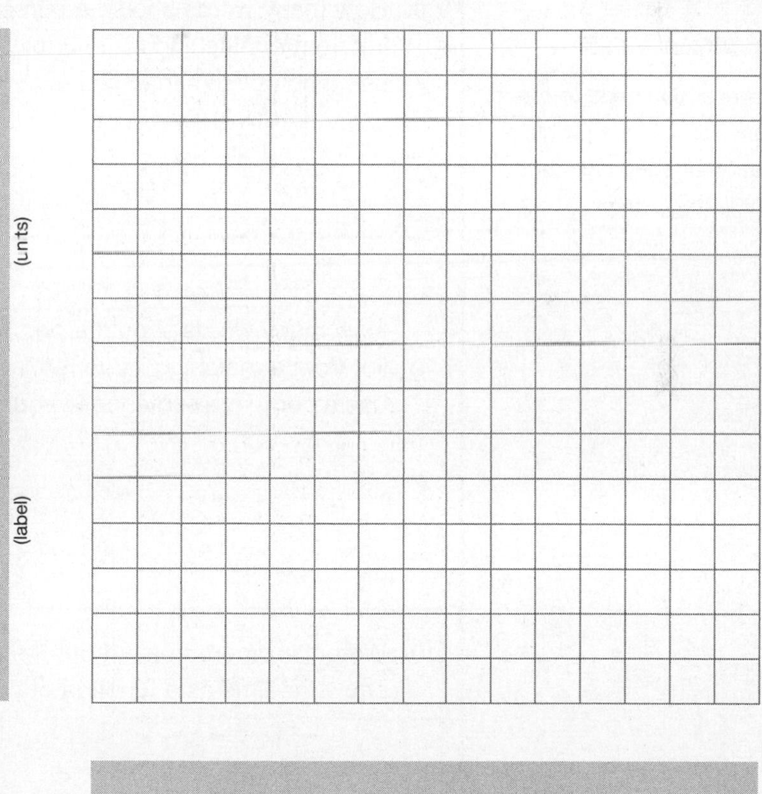

5. Use a ruler to draw the line of best fit. Then write the equation of your line.

6. Find the y-intercept of your line. What does the y-intercept represent in this situation? Use complete sentences in your answer.

Investigate Problem 1

7. Find the slope of your line. What does the slope represent in this situation? Use complete sentences in your answer.

8. How many seconds should it take a person to say the color of the ink of a matching list of 25 words? Show all your work and use a complete sentence in your answer.

   How many seconds should it take a person to say the color of the ink of a matching list of 10 words? Show all your work and use a complete sentence in your answer.

Take Note

Whenever you need to round an answer, use the problem situation and the units of the variable to guide you.

9. How many words should a person be able to say the color of the ink from a matching list in 2 minutes? Show all your work and use a complete sentence in your answer.

   How many words should a person be able to say the color of the ink from a matching list in 5 minutes? Show all your work and use a complete sentence in your answer.

10. Write the ordered pairs from the non-matching lists table that show the time as a function of the length of the list.

11. Create a scatter plot of the ordered pairs on the grid on the next page. First, choose your bounds and intervals. Be sure to label your graph clearly.

Variable quantity	Lower bound	Upper bound	Interval

6

Investigate Problem 1

12. Use a ruler to draw the line of best fit. Then write the equation of your line.

13. Find the y-intercept of your line. What does the y-intercept represent in this situation? Use a complete sentence in your answer.

14. Find the slope of your line. What does the slope represent in this situation? Use a complete sentence in your answer.

15. How many seconds should it take a person to say the color of the ink for a non-matching list of 25 words? Show all your work and use a complete sentence in your answer.

    How many seconds should it take a person to say the color of the ink for a non-matching list of 10 words? Show all your work and use a complete sentence in your answer.

6

Investigate Problem 1

16. How many words should a person be able to say the color of the ink from a non-matching list in 2 minutes? Show all your work and use a complete sentence in your answer.

How many words should a person be able to say the color of the ink from a non-matching list in 5 minutes? Show all your work and use a complete sentence in your answer.

17. Compare your results for the matching lists to the results for the non-matching lists. Do your results seem reasonable? Use complete sentences to explain your reasoning.

18. Are the results what you expected? Use complete sentences to explain your reasoning.

19. What conclusions do you think a cognitive psychologist might draw from your experiment results? Use complete sentences in your answer.

6.4 Jumping

Correlation

Objectives

In this lesson, you will:

- Draw a line of best fit.
- Find and use an equation of a line of best fit.
- Determine whether data are positively correlated, negatively correlated, or not correlated.

Key Terms

- correlation
- positively correlated
- negatively correlated

SCENARIO Your class is debating whether a person's height affects the height to which a person can jump. Your class decides to run an experiment and collect and analyze the data to find the answer.

Problem 1 How High Can You Jump?

A. Create a table that you can use for your experiment. The table should include columns for the person's name, the person's height in inches, and the height jumped in inches.

B. Perform the experiment and record the results in the table. Use complete sentences to describe the method that you used to determine the jump height.

Investigate Problem 1

1. Write the ordered pairs from the table that show the jump height as a function of the person's height. Copy the ordered pairs into the margin on page 275.

Investigate Problem 1

2. When data points are clustered together but are far from the origin, it can be hard to draw a line of best fit if the portion of the graph from the origin is included in the graph. So, you can break the graph and show the portion where the data appear. For instance, consider the two graphs below that display the same data.

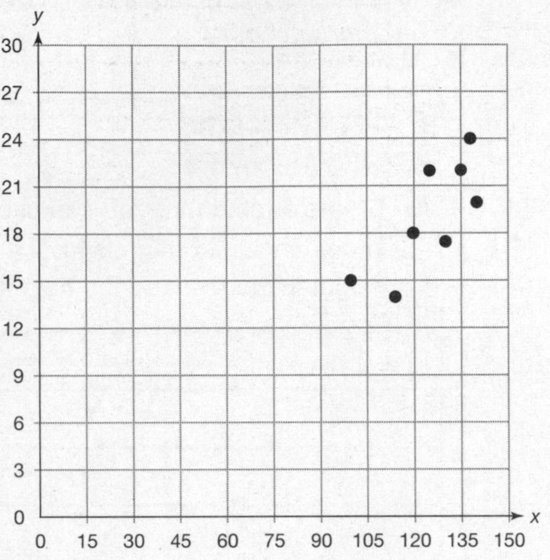

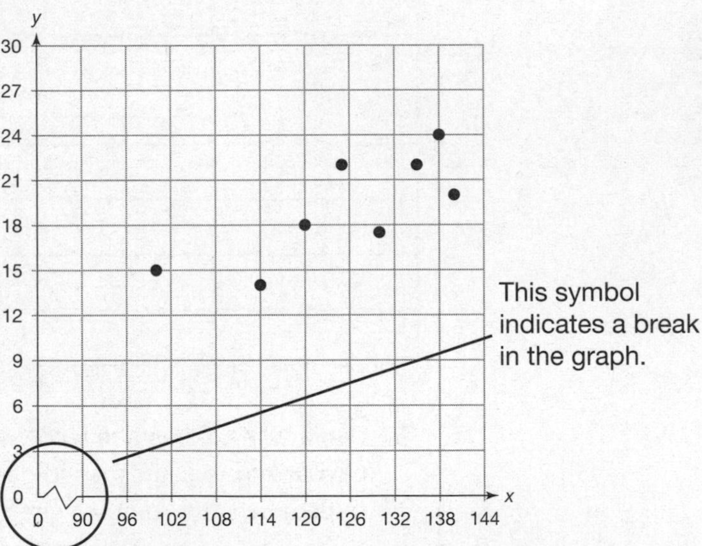

What is the advantage of using a graph with a break in it? Use a complete sentence in your answer.

What is the disadvantage of using a graph with a break in it? Use a complete sentence in your answer.

Investigate Problem 1

3. Create a scatter plot of the ordered pairs from Question 1 on the grid below. First, choose your bounds and intervals, using 52 as the lower bound for the person height. Be sure to label your graph clearly.

Variable quantity	Lower bound	Upper bound	Interval
Person height	52		

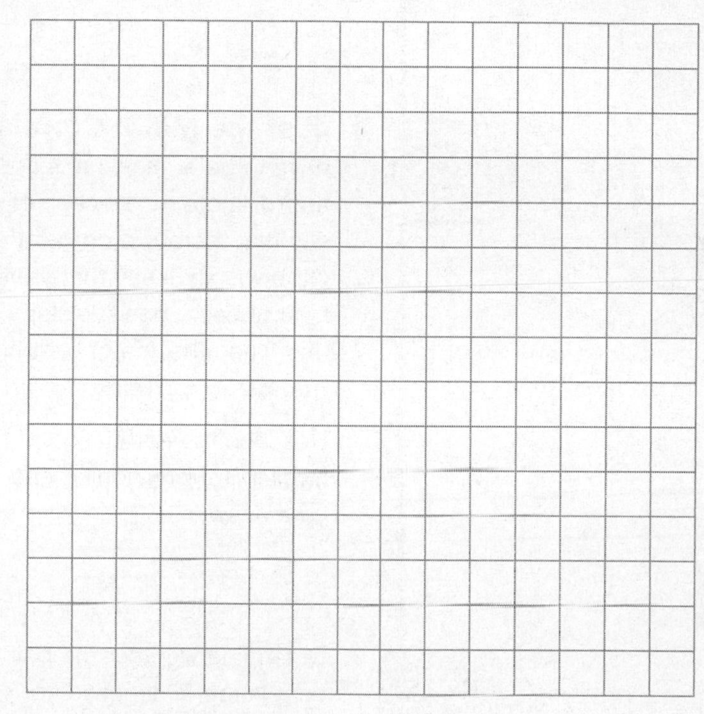

4. Use a ruler to draw the line of best fit. Then write the equation of your line.

5. Describe the slope of your line. Use a complete sentence in your answer.

6. What does your graph and line of best fit indicate about the relationship between a person's height and the height to which the person can jump? Use a complete sentence in your answer.

6

Investigate Problem 1

7. What factors could cause an incorrect jump height measurement or an inconsistency in the measurements? Use complete sentences in your answer.

Use complete sentences to describe situations in which these errors or inconsistencies could occur.

8. **Just the Math: Correlation** In many situations, you will have to determine if it is appropriate to use a line of best fit to approximate a collection of points. When it *is* appropriate, we say that there is a **correlation** between the *x*- and *y*-values. Otherwise, we say that there is no correlation. When the line of best fit has a positive slope, the points are **positively correlated,** and when the line of best fit has a negative slope, the points are **negatively correlated.**

Describe the correlation of the points in your graph in Question 3. Explain your reasoning and use a complete sentence in your answer.

9. Determine whether the points in each scatter plot have a positive correlation, a negative correlation, or no correlation.

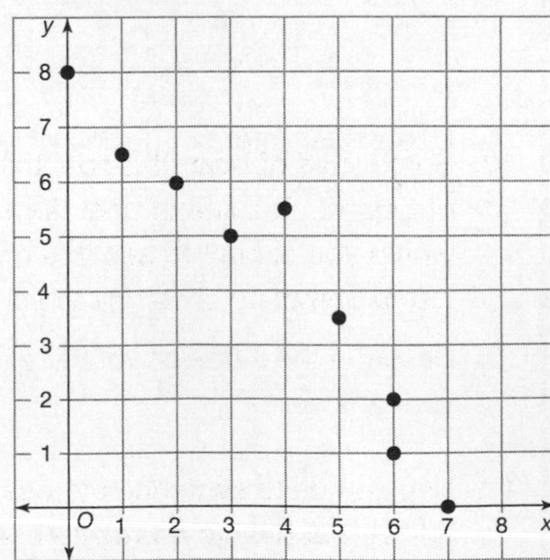

Investigate Problem 1

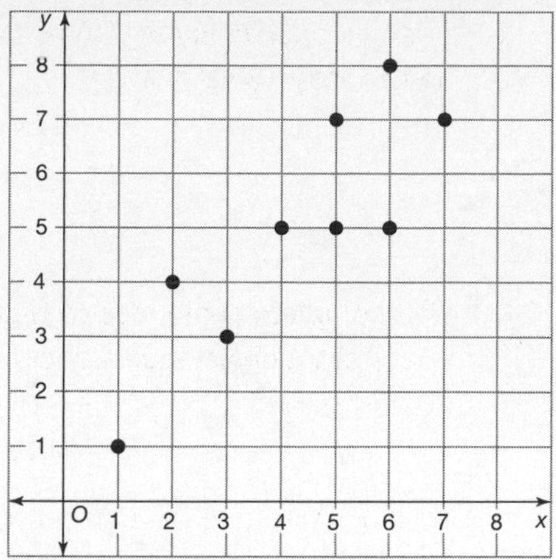

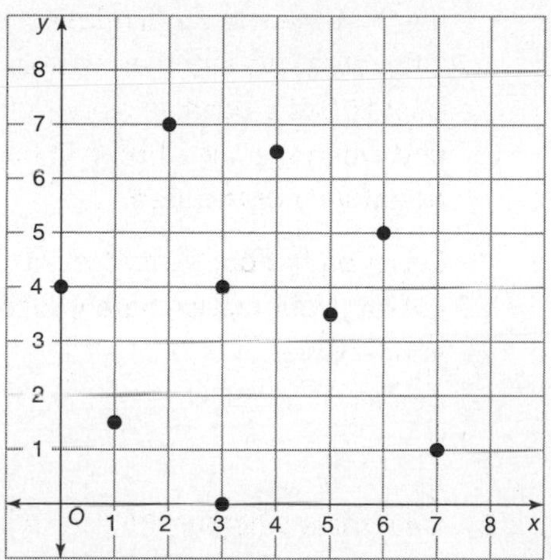

10. Some lines of best fit model their data better than other lines of best fit. If a line of best fit models the data very well, what would you expect to see in a graph of the data and the line? Use a complete sentence in your answer.

11. Use complete sentences to describe the graph of a collection of points that has no correlation.

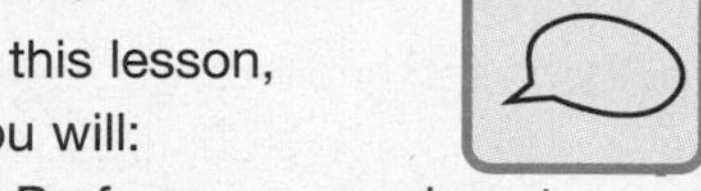

6.5 Human Chain: Wrist Experiment

Using Technology to Find a Linear Regression Equation, Part I

Objectives

In this lesson, you will:

- Perform an experiment.
- Use technology to find a linear regression equation.
- Use a linear regression equation to predict results.

Key Terms

- least squares method
- linear regression equation
- correlation coefficient

SCENARIO Your class is going to explore the speed of nerve impulses in the body by performing an experiment that involves a human chain.

Problem 1 A Chain Connected at the Wrist

In this experiment, a group of people forms a circle with each person gently holding the wrist of the person to his or her right. One person is the beginning of the chain and another person is the end of the chain. The group must keep their eyes closed. When the experiment begins, someone says "go" and the first person carefully but quickly squeezes the next person's wrist, this next person squeezes a wrist, and so on. After the last person's wrist is squeezed, he or she should say "stop" and let go of the next person's wrist. The amount of time from when the word "go" is spoken until the word "stop" is spoken (the amount of time it takes to complete the chain) is recorded.

A. Run the experiment ten times, using a different number of people in the chain each time. Record the data for the experiment in the table below. Then find the average of each row of times and record the result in the last column of the table. Round your average times to the nearest hundredth, if necessary.

Chain length (people)	Time 1 (seconds)	Time 2 (seconds)	Time 3 (seconds)	Average time (seconds)

6

Problem 1 A Chain Connected at the Wrist

B. Write the ordered pairs from the table that show the average time as a function of the chain length.

C. Create a scatter plot of the ordered pairs on the grid below. First, choose your bounds and intervals. Be sure to label your graph clearly.

Variable quantity	Lower bound	Upper bound	Interval

D. Use a ruler to draw the line of best fit. Then write the equation of your line.

6

Investigate Problem 1

1. Just the Math: Linear Regression Equation
You can use a graphing calculator or other technology, such as a spreadsheet program, to find a line of best fit. The method used by a calculator or spreadsheet program to find the line of best fit is called the **least squares method** and the equation is called the **linear regression equation.**

L1	L2	L3 2
5	1.55	
40	10.77	
30	8.86	
60	16.05	
22	7.72	
44	12.52	

L2(11)=

```
LinReg
 y=ax+b
 a=.2565228417
 b=1.030449264
 r²=.9751652654
 r=.9875045647
```

To find the linear regression equation for the ordered pairs in part (B), you must first enter the data into your calculator. Most calculators have a "list" feature that you can use to enter the data. Typically, all the *x*-values are entered into one list, and all the *y*-values are entered into a different list. A sample screen of what you might see is shown at the top left.

After you have entered your data, use the linear regression feature of your calculator to find the linear regression equation. The calculator will give you the values for the slope and *y*-intercept of the linear equation. A sample screen of what you might see is shown at the bottom left. In this case, the slope is the value for *a* and the *y*-intercept is the value for *b*.

Use your calculator to find the linear regression equation. You can round the values of the slope and *y*-intercept to the nearest hundredth.

2. Just the Math: Correlation Coefficient In the screen at the bottom left, you see a value for the variable *r*. The variable *r* is called the **correlation coefficient** and indicates how close the data are to forming a straight line. The value of *r* is between 0 and 1 if the linear regression equation has a positive slope and is between 0 and –1 if the linear regression equation has a negative slope. The closer *r* is to 1 (if the data are positively correlated) or –1 (if the data are negatively correlated), the closer the data are to being in a straight line.

What is the value of *r* for your linear regression equation?

How close are the data to being in a straight line? Use a complete sentence in your explanation.

3. Graph the linear regression equation on your graph. How do the lines compare? Use complete sentences in your answer.

Investigate Problem 1

4. Why should the lines be different? Use complete sentences in your answer.

5. What is the shortest chain length that is possible? Use a complete sentence to explain your reasoning.

What does this tell you about the domain of your linear regression equation? Use complete sentences in your answer.

6. What is the slope of the linear regression equation? Use a complete sentence in your answer.

What does the slope mean in this problem situation? Use a complete sentence in your answer.

7. Use your linear regression equation to determine the number of seconds it should take to perform the experiment if 100 people are in the chain. Show all your work and use a complete sentence in your answer.

Use your linear regression equation to determine the number of seconds it should take to perform the experiment if 50 people are in the chain. Show all your work and use a complete sentence in your answer.

Use your linear regression equation to determine the number of seconds it should take to perform the experiment if 10,000 people are in the chain. Show all your work and use a complete sentence in your answer.

Investigate Problem 1

8. Use your linear regression equation to determine the number of seconds it should take to perform the experiment if four billion people (the world's population) are in the chain. Show all your work and use a complete sentence in your answer.

   Write your answer to Question 8 in years. Show all your work and use a complete sentence in your answer.

9. Use your linear regression equation to determine the length of the chain if it takes one hour to complete the chain. Show all your work and use a complete sentence in your answer.

   Use your linear regression equation to determine the length of the chain if it takes one day to complete the chain. Show all your work and use a complete sentence in your answer.

   Use your linear regression equation to determine the length of the chain if it takes one year to complete the chain. Show all your work and use a complete sentence in your answer.

Investigate Problem 1

10. Could you perform the experiment to test your answers to Questions 7 through 9? Use complete sentences to explain your answer.

What does this tell you about the value of being able to find a line of best fit? Use complete sentences in your answer.

11. Why do you think it is necessary to have three different people time the experiment? Use complete sentences to explain your reasoning.

12. In one run of the experiment, why are the three times different? Use complete sentences to explain your reasoning.

13. Use complete sentences to explain why the data points do not form a straight line.

14. Suppose that you performed this experiment all over again. Would you get the same linear regression equation? Use complete sentences to explain your reasoning.

Would you get the same correlation coefficient? Use complete sentences to explain your reasoning.

6

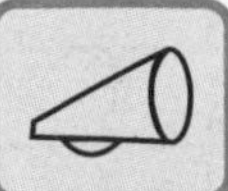

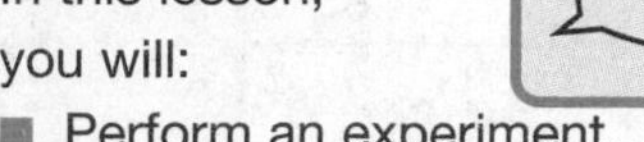

6.6 Human Chain: Shoulder Experiment

Using Technology to Find a Linear Regression Equation, Part 2

Objectives

In this lesson, you will:

- Perform an experiment.
- Use technology to find a linear regression equation.
- Use a linear regression equation to predict results.

Key Term

- linear regression equation

SCENARIO Your class is again going to explore nerve impulse speed in the body by performing an experiment.

Problem 1 A Chain Connected at the Shoulder

In this experiment, a group forms a circular chain with each person gently holding the *shoulder* of the person to his or her right. One person begins and another person ends the chain. The group must keep their eyes closed. To begin, someone says "go" and the first person carefully but quickly squeezes the next person's shoulder, this next person squeezes a shoulder, and so on. Once the last person's shoulder is squeezed, he or she should stay "stop" and let go of the next person's shoulder. The amount of time it takes to complete the chain is recorded.

A. How do you think this experiment's results will be different from the results in the wrist experiment in Lesson 6.5? Use complete sentences in your explanation.

B. Run the experiment ten times, using different chain lengths each time. Record the data in the table below. Then find the average of each row and record the results in the table. Round your averages to the nearest hundredth, if necessary.

Chain length (people)	Time 1 (seconds)	Time 2 (seconds)	Time 3 (seconds)	Average time (seconds)

6

Problem 1 A Chain Connected at the Shoulder

C. Write the ordered pairs from the table that show the average time as a function of the chain length.

Investigate Problem 1

1. Create a scatter plot of the ordered pairs on the grid below. Then sketch a line of best fit that you estimate without using technology. First, choose your bounds and intervals. Be sure to label your graph clearly.

Variable quantity	Lower bound	Upper bound	Interval

(label) (units)

(label) (units)

2. Use a graphing calculator to find the linear regression equation and correlation coefficient for the data. Then graph the line on the grid above.

Investigate Problem 1

3. How close are the data to forming a straight line? Use a complete sentence to explain your reasoning.

4. How close is the line you drew to the graph of the linear regression equation? Use a complete sentence in your answer.

5. What is the shortest chain length that is possible? Use a complete sentence to explain your reasoning.

   What does this tell you about the domain of your linear regression equation? Use complete sentences in your answer.

6. What is the slope of the linear regression equation? Use a complete sentence in your answer.

   What does the slope mean in the problem situation? Use a complete sentence in your answer.

7. Use your linear regression equation to determine the number of seconds it should take to perform the experiment if 100 people are in the chain. Show all your work and use a complete sentence in your answer.

   Use your linear regression equation to determine the number of seconds it should take to perform the experiment if 50 people are in the chain. Show all your work and use a complete sentence in your answer.

   Use your linear regression equation to determine the number of seconds it should take to perform the experiment if 10,000 people are in the chain. Show all your work and use a complete sentence in your answer.

Investigate Problem 1

8. Use your linear regression equation to determine the number of seconds it should take to perform the experiment if four billion people (the world's population) are in the chain. Show all your work and use a complete sentence in your answer.

   Write your answer to Question 8 in years. Show all your work and use a complete sentence in your answer.

9. Use your linear regression equation to determine the length of the chain if it takes one hour to complete the chain. Show all your work and use a complete sentence in your answer.

   Use your linear regression equation to determine the length of the chain if it takes one day to complete the chain. Show all your work and use a complete sentence in your answer.

   Use your linear regression equation to determine the length of the chain if it takes one year to complete the chain. Show all your work and use a complete sentence in your answer.

Investigate Problem 1

10. How does this experiment differ from the wrist experiment in the previous lesson? Use a complete sentence to explain.

11. Graph the equation of the line of best fit from the wrist experiment in the previous lesson and the equation from Question 2 on the grid below. First, choose your bounds and intervals. Be sure to label your graph clearly.

Variable quantity	Lower bound	Upper bound	Interval

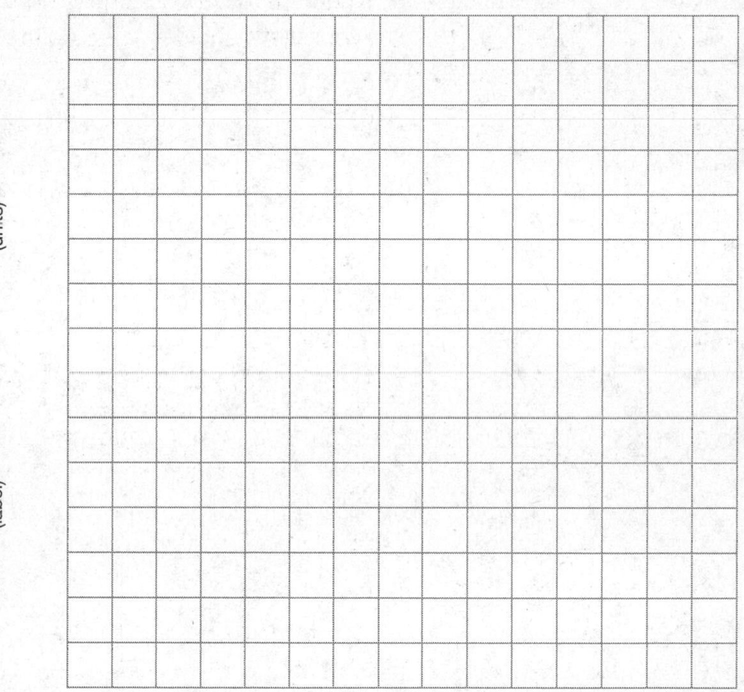

12. What do the slopes in each experiment (wrist and shoulder) represent? What do you think is the cause of the difference between the slopes? Use complete sentences in your answer.

6

6.7 Making a Quilt

Scatter Plots and Non-Linear Data

Objectives

In this lesson, you will:

- Create scatter plots of linear and non-linear data.
- Draw lines of best fit.

Key Terms

- perimeter
- area
- scatter plot
- line of best fit
- correlation coefficient

Take Note

The **perimeter** of a square is the sum of all the side lengths. The **area** of a square is the side length multiplied by itself.

SCENARIO Your class is making quilts for orphaned children as a community service project. In the bags of quilting squares, each square is just over two inches long and two inches wide. When the squares are attached to the backing and each other, the resulting squares are exactly two inches by two inches.

Problem 1 Square Quilts

A. Your class begins with one quilting square. Write a complete sentence to explain the length and width of the quilt at this point.

What are the perimeter and area of the quilt at this point? Show your work and use a complete sentence in your answer.

B. Next, you form a quilt that is two quilting squares long and two quilting squares wide. What are the perimeter and area of this quilt? Show all your work and write your answer using a complete sentence.

C. You continue by forming a quilt that is three quilting squares long and three quilting squares wide. What are the perimeter and area of this quilt? Show all your work and use a complete sentence in your answer.

D. Explain how you found the length and width of each quilt. Then, explain how you found the perimeter and area of each quilt. Use complete sentences in your answer.

6

Problem 1 Square Quilts

E. Complete the table below that shows the perimeter and area of square quilts of different sizes that can be made from the quilting squares. Use your answers to parts (A) through (C) for the first three rows.

Length	Width	Perimeter	Area
inches	inches	inches	square inches
2			
4			
6			
8			
10			
12			
14			

F. What happens to the perimeter as the length increases? Use a complete sentence in your answer.

G. What happens to the area as the length increases? Use a complete sentence in your answer.

H. Which is changing faster as the length changes, the perimeter or the area? Use complete sentences to explain your reasoning.

Investigate Problem 1

1. Write the ordered pairs that show the perimeter as a function of the quilt length.

Investigate Problem 1

2. Create a scatter plot of the ordered pairs on the grid below. First, choose your bounds and intervals. Be sure to label your graph clearly.

Variable quantity	Lower bound	Upper bound	Interval

(label) (units)

(label) (units)

3. Use a ruler to draw a line of best fit on your graph in Question 2. How well are the data correlated? Use a complete sentence in your answer.

4. If you were to use a graphing calculator would you get the same line? Use complete sentences to explain your reasoning.

6

Investigate Problem 1

5. Write the ordered pairs that show the area as a function of the quilt length for quilt lengths up to and including 12 inches.

6. Create a scatter plot of the ordered pairs on the grid below. Choose your bounds and intervals and label your graph clearly.

Variable quantity	Lower bound	Upper bound	Interval

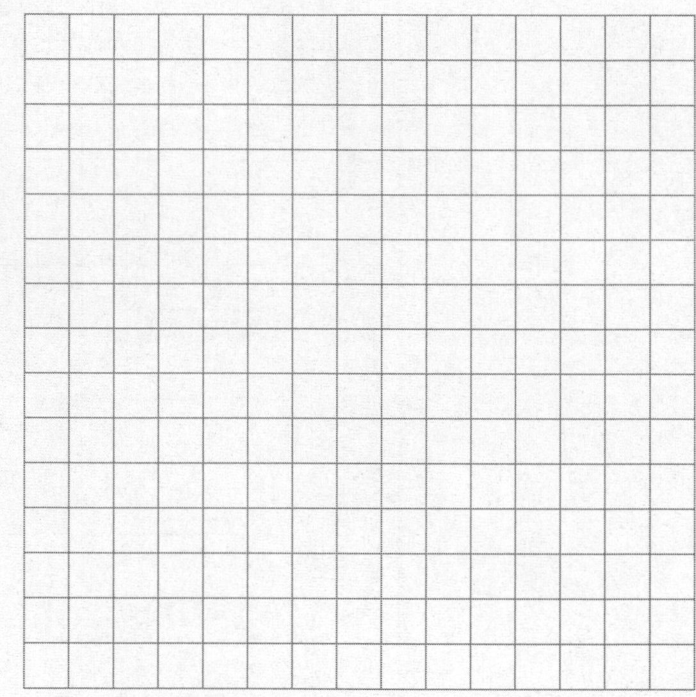

7. Use a ruler to draw a line of best fit on the graph in Question 6. Then write the equation of your line.

8. Use a complete sentence to describe the shape of the graph of the data in Question 6.

Investigate Problem 1

9. Find the area of a quilt that is 25 quilting squares long and 25 quilting squares wide as you did in part (D). Then use the equation that you wrote in Question 7 to find the area. What can you conclude about making a prediction with your linear model?

There is a pattern to the data in the graph in Question 6, but the pattern is non-linear. The graph below shows the ordered pairs from Question 5. Draw a smooth curve through the points. In Chapter 8, you will learn about non-linear equations and functions, including a function that accurately models the data below.

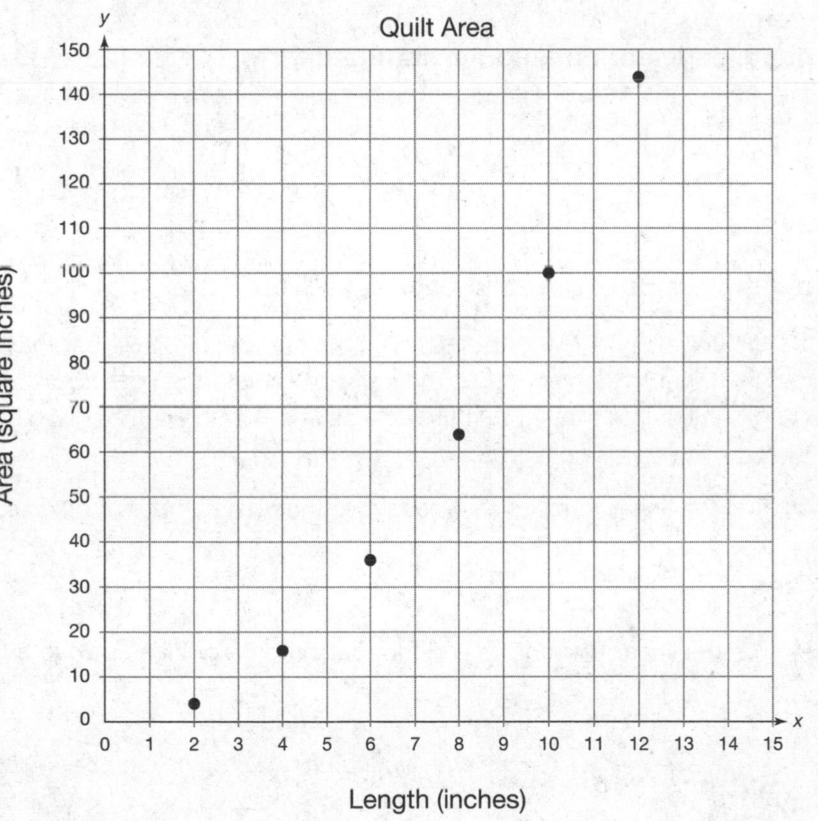

6

Looking Ahead to Chapter 7

7

Focus In Chapter 7, you will learn to write, graph, and solve systems of equations both graphically and algebraically. You will also learn how to write, graph, and solve systems of linear inequalities, as well as identify solutions to linear inequalities.

Chapter Warm-up

Answer these questions to help you review skills that you will need in Chapter 7.

Use the distributive property to simplify each expression.

1. $3(5x + 7)$

2. $-2(10 + 4y)$

3. $-\frac{1}{6}(3x - 12)$

Write each linear equation in standard form.

4. $y = -4x + 7$

5. $2y - 4 = 3x + 23$

6. $-8y = \frac{3}{5}x + \frac{1}{5}$

Read the problem scenario below.

A bicycle company is trying to determine the number of bikes that they have sold. The company began in 1995. In the year 1997, the company sold a total of 285 bikes, and in the year 2000, the company sold a total of 684 bikes. Assume that the number of bikes sold is a linear function of the time in years since 1995.

7. Find the linear function that describes the total number of bikes sold as a function of the time in years since 1995.

8. Use the linear function to find the total number of bikes sold in 2010.

Key Terms

CHAPTER

7

Systems of Equations and Inequalities

The earliest known bricks were made of mud. Today, most bricks are made of clay or ground shale. In Lesson 7.2, you will compare the number of bricks that can be laid by a novice bricklayer and an experienced bricklayer.

7.1 Making and Selling Markers and T-Shirts

Using a Graph to Solve a Linear System

7

Objectives

In this lesson, you will:

- Analyze cost and income equations.
- Graph cost and income equations on the same graph.
- Find the break-even point graphically.

Key Terms

- income
- profit
- point of intersection
- break-even point

SCENARIO You have a part-time job at a company that makes and sells color art markers. As part of your job, you are studying the company's production costs. The markers are made one color at a time. It costs $2 to manufacture each marker and there is a $100 set-up cost for each color. You are also studying the **income,** or the amount of money that the company earns, from the sales of the markers. The company sells the markers to office and art supply stores for $3 per marker.

Problem 1 Making and Selling Markers

A. Write an equation that gives the production cost in dollars to make one color of marker in terms of the number of markers produced. Be sure to describe what your variables represent. Use a complete sentence in your answer.

B. Write an equation that gives the income in dollars in terms of the number of markers sold. Be sure to describe what your variables represent. Use a complete sentence in your answer.

C. Find the production cost to make 80 markers of the same color. Show all your work and use a complete sentence in your answer.

Find the income from selling the 80 markers that you made. Show all your work and use a complete sentence in your answer.

Find the profit from the sale of the 80 markers that you made. Show all your work and use a complete sentence in your answer.

Take Note

Remember that the **profit** is the amount of money that is left from sales (income) after the production costs are subtracted.

7

Problem 1 Making and Selling Markers

D. Find the production cost to make 100 markers of the same color. Show all your work and use a complete sentence in your answer.

Find the income from selling the 100 markers that you made. Show all your work and use a complete sentence in your answer.

Find the profit if 100 markers are made and sold. Show all your work and use a complete sentence in your answer.

Investigate Problem 1

1. Complete the table of values that shows the production cost and income for different numbers of markers of the same color.

Quantity Name	**Number of markers**	**Product cost**	**Income**
Unit	**markers**	**dollars**	**dollars**
Expression	x		
	0		
	20		
	30		
	35		
	55		
	125		
	200		
	400		

Investigate Problem 1

2. Create a graph of both the production cost and income equations on the grid below. Use the bounds and intervals below. Be sure to label your graph clearly.

Variable quantity	Lower bound	Upper bound	Interval
Markers	0	150	10
Money	0	450	30

(label) (units)

(label) (units)

3. Use your graph to determine the numbers of markers for which the production cost is greater than the income. Use a complete sentence in your answer.

Use complete sentences to explain how you found your answer.

7

Investigate Problem 1

4. Use your graph to determine the numbers of markers for which the income is greater than the production cost. Use a complete sentence in your answer.

Use complete sentences to explain how you found your answer.

5. Use your graph to determine the number of markers for which the income is equal to the production cost. Use a complete sentence in your answer.

Use complete sentences to explain how you found your answer.

Take Note

Whenever you see the share with the class icon, your group should prepare a short presentation to share with the class that describes how you solved the problem. Be prepared to ask questions during other groups' presentations and to answer questions during your presentation.

6. Describe the numbers of markers that must be sold in order for your profit to be at least $0. Use complete sentences to explain how you found your answer.

Problem 2 Making and Selling T-Shirts

Your work at the marker company has inspired you to start your own business. You decide to design and sell customized T-shirts. The company that supplies your T-shirts charges you $7.50 for each T-shirt and a set-up cost of $22.50 for a new design. You decide to sell the T-shirts for $8.25 each.

A. Write an equation that gives the production cost in dollars to make one design of T-shirt in terms of the number of T-shirts made. Be sure to describe what your variables represent. Use a complete sentence in your answer.

B. Write an equation that gives the income (the amount of money that you earn) in dollars in terms of the number of T-shirts sold. Be sure to describe what your variables represent. Use a complete sentence in your answer.

C. Find the production cost to make 15 T-shirts in the same design. Show all your work and use a complete sentence in your answer.

Find the income from selling the 15 T-shirts that you made. Show all your work and use a complete sentence in your answer.

Take Note

Remember that the profit is the amount of money that is left from sales (income) after the production costs are subtracted.

Find the profit from the sale of the 15 T-shirts that you made. Show all your work and use a complete sentence in your answer.

D. Find the production cost to make 30 T-shirts in the same design. Show all your work and use a complete sentence in your answer.

Find the income from selling the 30 T-shirts that you made. Show all your work and use a complete sentence in your answer.

Find the profit if 30 T-shirts are made and sold. Show all your work and use a complete sentence in your answer.

Investigate Problem 2

1. Complete the table of values on the next page that shows the production cost and income for different numbers of T-shirts in the same design.

7

Investigate Problem 2

Quantity Name	Number of T-shirts	Product cost	Income
Unit	T-shirts	dollars	dollars
Expression	x		
	0		
	20		
	25		
	30		
	100		
	200		
	400		

2. Create a graph of both the production cost and income equations on the grid below. Use the bounds and intervals below. Be sure to label your graph clearly.

Variable quantity	Lower bound	Upper bound	Interval
T-shirts	0	45	3
Money	0	375	25

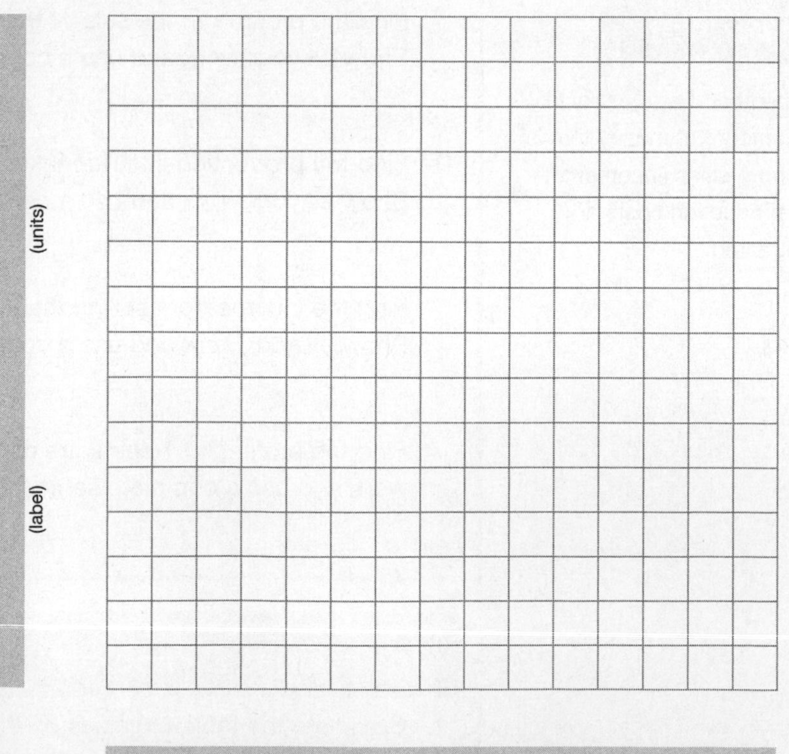

Investigate Problem 2

7

3. Use your graph to determine the numbers of T-shirts for which the production cost is greater than the income. Use a complete sentence in your answer.

Use complete sentences to explain how you found your answer.

4. Use your graph to determine the numbers of T-shirts for which the income is greater than the production cost. Use a complete sentence in your answer.

Use complete sentences to explain how you found your answer.

5. Use your graph to determine the number of T-shirts for which the income is equal to the production cost. Use a complete sentence in your answer.

Use complete sentences to explain how you found your answer.

Investigate Problem 2

6. Describe the numbers of T-shirts that must be sold in order for your profit to be at least \$0. Use complete sentences to explain how you found your answer.

7. **Just the Math: Break-Even Point** When two graphs cross (or intersect) each other, the point where they cross is called a **point of intersection.** When one line represents the production cost of an item and the other line represents the income from selling the item, the *x*-coordinate of this point is called the break-even point. What is the **break-even point** for making and selling markers? Use a complete sentence in your answer.

What is the company's profit at the break-even point? Show all your work and use a complete sentence in your answer.

What is the break-even point for making and selling T-shirts? Use a complete sentence in your answer.

What is your profit from the T-shirts at the break-even point? Show your work and use a complete sentence in your answer.

7.2 Time Study

Graphs and Solutions of Linear Systems

7

Objectives

In this lesson, you will:

- Determine the number of solutions of a linear system.
- Identify parallel and perpendicular lines.

Key Terms

- system of linear equations
- linear system
- solution
- point of intersection
- parallel lines
- perpendicular lines
- reciprocals

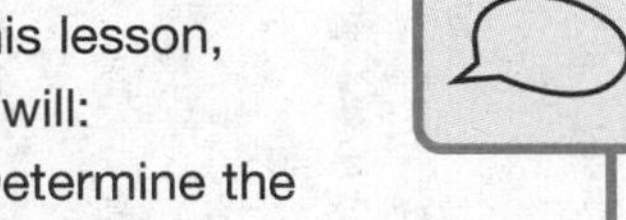

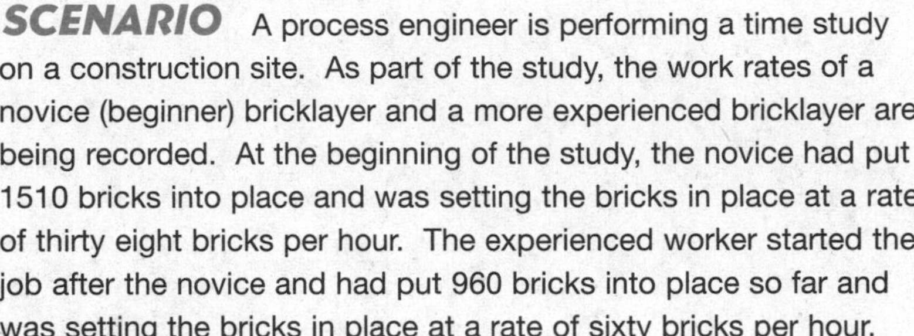

SCENARIO A process engineer is performing a time study on a construction site. As part of the study, the work rates of a novice (beginner) bricklayer and a more experienced bricklayer are being recorded. At the beginning of the study, the novice had put 1510 bricks into place and was setting the bricks in place at a rate of thirty eight bricks per hour. The experienced worker started the job after the novice and had put 960 bricks into place so far and was setting the bricks in place at a rate of sixty bricks per hour.

Problem 1 The Novice and the Pro

A. For each worker, write an equation that gives the total number of bricks y set in place in terms of the time x in hours after the beginning of the time study.

B. After eight hours of the time study, how many bricks in all will each worker have set into place? Show all your work and use complete sentences in your answer.

Which worker has set more bricks into place after eight hours of the time study? Use a complete sentence in your answer.

C. After forty hours of the time study, how many bricks in all will each worker have set into place? Show all your work and use complete sentences in your answer.

Which worker has set more bricks into place after forty hours of the time study? Use a complete sentence in your answer.

7

Problem 1 The Novice and the Pro

D. Find the number of hours that the time study would need to run in order for each worker to set a total of 2460 bricks. Show all your work and use complete sentences in your answer.

Investigate Problem 1

1. Create a graph of both equations on the grid below. First, choose your bounds and intervals. Be sure to label your graph clearly.

Variable quantity	Lower bound	Upper bound	Interval

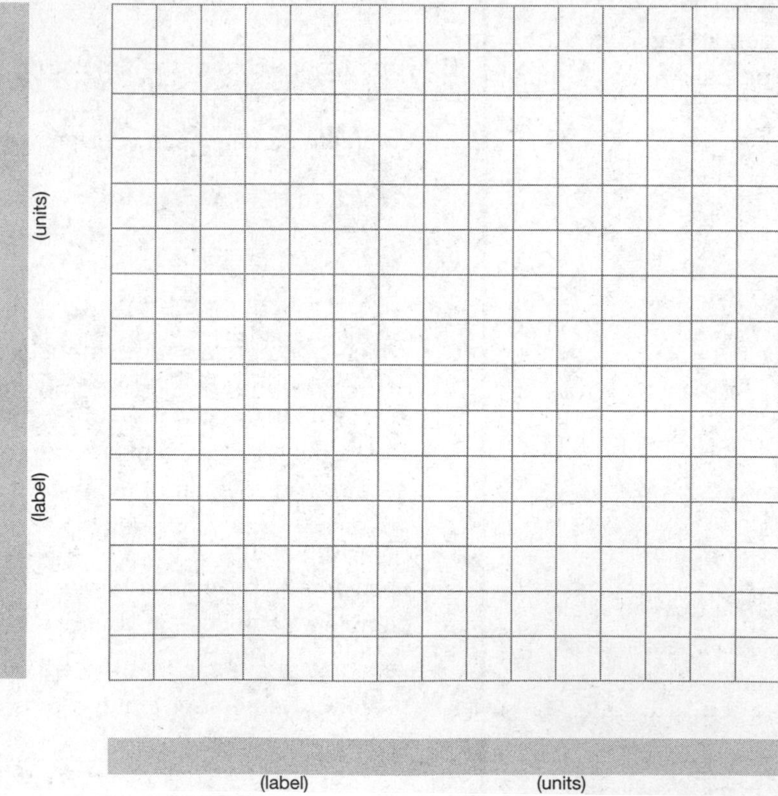

2. Find the amount of time that it will take in the time study for the number of bricks set by each worker to be the same. Use a complete sentence to explain how you found your answer.

Investigate Problem 1

7

3. What does the slope of each line represent in this problem situation? Use a complete sentence in your answer.

Which worker sets bricks faster? How do you know? Use a complete sentence in your answer.

4. What does the *y*-intercept of each line represent in this problem situation? Use a complete sentence in your answer.

How do the *y*-intercepts of the lines compare? What does this mean in the problem situation? Use complete sentences in your answer.

5. Just the Math: Systems of Linear Equations
In this lesson and in Lesson 7.1, you considered the graphs of two linear equations together. When you do this, you form a **system of linear equations** or a **linear system.** Write the linear system represented by the graph in Problem 1.

6. Just the Math: Solution of a Linear System
The **solution** of a linear system is an ordered pair (x, y) that is a solution to *both* equations in the system. Graphically, the solution is the **point of intersection** of the system. What is the solution of the linear system in this problem situation? Use your graph to help you. Write your answer using a complete sentence.

Algebraically, verify that the ordered pair is a solution of your system. Remember that the ordered pair needs to be a solution of both equations.

Take Note

Recall that to algebraically verify that an ordered pair is a solution of an equation, substitute the values given by the ordered pair for x and y in the equation. These values should give you a true statement.

Problem 2 The Pros

A. Another experienced bricklayer is having her time recorded as a part of the time study. At the beginning of the study, this worker had set 600 bricks so far and can set 60 bricks in one hour. Write an equation that gives the total number of bricks y set in place in terms of the time x in hours after the beginning of the time study.

B. Write a linear system that shows the total number of bricks set in terms of time for both experienced workers.

C. Create a graph of the linear system on the grid below. First, choose your bounds and intervals. Be sure to label your graph clearly.

Variable quantity	Lower bound	Upper bound	Interval

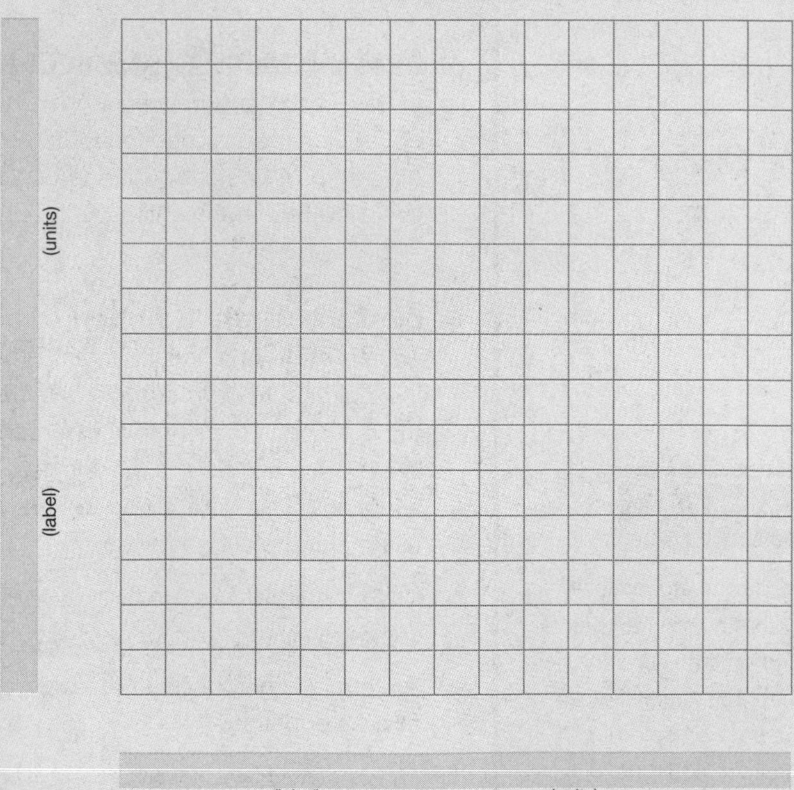

Investigate Problem 2

1. What does the slope of each line represent in this problem situation? Use a complete sentence in your answer.

   Which worker sets bricks faster? How do you know? Use a complete sentence in your answer.

2. What does the *y*-intercept of each line represent in this problem situation? Use a complete sentence in your answer.

   How do the *y*-intercepts of the lines compare? What does this mean in the problem situation? Use complete sentences in your answer.

3. Does there appear to be any point of intersection of the lines?

4. Use complete sentences to describe how the lines are related to each other.

5. **Just the Math: Parallel Lines** The lines that you graphed in part (C) are *parallel lines*. Two lines in the same plane are **parallel** to each other if they do not intersect. What can you conclude about the slopes of parallel lines? Use a complete sentence in your answer.

6. Does the linear system for the two experienced workers have a solution? Use complete sentences to explain your reasoning.

7. Will the two experienced workers ever set the same number of bricks during the time study? Use complete sentences to explain your reasoning.

7

Investigate Problem 2

8. Just the Math: Number of Solutions of a Linear System So far in this lesson, we have seen a linear system with one solution and a linear system with no solution. Use complete sentences to describe the graphs of these kinds of linear systems.

Consider the following linear system:

$y = 2x - 4$ and $y = -2(2 - x)$.

Complete the table of values for this linear system.

Expression	x	$2x - 4$	$-2(2 - x)$
	-5		
	0		
	5		
	10		
	12		
	15		

What can you conclude about the number of solutions of this linear system? Use a complete sentence in your answer.

Because every point on the graph of $y = 2x - 4$ is on the graph of $y = -2(2 - x)$, we can say that this system has an *infinite number* of solutions. Use a complete sentence to explain why you think this is true.

Problem 3 When Is the Job Done?

A. The experienced bricklayer who sets bricks at a rate of 60 bricks per hour and has set 960 bricks so far must set approximately 20,000 additional bricks before the job is done. Write an equation that gives the total number of bricks y left to set in terms of the time x in hours after the beginning of the time study.

Problem 3 When Is the Job Done?

B. Form a linear system with the equation in part (A) and the equation from Problem 1, part (A) that gives the total number of bricks set by this worker in terms of the time after the beginning of the time study.

7

Investigate Problem 3

1. Create a graph of the linear system on the grid below. First, choose your bounds and intervals. Be sure to label your graph clearly

Variable quantity	Lower bound	Upper bound	Interval

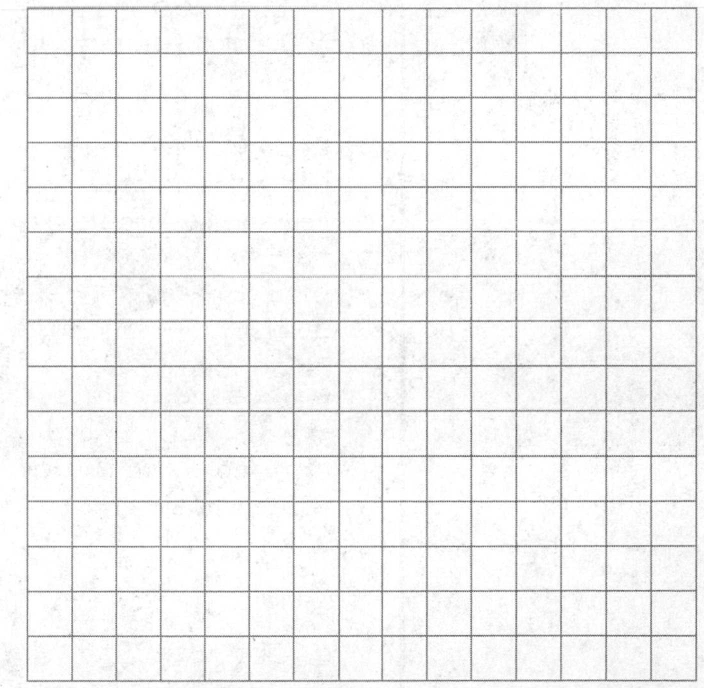

2. What does the point of intersection of the lines represent?

3. Compare the slopes of the lines. Use a complete sentence in your answer.

7

Investigate Problem 3

4. Are the lines *perpendicular*? That is, do they intersect at a right angle?

5. Consider the graph of your linear system and the equations of the lines. What do you notice about the slopes of perpendicular lines?

Take Note

Two numbers are **reciprocals** if their product is 1.

6. **Just the Math: Perpendicular Lines** A property of **perpendicular lines** is that the product of their slopes must be –1. So, this means that the slopes must have opposite signs and must be **reciprocals** of each other. For instance, the lines

   $y = -3x + 4$ and $y = \frac{1}{3}x + 1$ are perpendicular because

   $-3\left(\frac{1}{3}\right) = -1$. Algebraically show that the lines in your graph in Question 1 are *not* perpendicular. Show your work.

7. Determine whether the graphs of each pair of equations are parallel, perpendicular, or neither. Show your work and use a complete sentence to explain your reasoning.

   $y = \frac{2}{3}x + 4$ and $y = -\frac{3}{2}x + 1$

   $y = 5x - 4$ and $y = -5x + 4$

   $y = 4x$ and $y = \frac{1}{4}x - 2$

   $y = -1.8x + 15$ and $y = 6 - 1.8x$

7.3 Hiking Trip

Using Substitution to Solve a Linear System

7

Objective

In this lesson, you will:

- Solve linear systems by using substitution.

Key Terms

- standard form of a linear equation
- substitution method

Take Note

A linear equation is in **standard form** if it is written as $Ax + By = C$, where A, B, and C are constants and A and B are not both zero.

SCENARIO The Outdoor Club at school is going on a hiking trip and is making trail mix as part of the food that they will take. The trail mix will be made up of nuts and dried fruits, such as raisins, dried cherries, and banana chips. The nuts cost $4.50 per pound and the dried fruits cost $3.25 per pound. The group can spend $15 on the trail mix.

Problem 1 Making Trail Mix

A. Write an equation in standard form that relates the numbers of pounds of nuts and dried fruits that can be bought for $15. Use x to represent the number of pounds of nuts and y to represent the number of pounds of dried fruits that can be bought.

B. The group agreed to have one and a half times as much dried fruits as nuts in the mix. Write an equation in x and y as defined in part (A) that represents this situation.

C. Will two pounds of nuts and three pounds of dried fruits satisfy both of your equations? Show all your work.

D. Will two and one quarter pounds of nuts and one and a half pounds of dried fruits satisfy both of your equations? Show all your work.

7

Problem 1 Making Trail Mix

E. Create a graph of both equations on the grid below. First, choose your bounds and intervals. Be sure to label your graph clearly.

Variable quantity	Lower bound	Upper bound	Interval

F. Can you determine the solution of this linear system exactly from your graph? Use a complete sentence to explain your answer.

Investigate Problem 1

1. Estimate the point of intersection from your graph.

   Check your point in each of the equations. Is your point the solution of the linear system?

2. **Just the Math: Substitution Method** In many systems it is difficult to determine the solution from the graph, so there is an algebraic method for finding the solution. Consider the linear system for this problem situation:

   $4.50x + 3.25y = 15$

   $y = 1.5x.$

   Because y is equal to $1.5x$, we can substitute $1.5x$ for y in the first equation.

   $4.50x + 3.25y = 15$

   $4.50x + 3.25(1.5x) = 15$

   You now have an equation in x only. Solve this equation for x. Show all your work.

Take Note

It does not matter which equation from the linear system that you use to find the value of y. You could have used the equation $4.50x + 3.25y = 15$ to find the value of y.

   Now that you have the x-value of the solution, find the y-value by substituting your result for x into the equation $y = 1.5x$. Show all your work.

   So, the solution to the linear system is (1.6, 2.4). Is this solution confirmed by your graph?

3. Interpret the solution of the linear system in the problem situation. Use a complete sentence in your answer.

7

Investigate Problem 1

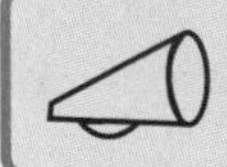

4. How many pounds of trail mix will the club have? Use a complete sentence to explain how you found your answer.

Problem 2 Hiking the Trail

The Outdoor Club splits up into two smaller groups to hike the trail. The first group leaves the beginning of the trail and hikes at a rate of 2.5 miles per hour. The second group leaves 30 minutes later and hikes at a rate of 2.5 miles per hour.

A. Write an equation for the first group that gives the distance hiked y in miles in terms of the amount of time x in hours that the group has been hiking.

B. How far will the first group have traveled after 30 minutes of hiking? Show your work and use a complete sentence in your answer.

C. Write an equation for the second group that gives the distance hiked y in miles in terms of the amount of time since the first group started hiking x.

D. How far will each group have traveled 45 minutes after the first group started hiking? Show all your work and use a complete sentence in your answer.

How far will each group have traveled after 2 hours? Show all your work and use a complete sentence in your answer.

E. Will the second group catch up to the first group? Use complete sentences to explain your reasoning.

Investigate Problem 2

1. Solve the linear system by using the substitution method. First, write your system below.

   Next, because you have an expression for y in terms of x, substitute your expression for y from the first equation into the second equation.

   Now solve the equation for x. What is the result? Use a complete sentence in your answer.

2. Create a graph of your linear system on the grid below. First, choose your bounds and intervals. Be sure to label your graph clearly.

Variable quantity	Lower bound	Upper bound	Interval

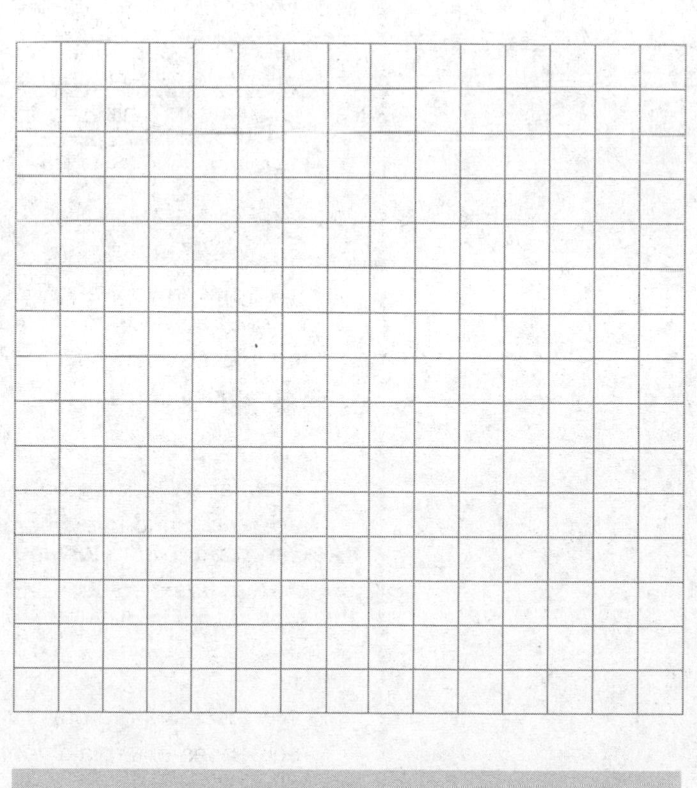

7

Investigate Problem 2

3. What is the relationship between the lines in the graph? Use a complete sentence in your answer.

4. What is the solution of the linear system? Use a complete sentence in your answer.

5. What is the result when you try to algebraically solve a linear system that has no solution? Use a complete sentence in your answer.

Problem 3 Camping

Another community group joins the Outdoor Club at the campsite. The new group has rented six tents and twenty four sleeping bags for $186. The Outdoor Club rented from the same place and rented eight tents and thirty sleeping bags for $236. Each tent costs the same, and each sleeping bag costs the same.

A. For each group, write an equation in standard form for this problem situation. Use x to represent the cost of one tent in dollars and use y to represent the cost of one sleeping bag in dollars.

B. Without solving the linear system, interpret the solution of the linear system in part (A). Use a complete sentence in your answer.

C. Can you tell from looking at the equations whether the linear system has a solution? Use a complete sentence to explain your reasoning.

Investigate Problem 3

1. How does this linear system differ from the linear systems that you wrote in Problems 1 and 2? Use complete sentences in your answer.

2. To solve this linear system by using the substitution method, what do you think you would have to do first? Use a complete sentence in your answer.

3. Write the equation for the community group in slope-intercept form. Show all your work.

4. Now, use the substitution method to solve the linear system. Begin by substituting your expression from Question 3 for y in terms of x into the equation for the Outdoor Club.

   $8x + 30(\boxed{}) = 236$

   Now solve this equation for x. Show all your work.

   Finally, find the value for y. Show all your work.

5. Check your answer algebraically. Show all your work.

6. Interpret the solution of the linear system in the problem situation. Use complete sentences in your answer.

Take Note

Whenever a product involves a sum, such as $4(x + 3)$, you must use the distributive property to simplify: $4(x + 3) = 4(x) + 4(3)$.

7

Investigate Problem 3

7. If possible, solve each linear system by using the substitution method. Show all your work and use a complete sentence in your answer. Then check your answer algebraically.

$4x + 3y = 10$
$y = 2x$

$y = 2x - 1$
$y = 3x + 1$

$8x - 2y = 7$
$2x + y = 4$

$6x + 3y = 5$
$y = -2x + 1$

7.4

Basketball Tournament

Using Linear Combinations to Solve a Linear System

7

Objective

In this lesson, you will:

- Solve a linear system by using linear combinations.

Key Terms

- standard form of a linear equation
- linear combinations method
- linear combination

SCENARIO Your school hosted a basketball tournament. Tickets were sold before the tournament and at the door. More tickets were bought before the tournament than were bought at the door. In fact, there was a difference of 84 tickets between the two kinds of tickets sold. A total of 628 tickets were sold.

Problem 1 Ticket Sales

A. Write an equation in standard form that represents the total number of tickets sold. Use x to represent the number of tickets sold before the tournament and use y to represent the number of tickets sold at the door.

B. Write an equation in standard form that represents the difference in the numbers of tickets sold.

C. How are these equations different? How are they the same? Use complete sentences in your answer.

Investigate Problem 1

1. Write the linear system for this problem situation below.

Now, add the equations together.

Solve the resulting equation. Use a complete sentence in your answer.

7

Investigate Problem 1

Now find the value for y by substituting your value for x into one of the original equations.

What is the solution of your linear system? Use a complete sentence in your answer.

2. Check your solution algebraically.

3. Check your solution by creating a graph of your linear system on the grid below. First, choose your bounds and intervals. Be sure to label your graph clearly.

Variable quantity	Lower bound	Upper bound	Interval

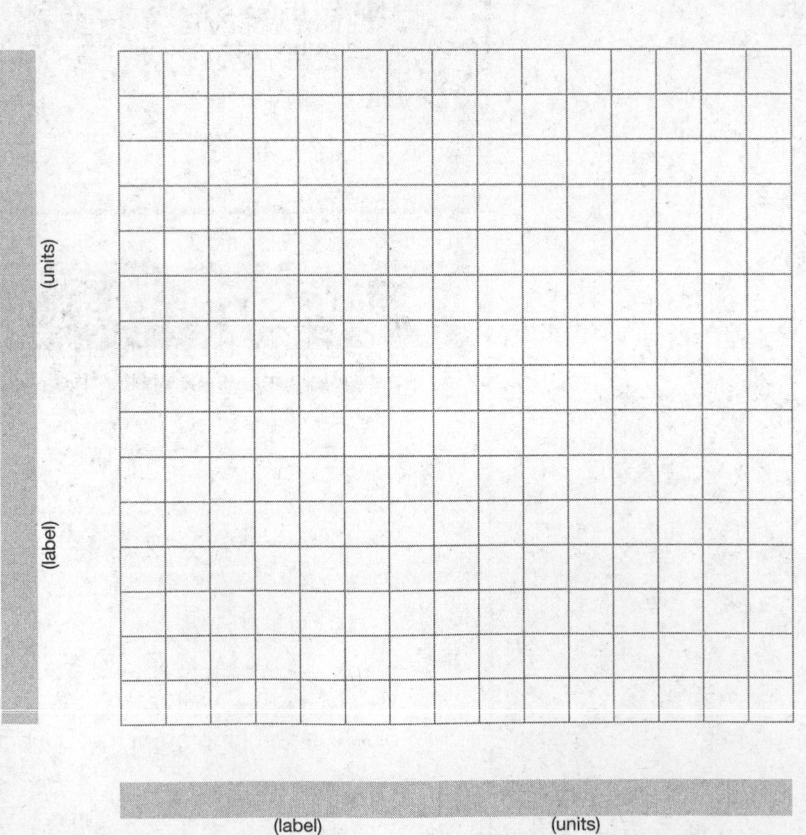

7

Investigate Problem 1

4. Interpret the solution of the linear system in the problem situation. Use a complete sentence in your answer.

5. What effect did adding the equations together have? Use complete sentences in your answer.

6. Describe how the coefficients of y in the original system are related. Use a complete sentence in your answer.

Problem 2 Traveling to the Tournament

A team that entered the tournament sold popcorn and mixed nuts to raise enough money to travel to the tournament. They made \$1.50 from each tin of popcorn and \$2 from each tin of mixed nuts. They raised a total of \$655 and sold 390 tins.

A. Write an equation in standard form that represents the total amount of money raised. Use x to represent the number of tins of popcorn sold and use y to represent the number of tins of nuts sold.

B. Write an equation in standard form that represents the total number of tins sold.

C. How are these equations different? How are they the same? Use complete sentences in your answer.

Investigate Problem 2

1. Multiply each side of the equation that represents the total number of tins sold by –2. Show your work.

7

Investigate Problem 2

2. Write a linear system from the equation in part (A) and the equation in Question 1.

Take Note

When a variable is multiplied by a number, the number is called the **coefficient.**

3. How do the coefficients of the equations in your linear system compare? Use complete sentences in your answer.

4. Add the equations in your linear system together. Then simplify the result. Show your work.

5. What does the result in Question 4 represent? Use a complete sentence in your answer.

6. Find the value for *y* by substituting your value for *x* into the original equation from part (B). Show your work.

7. What is the solution of the linear system? Interpret the solution of the linear system in the problem situation. Use complete sentences in your answer.

8. Check your solution algebraically. Show all your work.

9. **Just the Math: Linear Combinations Method**
The method you used to solve the linear systems in Problems 1 and 2 is called the **linear combinations method.** A **linear combination** is an equation that is the result of adding two equations to each other. The goal of adding the equations together is to get an equation in one variable. Then you can find the value of one variable and use it to find the value of the other variable.

Investigate Problem 2

7

In many cases, one (or both) of the equations in the system must be multiplied by a constant so that when the equations are added together, the result is an equation in one variable. For instance, consider the system

$4x + 2y = 3$
$5x - 3y = 1.$

What is the least common multiple of 2 and 3?

What do you have to multiply 2 by to get 6? What do you have to multiply 3 by to get 6?

So, multiply the first equation by 3 and multiply the second equation by 2. Complete the steps below.

$3(4x + 2y) = 3(3)$ 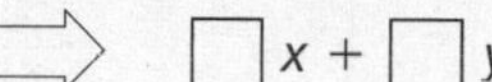 $\square x + \square y = \square$

$2(5x - 3y) = 2(1)$ 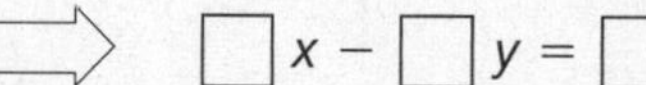 $\square x - \square y = \square$

Now, solve the new linear system. Show all your work and use a complete sentence in your answer.

10. For each linear system below, describe the first step you would take to solve the system by using the linear combinations method. Identify the variable that will be solved for when you add equations. Use complete sentences in your answer.

$4x - 3y = 8$ and $2x - 3y = 1$

$3x + 4y = 2$ and $2x - y = 4$

$6x + 5y = 1$ and $3x + 4y = 2$

$8x + 3y = 2$ and $-7x + 4y = 5$

7

Investigate Problem 2

11. Solve each linear system using linear combinations. Show all your work.

$$-5x + 2y = -10$$
$$3x - 6y = -18$$

$$7x - 4y = -3$$
$$2x + 5y = -7$$

12. Describe the kinds of linear systems for which you would use the substitution method you learned in the last lesson to solve the system. Describe the kinds of linear systems for which you would use the linear combinations method to solve the system. Use complete sentences in your answer.

7.5 Finding the Better Paying Job

Using the Best Method to Solve a Linear System, Part I

Objective

In this lesson, you will:

- Solve a linear system by using an algebraic method.

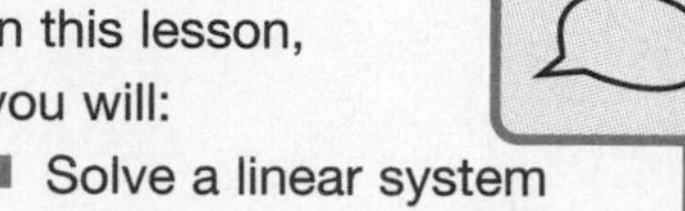

Key Terms

- linear system
- inequality

SCENARIO A friend of yours interviewed for two different sales positions at competing companies. One of the companies, Stellar, pays \$500 per week plus a 10% commission on the total sales per week in dollars. The other company, Lunar, pays \$200 per week plus a 20% commission on the total sales per week in dollars.

Problem 1 Comparing Salaries

A. Write an equation that gives the weekly salary from Stellar in dollars in terms of the weekly total sales in dollars. Be sure to define your variables. Use a complete sentence in your answer.

B. Write an equation that gives the weekly salary from Lunar in dollars in terms of the weekly total sales in dollars. Be sure to define your variables. Use a complete sentence in your answer.

C. Find the salary from Stellar if the total sales are \$1200 in one week. Show your work and use a complete sentence in your answer.

Find the salary from Lunar if the total sales are \$1200 in one week. Show your work and use a complete sentence in your answer.

D. Find the total sales from Lunar if the weekly salary was \$1200. Show your work and use a complete sentence in your answer.

7

Problem 1 Comparing Salaries

E. The salary from Stellar for one week is $540. Find the salary at Lunar if the total sales at Lunar are the same as the total sales at Stellar for this week. Show all your work and use a complete sentence in your answer.

Investigate Problem 1

1. Use an algebraic method to determine whether the salary from Lunar will ever be the same as the salary at Stellar. Show all your work and use a complete sentence in your answer.

If the salaries will be the same, what will the salaries be? Show all your work and use a complete sentence in your answer.

2. Which method did you use to find the answer to Question 1? Use a complete sentence to explain your choice.

3. Check your solution by creating a graph of your linear system on the grid on the next page. First, choose your bounds and intervals. Be sure to label your graph clearly.

Variable quantity	Lower bound	Upper bound	Interval

Investigate Problem 1

7

(label) (units)

(label) (units)

Is your solution confirmed by your graph?

4. Complete the table of values that shows the salaries from both companies for different sales amounts.

Quantity Name	Total sales	Stellar salary	Lunar salary
Unit	dollars	dollars	dollars
Expression	x		
	0		
	100		
	500		
	2500		
	10,000		

7

Investigate Problem 1

5. Which company would you recommend to your friend? Why? Use complete sentences in your answer.

6. Your friend interviews at a third company, Solar. Solar pays a salary of $750 per week with no commissions. Write an equation that gives the salary in dollars in terms of the total sales in dollars. Then add the graph of this equation to your graph in Question 3.

7. Describe the conditions for which the salary from Solar is better than the salaries at Stellar and Lunar. Show all your work and use complete sentences in your answer.

8. Your friend takes the job with Stellar and wants to earn at least $975 each week. Write an **inequality** that represents this situation.

Solve the inequality. Then use a complete sentence to explain what the solution means in the problem situation.

7.6 World Oil: Supply and Demand

Using the Best Method to Solve a Linear System, Part 2

Objective

In this lesson, you will:

- Solve a linear system by using an algebraic method.

Key Term

- linear system

SCENARIO In 2003, there were approximately 28,179.4 million barrels of oil being produced in the world. In 1965, there were approximately 15,856 million barrels of oil being produced in the world.

Problem 1 Supply and Demand

A. What is the rate of change in the amount of oil being produced in millions of barrels per year from 1965 to 2003? Show all your work and use a complete sentence in your answer. Round your answer to the nearest tenth, if necessary.

B. The amount of oil being produced is called the *supply* of oil. Write an equation that gives the supply in millions of barrels in terms of the number of years since 1965. Assume that the rate of change in the supply is the same as the rate of change from 1965 to 2003. Be sure to define your variables. Show all your work and use complete sentences in your answer.

C. The amount of oil that the world uses is called the *demand* for oil. In 1965, the demand was approximately 15,179 million barrels per year and was increasing at a rate of 360.1 million barrels per year. Write an equation that gives the demand in millions of barrels in terms of the number of years since 1965. Be sure to define your variables and use a complete sentence in your answer.

Investigate Problem 1

1. In which year was the supply 18,000 million barrels? Show all your work and use a complete sentence in your answer.

2. In which year will the supply be 30,000 million barrels? Show all your work and use a complete sentence in your answer.

3. Find the demand in 1975. Show all your work and use a complete sentence in your answer.

4. Find the demand in 2010. Show all your work and use a complete sentence in your answer.

5. In which year was the demand 18,000 million barrels of oil? Show all your work and use a complete sentence in your answer.

Investigate Problem 1

7

6. In which year will the demand be 40,000 million barrels of oil? Show all your work and use a complete sentence in your answer.

7. Find the supply 25 years after 1965. Show all your work and use a complete sentence in your answer.

8. In which year was the demand 10,000 million barrels of oil? Show all your work and use a complete sentence in your answer.

9. Find the year in which the supply was 10,000 million barrels. Show all your work and use a complete sentence in your answer.

10. Write the linear system that represents the supply and the demand since 1965.

11. Do you think that the supply was ever the same as the demand? Use what you know about the equations of a linear system to explain your answer.

7

Investigate Problem 1

12. Complete the table of values below that shows the supply and the demand for different numbers of years.

Quantity Name	Years since 1965	Supply	Demand
Unit	years	million barrels	million barrels
Expression	x		
	1		
	10		
	40		
	50		

13. Use the table to decide whether the supply was ever the same as the demand. Use a complete sentence to explain your reasoning.

If so, determine the number of years that will pass before the supply and demand will be equal. Show all your work and use a complete sentence in your answer.

How did you find your answer? Use a complete sentence to explain.

What was the amount of oil when the supply and demand were equal? Show all your work and use a complete sentence in your answer.

Investigate Problem 1

7

14. Check your estimate by creating a graph of your linear system on the grid below. First, choose your bounds and intervals. Be sure to label your graph clearly.

Variable quantity	Lower bound	Upper bound	Interval

(label) (units)

(label) (units)

Is your estimate confirmed by your graph?

15. Do you think that your equations are accurate models for your data? Use complete sentences to explain your reasoning.

7

7.7 Picking the Better Option

Solving Linear Systems

7

Objective

In this lesson, you will:

- Use a system of linear equations to solve a problem.

Key Term

- break-even point

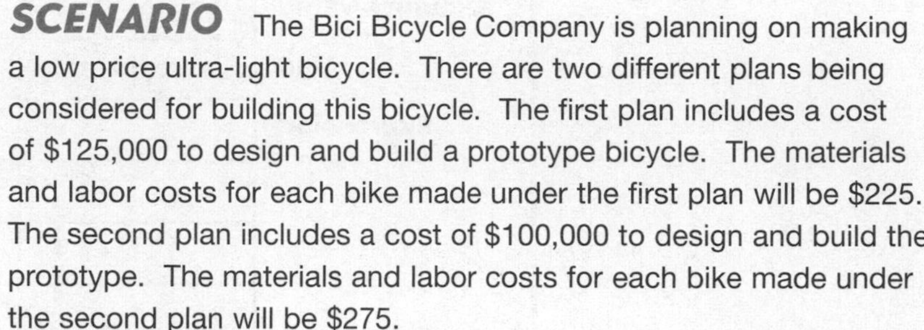

SCENARIO The Bici Bicycle Company is planning on making a low price ultra-light bicycle. There are two different plans being considered for building this bicycle. The first plan includes a cost of \$125,000 to design and build a prototype bicycle. The materials and labor costs for each bike made under the first plan will be \$225. The second plan includes a cost of \$100,000 to design and build the prototype. The materials and labor costs for each bike made under the second plan will be \$275.

Problem 1 Which Plan Is the Better Plan?

A. Before you begin comparing the plans, what factors do you think are important to consider? Use complete sentences in your answer.

B. For each plan, write an equation that gives the total cost in dollars in terms of the total number of bicycles made. Be sure to define your variables.

C. For each plan, what do the slope and y-intercept of the graph of the equation represent in the problem situation? Use complete sentences in your answer.

D. Will there be a number of bicycles for which the total costs are the same? How do you know? Use a complete sentence to explain your reasoning.

E. Describe the different methods you can use to find the number of bicycles for which the total costs are the same. Use a complete sentence in your answer.

7

Investigate Problem 1

1. Complete the table of values that shows the total cost of both plans for different numbers of bicycles.

Quantity Name	Bicycles made	Plan 1 cost	Plan 2 cost
Unit	bicycles	dollars	dollars
Expression			

2. Can you determine from your table the number of bicycles for which the total costs are the same? If so, describe the numbers of bicycles for which the first plan is better and the numbers of bicycles for which the second plan is better. If not, use an algebraic method to answer the question. Then describe the numbers of bicycles for which each plan is the better plan.

3. Create a graph of your linear system on the grid on the next page to verify your answer. First, choose your bounds and intervals. Be sure to label your graph clearly.

Variable quantity	Lower bound	Upper bound	Interval

Investigate Problem 1

4. Now consider the selling price of the bikes. Suppose that the company wants to sell the bikes for $525 each. Write an equation that gives the total earnings in dollars in terms of the number of bicycles sold.

5. For each plan, determine the break-even point. Show all your work. Use complete sentences in your answer.

Take Note

Recall that the *break-even point* is the *x*-coordinate of the point where the graph of the cost intersects the graph of the income.

7

Investigate Problem 1

6. Use a complete sentence to explain what the break-even point means in this situation.

7. Use the results from Questions 2 and 5 to describe the numbers of bicycles for which each plan is better. Use complete sentences in your answer.

8. Suppose that the company wants to change the total costs of each plan. The company wants to reduce the material and labor costs under each plan by $22.50. For each plan, write the new equation for the total cost in terms of the number of bicycles made. Then use your equations to determine the numbers of bicycles for which each plan is better. Use complete sentences in your answers.

Investigate Problem 1

7

9. Does this answer surprise you? Why or why not? Use complete sentences to explain your answer.

10. The company also decides to reduce the selling price under each plan to $450. For each new plan, determine the break-even point. Show all your work. Use complete sentences in your answer.

11. Use the results from Questions 8 and 10 to describe the numbers of bicycles for which each plan is better. Use complete sentences in your answer.

Investigate Problem 1

12. Create a graph of the linear system you found in Question 8 on the grid below. First, choose your bounds and intervals. Be sure to label your graph clearly.

Variable quantity	Lower bound	Upper bound	Interval

(label) (units)

(label) (units)

13. Estimate the point of intersection from your graph. Use complete sentences to compare the points of intersection that you found algebraically and graphically.

7.8 Video Arcade

Writing and Graphing an Inequality in Two Variables

7

Objectives

In this lesson, you will:

- Write an inequality in two variables.
- Graph an inequality in two variables.

Key Terms

- linear inequality in two variables
- inequality symbol
- linear equation
- coordinate plane
- half-plane

SCENARIO Your cousin's graduation party is at a restaurant that has a large video arcade. Each person at the party receives a card with fifty points on it to play the games in the arcade. One of your favorite games, a driving game, uses twelve card points per game. Another game that you like, a basketball game, uses eight points per game.

Problem 1 Playing Games

A. Can you play three driving games and two basketball games and not go over the number of points on the card? Show your work.

B. Can you play two driving games and three basketball games and not go over the number of points on the card? Show your work.

C. Can you play one driving game and four basketball games and not go over the number of points on the card? Show your work.

D. Write an expression that represents the total number of points used by playing *x* driving games and *y* basketball games.

E. What restrictions must be placed on this expression so that you do not go over the number of points on the card? Use a complete sentence in your answer.

F. One form of a **linear inequality in two variables** can be written as $Ax + By \le C$. Write an inequality in two variables that represents this problem situation.

Take Note

Recall that an **inequality** is a statement that is formed by placing an **inequality symbol** ($<$, $>$, $\le$, $\ge$) between two expressions.

Take Note

The forms of a linear inequality in two variables are:

$Ax + By < C$
$Ax + By > C$
$Ax + By \le C$
$Ax + By \ge C$

Investigate Problem 1

1. Complete the table on the next page that shows different numbers of driving and basketball games played and the numbers of points used.

7

Investigate Problem 1

Quantity Name	Driving games	Basketball games	Points used
Unit	games	games	points
	0	5	
	1	3	
	2	3	
	2	4	
	3	2	
	3	3	
	4	0	
	4	1	

2. Create a graph of the data in the table on the grid below. If the number of points used in a row does not exceed the card's points, draw a point for the numbers of games. If the number of points used does exceed the card's points, draw an "x" for the numbers of games. Use the bounds and intervals given below. Label your graph clearly.

Variable quantity	Lower bound	Upper bound	Interval
Driving game	0	7.5	0.5
Basketball game	0	7.5	0.5

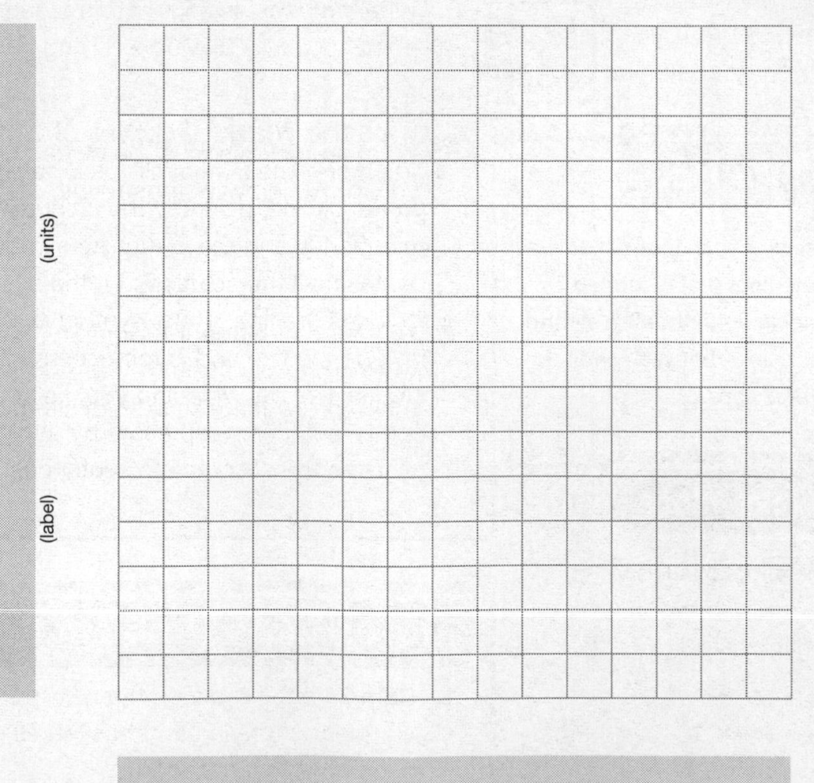

Investigate Problem 1

7

3. Write an equation that represents the number of driving games x and the number of basketball games y that can be played for exactly 50 points. Then add the graph of this equation to your graph in Question 2.

4. What do you notice about your graph? Use a complete sentence in your answer.

5. **Just the Math: Linear Inequality** Shade the side of the graph that contains all of the points. This graph is the graph of the *linear inequality* $12x + 8y \leq 50$. A linear inequality is the same as a linear equation except that an inequality symbol ($<$, $>$, $\leq$, or $\geq$) is used instead of an equals sign. How do the solutions of the linear equation $12x + 8y = 50$ differ from the solutions of the linear inequality $12x + 8y \leq 50$? Use complete sentences in your answer.

Take Note

A **linear equation** in two variables is an equation in which each of the variables is raised to the first power (such as x, rather than x^2) and, when in simplest form, each variable only appears once.

6. **Just the Math: Graphs of Linear Inequalities** The graph of a linear inequality is a **half-plane,** or half of a **coordinate plane**. A line, given by the inequality, divides the plane into two half-planes and the inequality symbol tells you which half-plane contains all the solutions. If the symbol is $\leq$ or $\geq$, the graph includes the line. If the symbol is $<$ or $>$, the graph does not include the line and is represented by a dashed line. For which inequalities below would you include the line? Which inequalities below would you represent by using a dashed line? Write your answers using complete sentences.

$y > -6 - x$ $\qquad$ $2x + 3y \geq 4$ $\qquad$ $x + 5y \leq 10$

$3x + 12y > 5$ $\qquad$ $y \geq -x + 2$ $\qquad$ $x - y < 3$

7

Investigate Problem 1

Consider the linear inequality $y < 4x + 3$. The line that divides the plane is given by $y = 4x + 3$. Should this line be a solid line or a dashed line? Use a complete sentence to explain. Then draw the correct type of line on the grid below.

After you draw the correct type of line, you need to decide which half-plane contains all the solutions, because this is the half-plane that you will shade. To make your decision, consider the point (0, 0). If (0, 0) is a solution, then the half-plane that contains (0, 0) contains all the solutions and should be shaded. If (0, 0) is not a solution, then the half-plane that does not contain (0, 0) contains all the solutions and should be shaded.

Is (0, 0) a solution? Show your work.

Now shade the correct half-plane on the grid below.

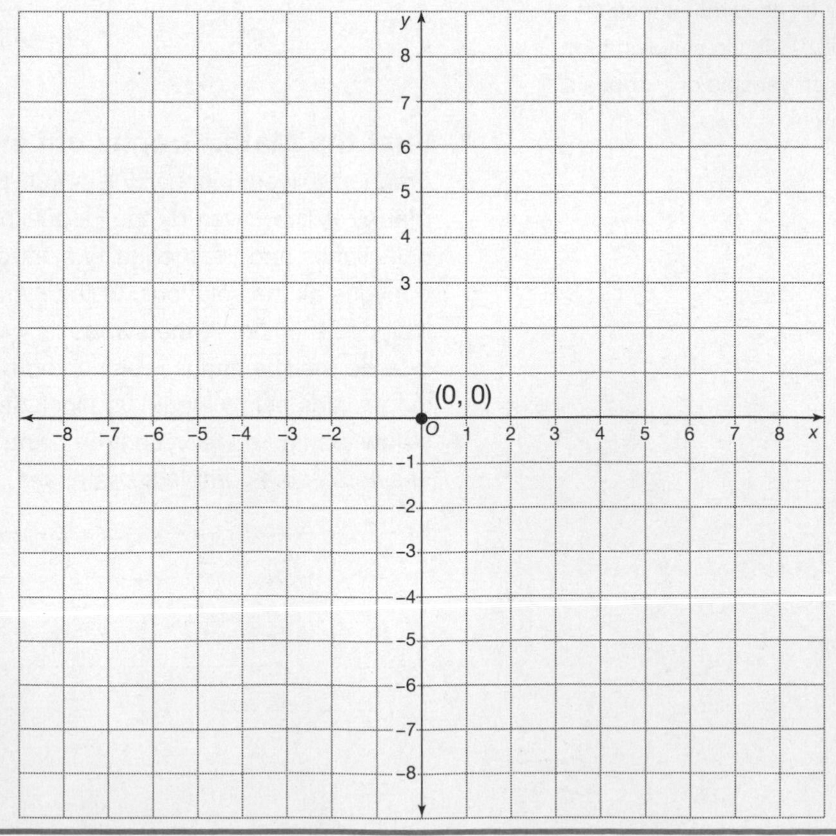

Investigate Problem 1

7. Graph each linear inequality.

$y > x + 2$

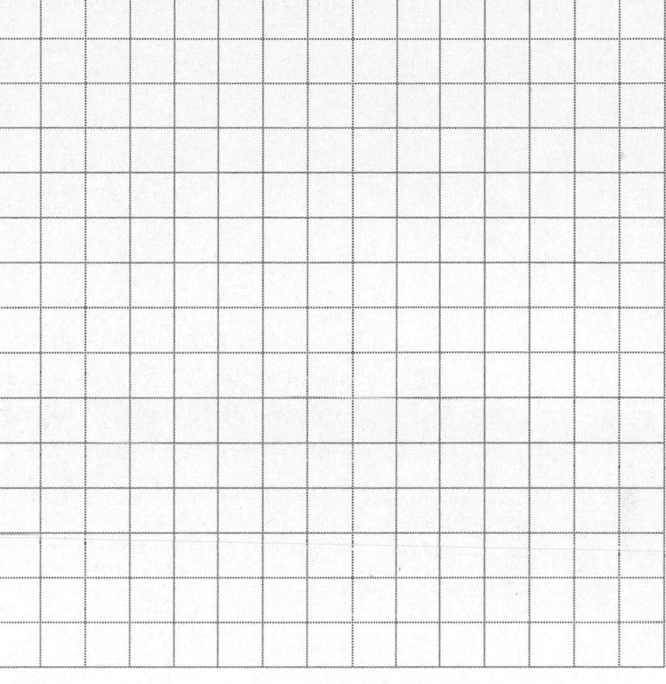

$y \le -x + 3$

7

7.9 Making a Mosaic

Solving Systems of Linear Inequalities

7

Objectives

In this lesson, you will:

- Write a system of linear inequalities.
- Graph a system of linear inequalities.
- Identify solutions of a system of linear inequalities.

Key Terms

- system of linear equations
- linear inequality
- system of linear inequalities

SCENARIO A local arts group is donating a mural that will be placed at the entrance to your school. The mural will be 6 feet tall and 12 feet wide. The group has calculated that they will need approximately 110 bags of tiles to complete the project. The mural will be made of glass and metallic tiles. Each bag of glass tiles costs \$10 and each bag of metallic tiles costs \$18. Another group has donated \$1500 for the purchase of the tiles.

Problem 1 Getting the Tiles

A. Write an equation that relates the numbers of bags of glass and metallic tiles that can be bought for \$1500. Use x to represent the number of bags of glass tiles and use y to represent the number of bags of metallic tiles that can be bought for the mural.

B. Write an equation that relates the numbers of bags of glass and metallic tiles to the total number of bags of tiles needed for the project.

C. What does the solution of the linear system formed by the equations in part (A) and part (B) represent?

D. Solve the linear system. Show all your work and use a complete sentence in your answer.

E. What does the solution mean in the problem situation? Use a complete sentence in your answer.

7

Investigate Problem 1

1. Suppose that the group wants to buy 75 bags of glass tiles and 35 bags of metallic tiles. Is this enough tile?

   Can the group afford this assortment of tile? Show all your work and use a complete sentence to explain your reasoning.

2. Suppose that the group wants to buy 90 bags of glass tiles and 25 bags of metallic tile. Is this enough tile?

   Can the group afford this assortment of tile? Show all your work and use a complete sentence to explain your reasoning.

3. Suppose that the group wants to buy 80 bags of glass tiles and 38 bags of metallic tiles. Is this enough tile?

   Can the group afford this assortment of tile? Show all your work and use a complete sentence to explain your reasoning.

4. Does the group have to spend all of the money to get enough tile? Use a complete sentence to explain your reasoning.

   Write an inequality that represents the amounts of money the group can spend on x bags of glass tiles and y bags of metallic tiles.

Investigate Problem 1

5. Can the group buy more bags of tiles than is needed and not spend all the money? Use a complete sentence to explain your reasoning.

Write an inequality that represents the total numbers of bags of tiles they can use to complete the project.

6. **Just the Math: System of Linear Inequalities**
Together, the linear inequalities in Questions 4 and 5 form a **system of linear inequalities.** Write the system of linear inequalities below.

What do you think it means to be a solution of a system of linear inequalities? Use a complete sentence in your answer.

Determine whether the numbers of bags of tiles given in Questions 1 through 3 are solutions of your system of inequalities. Show all your work.

7. How many solutions do you think a system of linear inequalities can have? Use complete sentences to explain your reasoning.

7

Investigate Problem 1

8. Create a graph of your system of inequalities on the grid below. Use a different color pen or pencil for each inequality. First, choose your bounds and intervals. Be sure to label your graph clearly.

Variable quantity	Lower bound	Upper bound	Interval

(label) (units)

(label) (units)

9. What part of the graph do you think represents the solution of the system of linear inequalities? Use a complete sentence in your answer.

10. Identify three different solutions of the system of inequalities. What do these solutions represent in the problem situation? Use complete sentences in your answer.

7

Looking Ahead to Chapter 8

Focus In Chapter 8, you will graph, solve, and analyze quadratic functions using methods such as factoring, extracting square roots, and the quadratic formula. You will also learn to find the vertex, and minimum and maximum values of a parabola.

Chapter Warm-up

Answer these questions to help you review skills that you will need in Chapter 8.

8

Find the square of each number.

1. 3 **2.** 11 **3.** –4

4. –8.64 **5.** 6.4 **6.** 12.5

Evaluate each expression when $x = 3$.

7. $4x^2 - 6$ **8.** $5x^2 + 8x + 1$ **9.** $2x^2 + 9x$

Read the problem scenario below.

You and your friends are playing soccer in a field by your house. You mark each corner of the field with a flag. Given the distances below, what is the area of your soccer field? Be sure to include the correct units in your answers. Write your answers using a complete sentence.

10. The length of the field is 150 feet, and the width is 50 feet.

11. The length of the field is 75 yards, and the width is 20 yards.

12. The length of the field is 80 meters, and the width is 25 meters.

Key Terms

CHAPTER

8

Quadratic Functions

When a musician plucks a guitar string, the string vibrates and transmits its vibration through the guitar. The sound is amplified and you hear a musical note. In Lesson 8.4, you will use an equation to find the tension of the string and wave speed of the vibrations.

8

8.1 Web Site Design

Introduction to Quadratic Functions

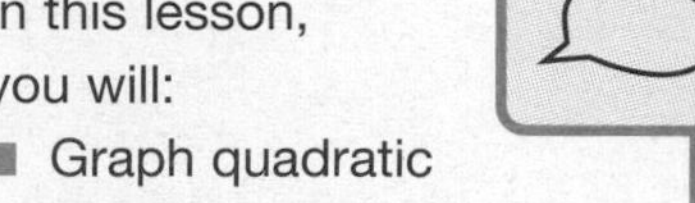

Objectives

In this lesson, you will:

- Graph quadratic functions.
- Identify coefficients in quadratic functions.
- Evaluate quadratic functions.

Key Terms

- rate of change
- quadratic function
- evaluate

SCENARIO Your brother is a graphic artist who works at a company that creates and maintains web sites. One of his jobs is to make art pieces that are put together to form movies (or animations) that are played on different pages of the web site. Each art piece is a frame of the animation. When the frames are displayed one after another, movement can be shown, and the animation is created. His current project is for a web site for a sporting goods company.

Problem 1 Creating an Animation

Your brother's first job on his current project is to create the frames for an animation of the company's logo that will play on the web site's main page. Some of the frames for the animation are shown. When the frames are displayed one after another, the logo will appear to grow.

The initial side length of the square logo is 1 inch. The side length grows by one inch in each frame.

A. Complete the table of values that shows the side length of the logo, the area of the logo, and the corresponding frame numbers. Copy the columns of the table into the correct columns in the margins of pages 361 and 362.

Quantity Name	**Frame**	**Length**	**Area**
Unit	**numbers**	**inches**	**square inches**
Expression	x		
	1		
	2		
	3		
	4		
	5		

Problem 1 Creating an Animation

B. How does the length grow as the frame number increases? How does the area grow as the frame number increases? Use complete sentences in your answer.

C. Find the **rate of change** in the length and find the rate of change in the area from the first frame to the second frame. Show all your work and include the units in your answer.

8

D. Find the rate of change in the length and find the rate of change in the area from the second frame to the third frame. Show all your work and include the units in your answer.

E. Find the rate of change in the length and find the rate of change in the area from the third frame to the fourth frame. Show all your work and include the units in your answer.

F. Find the rate of change in the length and find the rate of change in the area from the fourth frame to the fifth frame. Show all your work and include the units in your answer.

Problem 1 Creating an Animation

G. What do you notice about the rates of change in the length with respect to the frame number? What do you notice about the rates of change in the area with respect to the frame area? Use a complete sentence in your answer.

Quantity Name	Frame	Length
Unit	numbers	inches
Expression	x	
	1	
	2	
	3	
	4	
	5	

Investigate Problem 1

1. Create a scatter plot of the length as a function of the frame number on the grid below. First, choose your bounds and intervals. Be sure to label your graph clearly.

Variable quantity	Lower bound	Upper bound	Interval

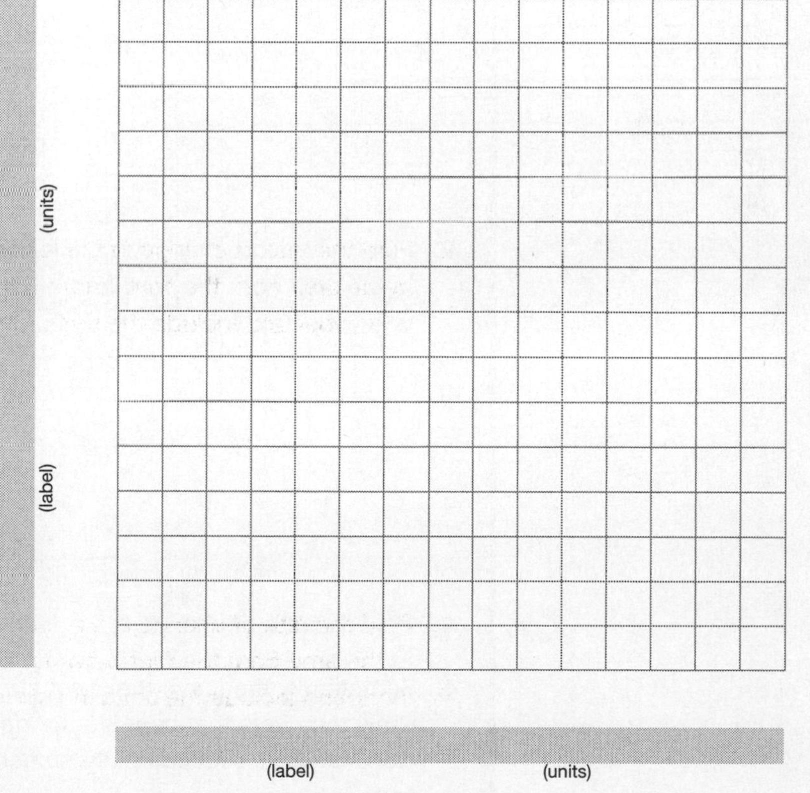

8

Take Note

A **curve** can be a straight line or a curved line.

8

Quantity Name	Frame	Area
Unit	numbers	square inches
Expression	x	
	1	
	2	
	3	
	4	
	5	

Investigate Problem 1

2. Draw the curve that best fits the data on your graph in Question 1. Use a complete sentence to describe the shape of your curve.

3. Create a scatter plot of the area as a function of the frame number on the grid below. First, choose your bounds and intervals. Be sure to label your graph clearly.

Variable quantity	Lower bound	Upper bound	Interval

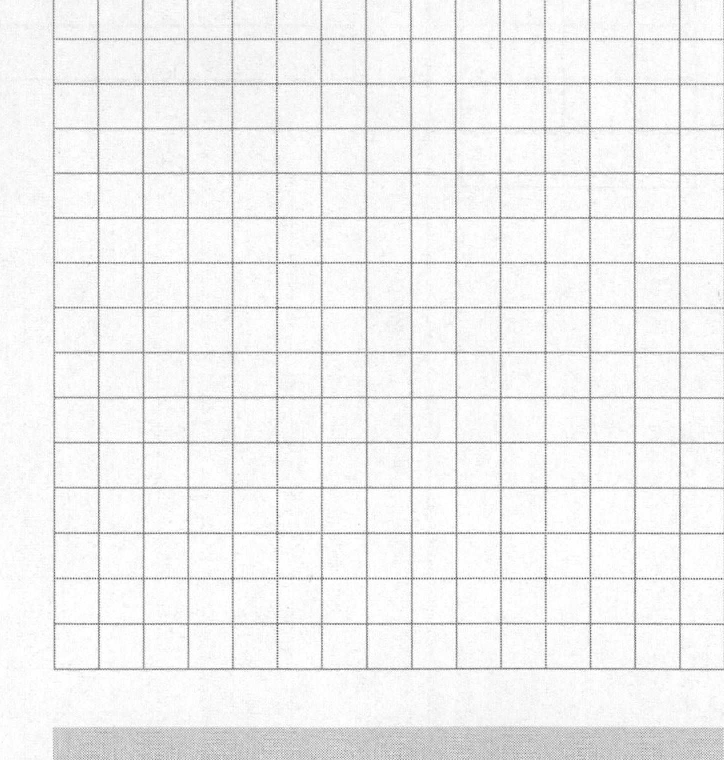

4. Sometimes, the curve that best fits the data is not a straight line. Draw the curve that best fits the data on your graph in Question 3. Use a complete sentence to describe the shape of your curve.

Investigate Problem 1

5. For each graph, write an equation that describes the problem situation. Be sure to define your variables. Write your answers using complete sentences.

6. **Just the Math: Quadratic Function** The equation that you wrote for the area, $y = x^2$, represents the simplest form of a *quadratic function*. A **quadratic function** is a function of the form $f(x) = ax^2 + bx + c$, where a, b, and c are constants with $a \neq 0$. The graph of a quadratic function is a U-shaped graph. What can you conclude about the rate of change of a quadratic function? Use a complete sentence in your answer.

8

7. Identify the values of a, b, and c in each quadratic function below.

$f(x) = 2x^2 + 3x + 5$ $\qquad$ $h(x) = x^2 + 4x - 1$

$g(x) = x^2 + 4$ $\qquad$ $f(x) = -x^2 - 2x + 8$

$h(x) = x^2 - 3x$ $\qquad$ $g(x) = 10 - x^2$

Problem 2 The Bouncing Ball

One of the programmers at your brother's company has the task of making the animations work on the web site. On one of the pages, he has to program an animation of a ball being thrown from one person to another person. The programmer uses a function to determine the path of the ball.

Problem 2 The Bouncing Ball

A. The table below shows some of the positions of the ball on the computer screen with respect to the origin as the animation plays. The origin represents the lower left-hand corner of the screen.

Quantity Name	**Horizontal position**	**Vertical position**
Unit	**pixels**	**pixels**
	10	20
	30	80
	50	100
	70	80
	90	20

Create a scatter plot of the path of the ball on the grid below. First, choose your bounds and intervals. Be sure to label your graph clearly.

Variable quantity	Lower bound	Upper bound	Interval

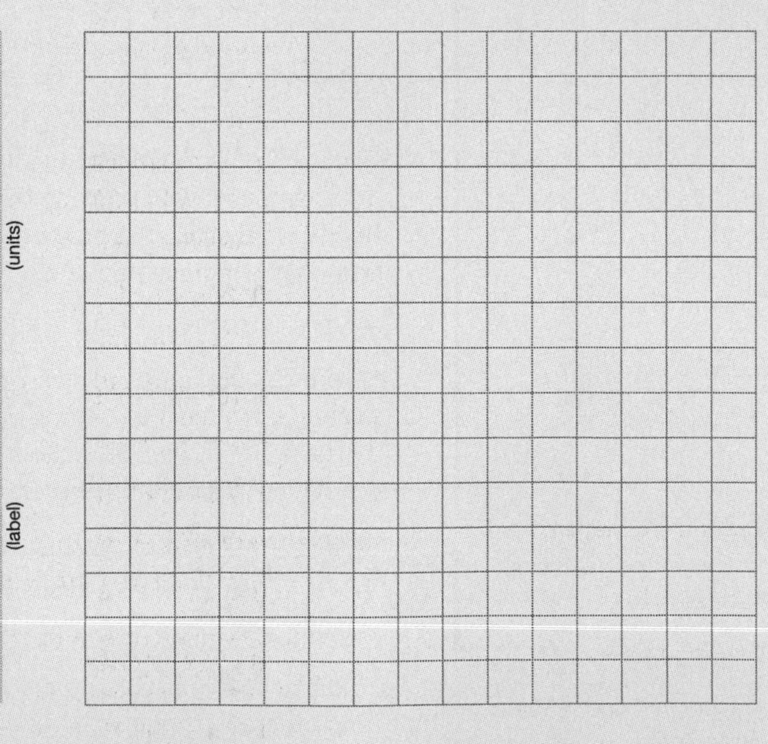

(label) (units)

Problem 2 The Bouncing Ball

B. Connect the points with a smooth curve.

C. Find the rates of change in the position of the ball as it moves from position to position. Record the results in the table.

Change in position	Rate of change
from (10, 20) to (30, 80)	
from (30, 80) to (50, 100)	
from (50, 100) to (70, 80)	
from (70, 80) to (90, 20)	

D. What do you notice about the rates of change? Use a complete sentence in your answer.

E. What kind of function is represented by your graph? Use a complete sentence in your answer.

8

Investigate Problem 2

1. The sporting goods company has seen the animation of the ball and wants the two people to be closer together and the ball to be thrown higher. The programmer has come up with a new path that is represented by the function

$f(x) = -0.05x^2 + 4x + 40.$

Before you can graph this new path, you need to be able to **evaluate** this function. In the order of operations, you should evaluate any powers first. So, to find the value of $f(10)$, substitute 10 for x and evaluate 10^2 first:

$$f(10) = -0.05(10^2) + 4(10) + 40$$
$$= -0.05(100) + 4(10) + 40$$

Then multiply and finally add and subtract from left to right. Show all your work.

Take Note

Order of Operations

1. Evaluate expressions inside grouping symbols such as ( ) or [ ].
2. Evaluate powers.
3. Multiply and divide from left to right.
4. Add and subtract from left to right.

8

Investigate Problem 2

2. Complete the table below to show some of the new positions of the path of the ball.

Quantity Name	**Horizontal position**	**Vertical position**
Unit	**pixels**	**pixels**
	10	
	20	
	40	
	60	
	70	

3. Create a graph of the path of the ball on the grid below. First, choose your bounds and intervals. Be sure to label your graph clearly.

Variable quantity	Lower bound	Upper bound	Interval

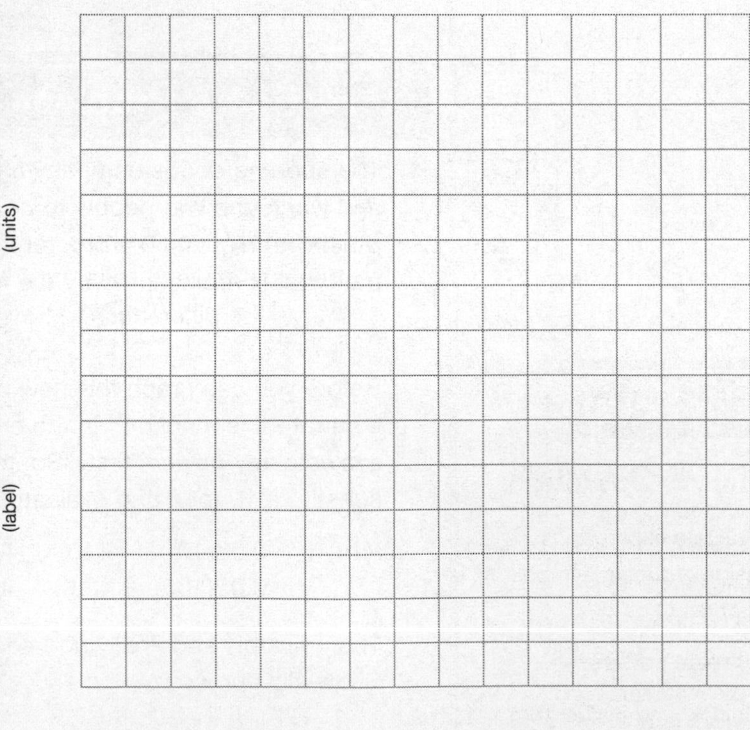

(label) (units)

Investigate Problem 2

4. Is the highest point in this graph higher than the highest point in the graph in part (A)? If so, what is the difference in the heights? Write your answer using a complete sentence.

5. Evaluate each of the following quadratic functions for the given value of x. Show all your work.

   $f(x) = x^2 + 5x + 7; f(4)$ $\qquad$ $g(x) = 25 - x^2; g(-5)$

   $h(x) = -x^2 + 4x - 1; h(-2)$ $\qquad$ $f(x) = 5x^2 - 18; f(0)$

   $g(x) = 8x^2 - 3x + 10; g(2)$ $\qquad$ $h(x) = -3x^2 + 15; h(10)$

Take Note

Whenever you see the share with the class icon, your group should prepare a short presentation to share with the class that describes how you solved the problem. Be prepared to ask questions during other groups' presentations and to answer questions during your presentation.

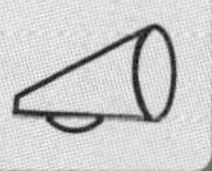

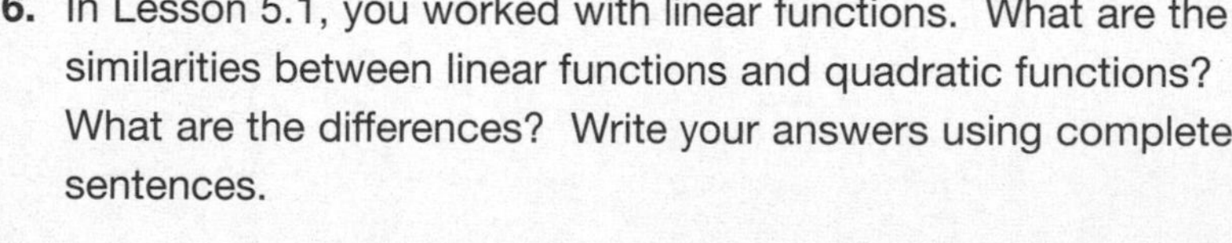

6. In Lesson 5.1, you worked with linear functions. What are the similarities between linear functions and quadratic functions? What are the differences? Write your answers using complete sentences.

8

8.2 Satellite Dish

Parabolas

Objectives

In this lesson, you will:

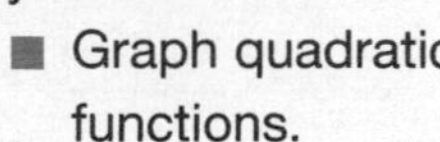

- Graph quadratic functions.
- Find the line of symmetry of a parabola.
- Find the vertex of a parabola.
- Identify the maximum or minimum value of a function.

Key Terms

- parabola
- line of symmetry
- vertical line
- vertex
- minimum
- maximum

SCENARIO A satellite dish is a type of antenna that transmits signals to and receives signals from satellites. Satellite dishes are most commonly used by people to receive satellite television transmissions. You can use a quadratic equation to model the profile, or outline, of a satellite dish.

Problem 1 Dish Design

A. You can model the profile of one type of satellite dish by using the function $y = \frac{1}{36}x^2$ where x is the number of inches to the right of the center of the dish and y is the number of units above the bottom of the dish. (A negative x-value indicates the number of units to the left of the center of the dish.) Complete the table of values that shows the profile of the satellite dish. Copy the values into the table on the next page.

Quantity Name	**Horizontal component**	**Vertical component**
Unit		
Expression		
	–24	
	–18	
	–12	
	–6	
	0	
	6	
	12	
	18	
	24	

Quantity Name	Horizontal component	Vertical component
Unit		
Expression		
	–24	
	–18	
	–12	
	–6	
	0	
	6	
	12	
	18	
	24	

8

Problem 1 Dish Design

B. Create a graph of the quadratic function on the grid below. First, choose your bounds and intervals. Be sure to label your graph clearly.

Variable quantity	Lower bound	Upper bound	Interval

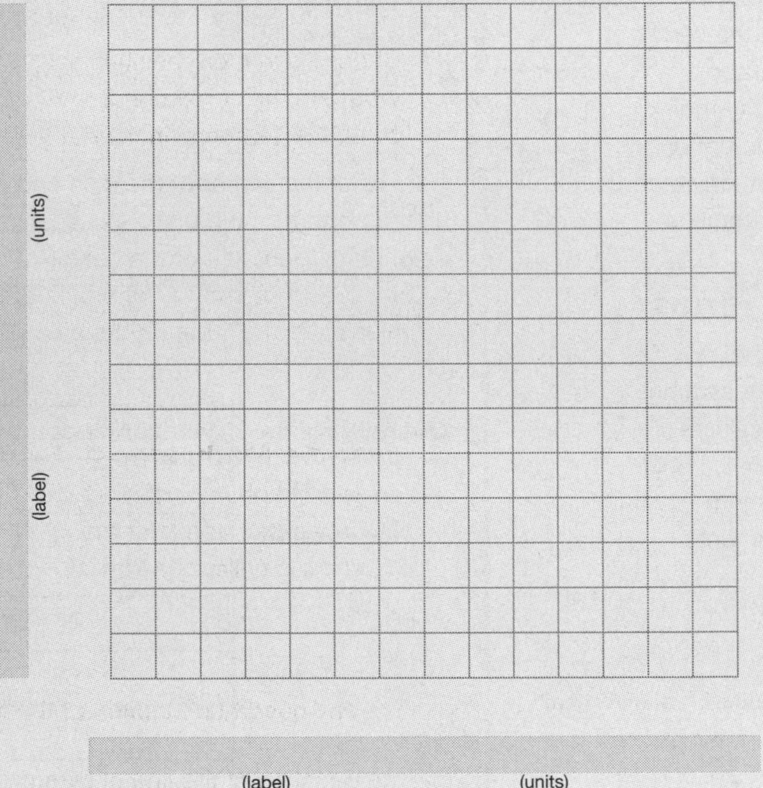

Investigate Problem 1

1. **Just the Math: Parabolas** Describe the shape of the graph. Use a complete sentence in your answer.

The graph of any quadratic function is called a **parabola.** How is the graph of a quadratic function different from the graph of a linear function? Use complete sentences in your answer.

Investigate Problem 1

2. Choose a positive height above the bottom of the dish. What are the corresponding x-values on the graph? Use a complete sentence in your answer.

Choose another positive height above the bottom of the dish. What are the corresponding x-values on the graph? Use a complete sentence in your answer.

Choose one more positive height above the bottom of the dish. What are the corresponding x-values on the graph? Use a complete sentence in your answer.

What do you notice about these x-values? Use a complete sentence in your answer.

3. **Just the Math: Line of Symmetry** Draw a dashed line on your graph in part (B) so that the graph on one side of the line is a mirror image of the graph on the other side of the line. Your line is called the **line of symmetry.** What is the equation of this line?

For any quadratic function of the form $y = ax^2 + bx + c$,

the equation of the line of symmetry is given by $x = -\frac{b}{2a}$.

Think about the function $y = \frac{1}{36}x^2$. What is the value of a for this function? What is the value of b for this function? Write your answers using complete sentences.

Use the values of a and b to write the equation of the line of symmetry. Write your answer using a complete sentence.

Take Note

The equation of a **vertical line** is $x = a$, where a is a real number.

8

Investigate Problem 1

Find the equation of the line of symmetry for each quadratic function. Show all your work.

$y = x^2 + 2x + 1$

$y = -3x^2 + 6x + 3$

$y = x^2 - 2x + 2$

$y = -x^2 - 4x - 1$

$y = 2x^2 - 20x + 54$

$y = -5x^2 + 8x - 10$

4. Just the Math: Vertex What is the lowest point on your graph in part (B)? This point is called the **vertex.** What is different about this point from the other points on the graph? Use a complete sentence in your answer.

The x-coordinate of the vertex is given by $x = -\frac{b}{2a}$. Does this make sense to you? Why? Use a complete sentence in your answer.

Find the vertex of the graph of each quadratic function. Show all your work.

$y = x^2 - 8$

$y = -2x^2 + 4x - 5$

Investigate Problem 1

5. **Just the Math: Maximum and Minimum** When the parabola opens upward, such as your graph in part (B), the *y*-coordinate of the vertex is called the **minimum,** or lowest value, of the function. When the parabola opens downward, such as the path of the ball in Lesson 8.1, the *y*-coordinate of the vertex is called the **maximum,** or highest value, of the function. Do the graphs of linear functions have maximum or minimum values? Use complete sentences to explain your reasoning.

6. What is the domain of the graph of your function in part (B)? What is the range of the graph of your function in part (B)? Do not consider the problem situation to answer the question. Use complete sentences in your answer.

7. The satellite dish is four inches tall. Use this information to find the domain and range of the function in the problem situation. Show all your work and use a complete sentence in your answer.

   How wide is the dish at its widest point? Use a complete sentence to explain your reasoning.

8. How is the domain of a linear function the same as or different from the domain of a quadratic function? Use a complete sentence in your answer.

   How is the range of a linear function the same as or different from the range of a quadratic function? Use complete sentences in your answer.

8

Investigate Problem 1

9. For each function, algebraically determine the vertex and the line of symmetry of the graph. Then draw the graph of the function. Identify the domain and range of the function. Use a complete sentence to tell whether the function has a maximum or minimum value.

$y = -x^2 + 4x$

Investigate Problem 1

$y = 2x^2 - 4x + 1$

10. How can you tell from the equation for the parabola whether the parabola opens upward or downward? Use complete sentences in your answer.

11. Find the vertex of the graph of the quadratic function. Then tell whether the y-coordinate of the vertex is a minimum or a maximum.

$y = 2x^2 + 8x - 3$ $\qquad$ $y = -x^2 + 10x + 3$

8

8.3 Dog Run

Comparing Linear and Quadratic Functions

Objectives

In this lesson, you will:

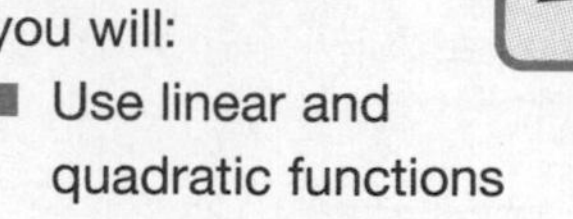

- Use linear and quadratic functions to model a situation.
- Determine the effect on the area of a rectangle when its length or width doubles.

Key Terms

- linear function
- quadratic function

SCENARIO Two dog owners have 16 yards of fencing to build a dog run beside their house. The dog owners want the run to be in the shape of a rectangle, and they want to use the side of their house as one side of the dog run. A rough sketch of what they have in mind is shown below.

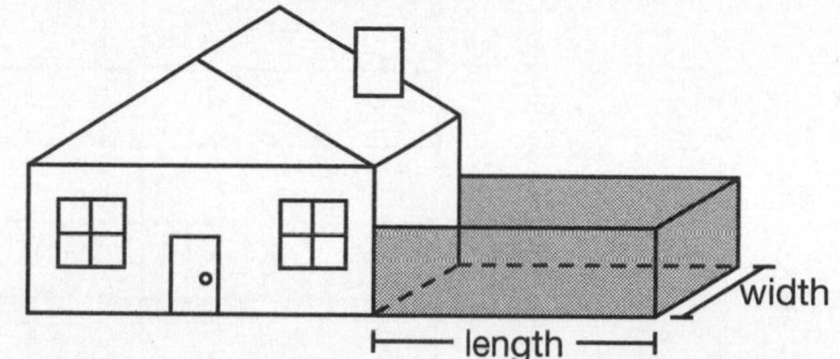

Problem 1 Deciding on the Dimensions

A. Suppose that the width of the dog run is 2 yards. Find the length of the dog run and the area of the dog run. Show all your work and use a complete sentence in your answer.

B. Suppose that the width of the dog run is 4 yards. Find the length of the dog run and the area of the dog run. Show all your work and use a complete sentence in your answer.

C. Suppose that the width of the dog run is 7 yards. Find the length of the dog run and the area of the dog run. Show all your work and use a complete sentence in your answer.

D. Suppose that the width of the dog run is 8 yards. Find the length of the dog run and the area of the dog run. Show all your work and use a complete sentence in your answer.

Problem 1 Deciding on the Dimensions

E. Complete the table below to show different widths, lengths, and areas that can occur with sixteen yards of fencing. Copy the Width and Area columns of the table into the correct columns in the margin of page 380.

Width	Length	Area
yards	yards	square yards

Investigate Problem 1

1. Describe what happens to the length as the width of the dog run increases. Why do you think this happens? Use complete sentences in your answer.

2. Describe what happens to the area as the width of the dog run increases. Use a complete sentence in your answer.

3. Describe what happens to the length and area as the width of the dog run decreases. Use complete sentences in your answer.

4. Describe what happens to the width and area as the length of the dog run *increases*. Describe what happens to the width and area as the length of the dog run *decreases*. Use complete sentences in your answer.

Investigate Problem 1

5. Compare how the area changes as the width changes to how the area changes as the length changes. Use complete sentences to explain your reasoning.

6. Create a graph that shows the length as a function of the width on the grid below. First, choose your bounds and intervals. Be sure to label your graph clearly.

Variable quantity	Lower bound	Upper bound	Interval

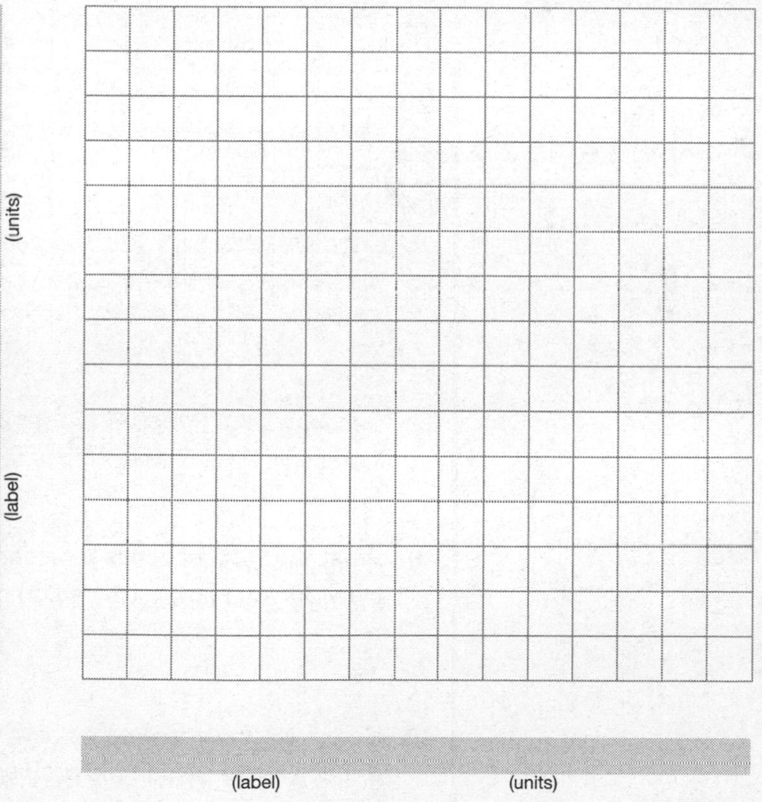

7. What kind of function is represented by the graph in Question 6? How do you know? Use a complete sentence in your answer.

8

Width	Area
yards	square yards

8

Investigate Problem 1

8. Create a graph that shows the area as a function of the width on the grid below. First, choose your bounds and intervals. Be sure to label your graph clearly.

Variable quantity	Lower bound	Upper bound	Interval

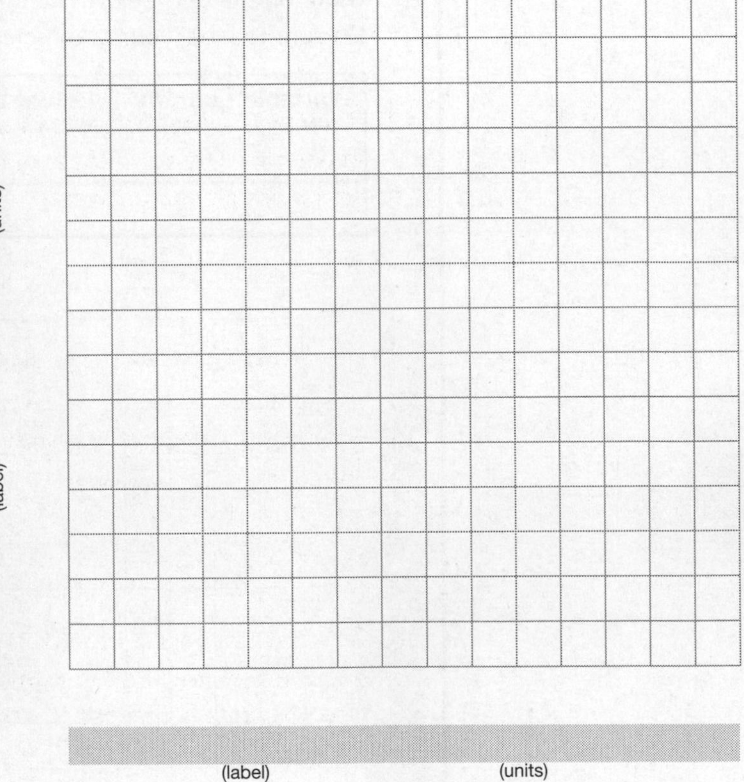

9. What kind of function is represented by the graph in Question 8? How do you know? Use a complete sentence in your answer.

10. Determine the x-intercepts of each graph. What is the meaning of each x-intercept in the problem situation? Use complete sentences in your answer.

Investigate Problem 1

11. How many x-intercepts can the graph of a linear function have? Use complete sentences to explain your reasoning.

12. How many x-intercepts can the graph of a quadratic function have? Use complete sentences to explain your reasoning.

8

13. Determine the y-intercepts of each graph. What is the meaning of each y-intercept in the problem situation? Use complete sentences in your answer.

14. Describe the rates of change for each graph. Use complete sentences in your answer.

15. What is the greatest possible area? What are the length and width of the dog run with the greatest possible area? Use complete sentences to explain how you found your answer.

Problem 2 A Change in Plans

The owners read about a sale on the same exact fencing that they already have and decide to buy an additional 16 yards of fencing.

A. How many yards of fencing do they have now? Use a complete sentence in your answer.

Problem 2 A Change in Plans

B. Complete the table below to show different widths, lengths, and areas that can be made with the new amount of fencing.

Width	Length	Area
yards	yards	square yards
0		
8		
16		
24		
32		

C. Create a graph that shows the length as a function of the width on the grid below. First, determine your bounds and intervals. Be sure to label your graph clearly.

Variable quantity	Lower bound	Upper bound	Interval

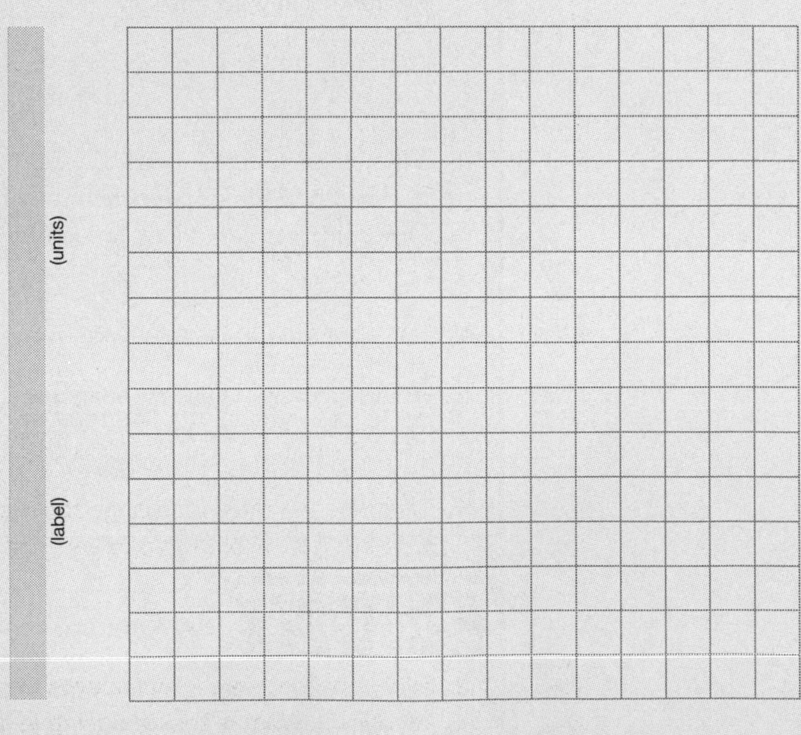

Problem 2 A Change in Plans

D. Create a graph that shows the area as a function of the width on the grid below. First, choose your bounds and intervals. Be sure to label your graph clearly.

Variable quantity	Lower bound	Upper bound	Interval

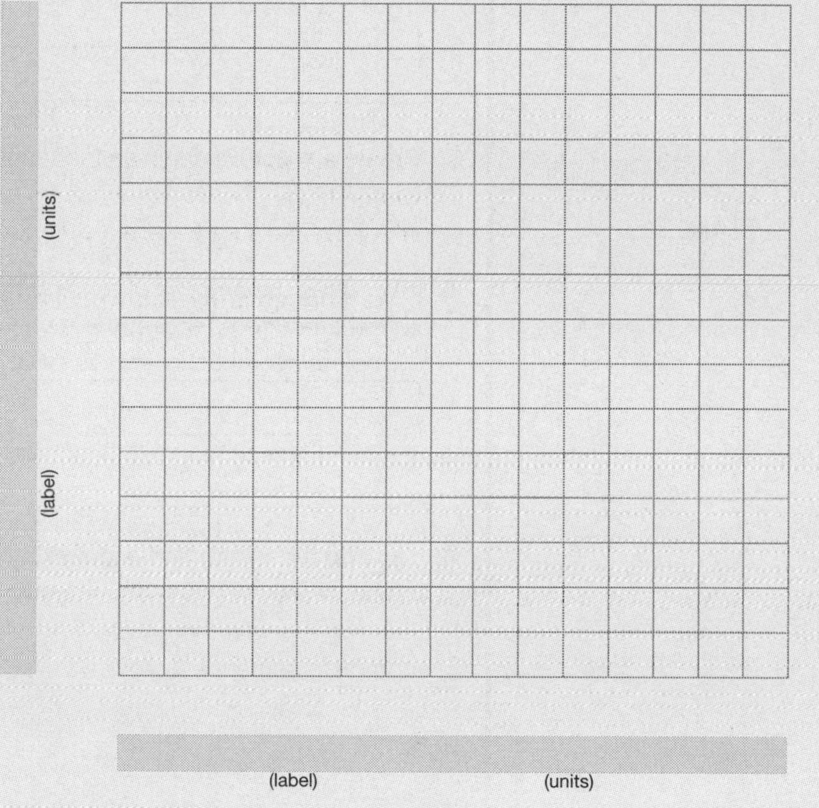

8

Investigate Problem 2

1. Describe the rates of change for each of the graphs. Use complete sentences in your answer.

2. What are the *x*- and *y*-intercepts of the graph of the linear function? What is their meaning in this problem situation? Use complete sentences in your answer.

8

Investigate Problem 2

3. What are the x- and y-intercepts of the graph of the quadratic function? What is their meaning in the problem situation? Use complete sentences in your answer.

4. What is the greatest possible area? What are the length and width of the dog run with the greatest possible area? Use a complete sentence to explain how you found your answer.

5. How does the amount of fencing the owners have now compare to the amount of fencing the owners had in Problem 1? Use a complete sentence in your answer.

6. How do the length and width of the dog run with the greatest possible area in this problem compare to the length and width of the dog run with the greatest possible area in Problem 1? Use a complete sentence in your answer.

7. How do the greatest possible areas in this problem and Problem 1 compare?

8. Use complete sentences to explain why the difference in the areas is more than the differences in the lengths and widths.

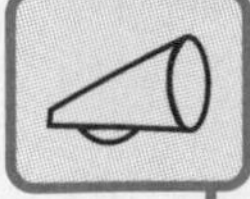

8.4

Guitar Strings and Other Things

Square Roots and Radicals

Objectives

In this lesson, you will:

- Evaluate the square root of a perfect square.
- Approximate a square root.

Key Terms

- square root
- positive square root
- negative square root
- principal square root
- radical symbol
- radicand
- perfect square

SCENARIO When you pluck a string on a guitar, the string vibrates and produces sound. When the string vibrates, the vibrations are repeating waves of movement up and down, as shown below.

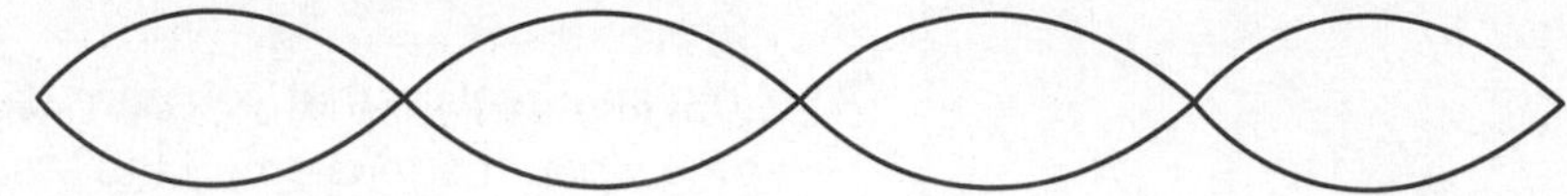

If the guitar is not tuned properly, the correct notes will not be played, and the result may not sound musical. To tune a guitar properly requires a change in the *tension* of the strings. The tension can be thought of as the amount of stretch on the string between two fixed points. A string with the correct tension produces the correct wave speed, which in turn produces the correct sounds.

8

Problem 1 Good Vibrations

Consider a string that weighs approximately 0.0026 pound per inch and is 34 inches long. An equation that relates the wave speed v in cycles per second and tension t in pounds is $v^2 = t$.

A. Find the tension of the string if the wave speed is 9.5 cycles per second. Show all your work and use a complete sentence in your answer.

B. Find the tension of the string if the wave speed is 8.5 cycles per second. Show all your work and use a complete sentence in your answer.

C. Find the tension of the string if the wave speed is 7.6 cycles per second. Show all your work and use a complete sentence in your answer.

D. What happens to the tension as the wave speed increases? Use a complete sentence in your answer.

Take Note

A *cycle* of a wave is the motion of the string up and then down one time.

Investigate Problem 1

1. Write an equation that you can use to find the wave speed of a string when the tension on the string is 81 pounds.

   What must the wave speed be? How do you know? Use a complete sentence in your answer.

2. Write an equation that you can use to find the wave speed of a string when the tension on the string is 36 pounds.

   What must the wave speed be? How do you know? Use a complete sentence in your answer.

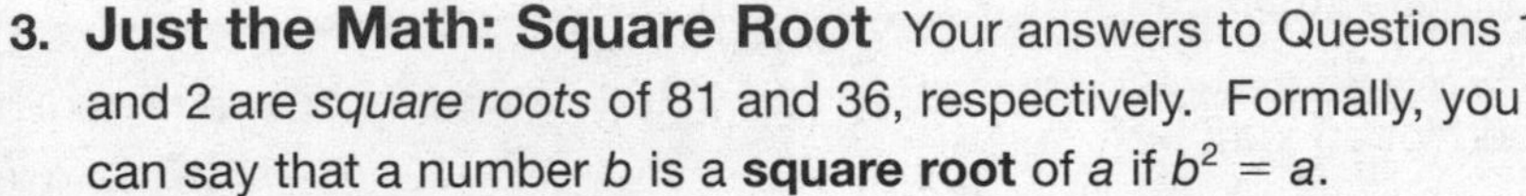

3. **Just the Math: Square Root** Your answers to Questions 1 and 2 are *square roots* of 81 and 36, respectively. Formally, you can say that a number b is a **square root** of a if $b^2 = a$.

   So, 9 is a square root of 81 because $9^2 = 81$ and 6 is a square root of 36 because $6^2 = 36$.

   Is there another number whose square is 81? If so, name the number.

   Is there another number whose square is 36? If so, name the number.

   Every positive number has two square roots: a **positive square root** and a **negative square root.** So, you can see that the square roots of 81 are 9 and –9, and the square roots of 36 are 6 and –6. The positive square root is called the **principal square root.** An expression such as $\sqrt{36}$ indicates that you should find the principal, or positive, square root of 36.

Take Note

Finding the square root of a number is the *inverse operation* of finding the square of a number.

4. Complete each statement below.

   $\sqrt{4} = \square$ $\qquad$ $-\sqrt{25} = \square$

   $-\sqrt{100} = \square$ $\qquad$ $\sqrt{49} = \square$

Take Note

The symbol, $\sqrt{}$, is called the **radical symbol.** The number underneath a radical symbol is called the **radicand.**

Investigate Problem 1

5. Each of the radicands in Question 4 is a **perfect square**. Can you explain why these numbers are called perfect squares? Use a complete sentence in your answer.

6. Write an equation that you can use to find the wave speed of a string when the tension on the string is 42 pounds.

What number represents the wave speed? Write your answer as a radical.

Can you write this number as a positive integer? Why or why not? Use a complete sentence in your answer.

7. Because 42 is not a perfect square, we have to approximate the value of $\sqrt{42}$. To do this, we will use perfect squares. Complete the statements below.

The perfect square that is closest to 42 and is less than 42 is ______ .

The perfect square that is closest to 42 and is greater than 42 is ______ .

So, 42 is between ______ and ______ and $\sqrt{42}$ is between $\sqrt{\square} = \square$ and $\sqrt{\square} = \square$.

Estimate $\sqrt{42}$ by choosing numbers between 6 and 7. Test each number by finding its square and seeing how close it is to 42.

$6.4^2 = \square$ $6.5^2 = \square$

Which number is closer to 42?

So, $\sqrt{42} \approx \square$.

8. What is the wave speed of a string if the tension is 42 pounds? Use a complete sentence in your answer.

9. What happens to the wave speed as the tension increases? Use a complete sentence in your answer.

Take Note

Remember that the symbol $\approx$ means "is approximately equal to."

8

8

Investigate Problem 1

10. Approximate $\sqrt{13}$ to the nearest tenth. First complete each statement below. Show all your work.

$\square < 13 < \square$

$\sqrt{\square} < \sqrt{13} < \sqrt{\square}$

$\square < \sqrt{13} < \square$

11. Approximate $\sqrt{30}$ to the nearest tenth. First complete each statement below. Show all your work.

$\square < 30 < \square$

$\sqrt{\square} < \sqrt{30} < \sqrt{\square}$

$\square < \sqrt{30} < \square$

12. Approximate $\sqrt{75}$ to the nearest tenth. First complete each statement below. Show all your work.

$\square < 75 < \square$

$\sqrt{\square} < \sqrt{75} < \sqrt{\square}$

$\square < \sqrt{75} < \square$

8.5 Tent Designing Competition

Solving by Factoring and Extracting Square Roots

Objectives

In this lesson, you will:

- Solve a quadratic equation by factoring.
- Solve a quadratic equation by extracting square roots.

Key Terms

- parabola
- intercepts
- pi

SCENARIO You and your friend are working together in a competition to design a camping tent. Your design is based on a *parabola*. Your idea is to take a part of a parabola that opens downward and rotate it around to create the shape of the tent as shown at the left.

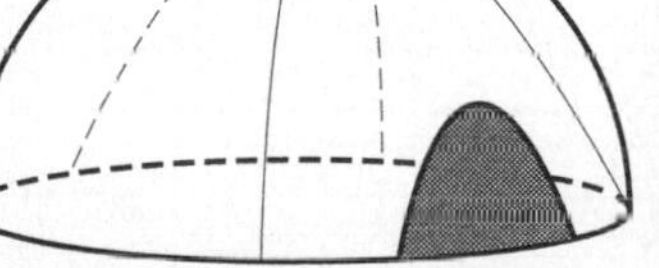

Take Note

The equation of the tent is a quadratic equation in *factored* form. You will learn more about factoring in Chapter 10.

8

Problem 1 Planning the Tent Shape

You are testing out different parabolic shapes for the tent. The first shape can be modeled by the equation $y = -\frac{1}{2}(x - 4)(x + 4)$, where x is the number of feet to the right of the center and y is the height of the tent in feet.

A. What is the height of the tent two feet to the right of the center? Show all your work and use a complete sentence in your answer.

B. What is the height of the tent two feet to the left of the center? Show all your work and use a complete sentence in your answer.

C. What is the height of the tent four feet to the right of the center? Show all your work and use a complete sentence in your answer.

D. What is the height of the tent four feet to the left of the center? Show all your work and use a complete sentence in your answer.

Problem 1 Planning the Tent Shape

E. What is the height of the tent at the center? What does this height represent? Show all your work and use a complete sentence in your answer.

8

Investigate Problem 1

1. Create a graph of the tent shape on the grid below. First, choose your bounds and intervals. Be sure to label your graph clearly.

Variable quantity	Lower bound	Upper bound	Interval

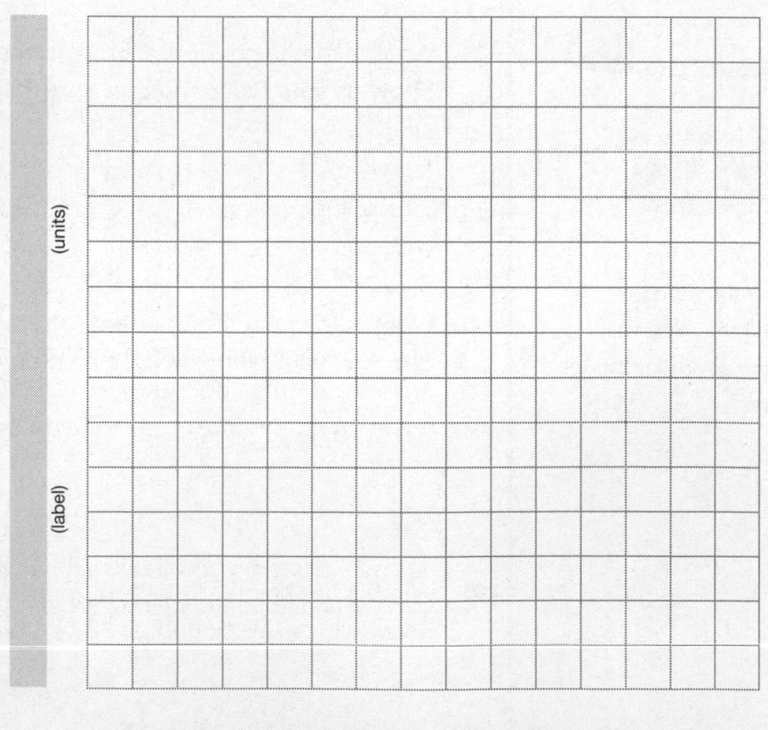

Investigate Problem 1

2. What is the y-intercept of the graph? What does it represent in the problem situation? Use complete sentences in your answer.

3. What are the x-intercepts of the graph? What do they represent in the problem situation? Use complete sentences in your answer.

How wide is your tent? Use a complete sentence in your answer.

8

4. Consider the equation below that you could use to *algebraically* find the x-intercepts of the graph. To do this, substitute 0 for y.

$$0 = -\frac{1}{2}(x - 4)(x + 4)$$

Substitute one of your x-intercepts into this equation. Then simplify.

$$0 = -\frac{1}{2}(\square - 4)(\square + 4)$$

$$0 = -\frac{1}{2}(\square)(\square)$$

$$0 = \square$$

Why is the product equal to zero? Use a complete sentence in your answer.

5. You are also considering a different parabolic tent design that is modeled by the equation $y = -0.24(x - 5)(x + 5)$. Write an equation that you can use to find the x-intercepts of the parabola.

What x-values do you think will be solutions of this equation? Use complete sentences to explain your reasoning.

Investigate Problem 1

Check your answers by substituting them into the equation that you wrote. Show all your work.

What do the x-intercepts mean in the problem situation? Use a complete sentence in your answer.

8

6. Algebraically find the y-intercept. What does it mean in the problem situation? Use a complete sentence to explain.

7. Create a graph of the new tent shape on the grid below. First, choose your bounds and intervals.

Variable quantity	Lower bound	Upper bound	Interval

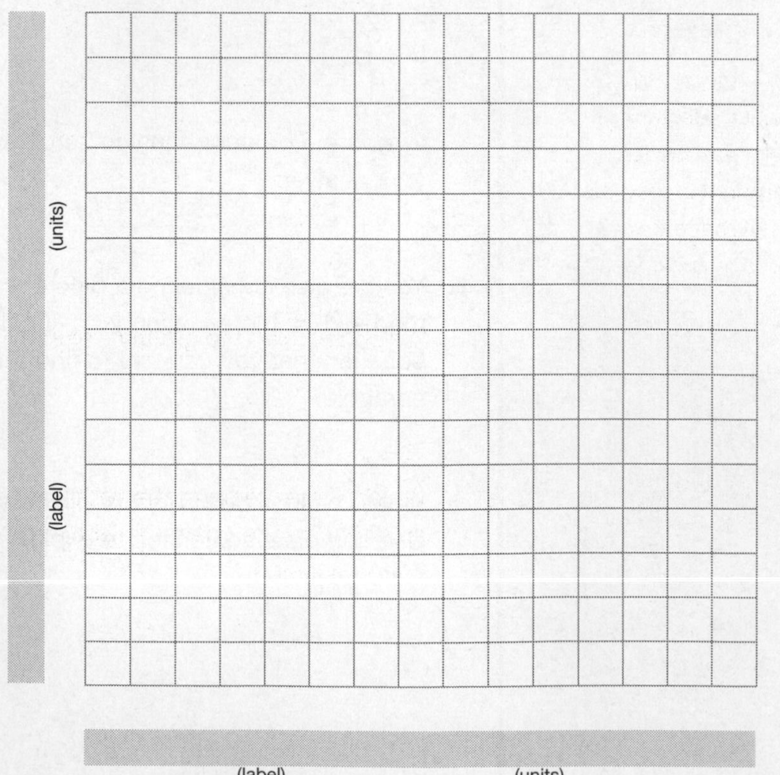

Problem 2 Tent Volume

Another consideration in your tent design is the tent's volume, or the amount of space inside the tent. The volume of your tent is related to the maximum tent width and maximum tent height by the equation $V = \frac{\pi}{8}w^2h$ where V is the volume, w is the maximum tent width, and h is the maximum tent height.

A. What are the maximum width and height of your first tent design in Problem 1? Use a complete sentence in your answer.

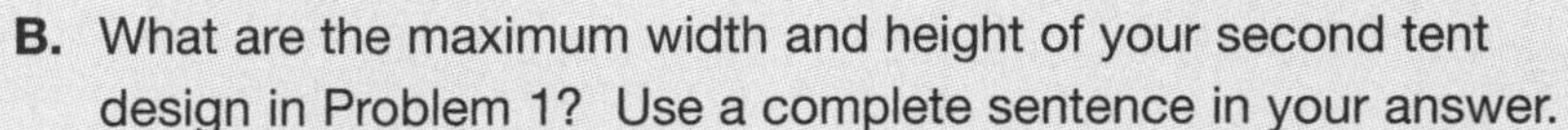

Take Note

Pi, written by using the Greek letter π, is a constant that is the ratio of a circle's circumference to its diameter.

Pi is an irrational number whose value is approximately 3.14.

B. What are the maximum width and height of your second tent design in Problem 1? Use a complete sentence in your answer.

C. Which tent do you expect to have more volume? Why? Use complete sentences in your answer.

D. Find the volume of each tent design in Problem 1. Use 3.14 for π. Show all your work and use complete sentences in your answer.

Take Note

Volume is measured in *cubic* units. Because the dimensions of the tent are measured in feet, the volume of the tent is measured in cubic feet.

Which tent has the greater volume?

Which measurement, the width or the height, has more of an effect on the volume? Use complete sentences to explain your reasoning.

8

Investigate Problem 2

1. You and your friend decide to create more tent designs based on the volume of the tent. Your first design based on the volume will have a volume of 392.5 cubic feet and a width of 10 feet. Write an equation that you can use to find the height of the tent.

   Find the height of the tent. Use 3.14 for π. Show all your work and use a complete sentence in your answer.

2. Your second design based on the volume will have a volume of 314 cubic feet and a height of 8 feet. Write an equation that you can use to find the width of the tent.

   Get the variable by itself on one side of the equation and simplify. Use 3.14 for π and show all your work.

   Can you visually tell which two numbers are the solutions of this equation? If so, what are the numbers? Use a complete sentence in your answer.

   Does each number represent the tent width? Use a complete sentence to explain your reasoning.

   What is the tent width? Use a complete sentence in your answer.

Investigate Problem 2

3. Your third design based on the volume will have a volume of 400 cubic feet and a height of 6 feet. Write an equation that you can use to find the width of the tent.

Isolate the variable on one side of the equation and simplify. Use 3.14 for π and show all your work. If necessary, round to the nearest whole number.

Can you visually tell which two numbers are the solutions of this equation?

A solution to your equation will be the number whose __________ is 170. So, one solution is the _______________ of 170. What is the other solution of this equation? Use a complete sentence in your answer.

Use a calculator to approximate the solutions of the equation to the nearest tenth.

What is the width of your tent? Use a complete sentence in your answer.

4. What is the solution of the equation $x^2 = 0$? Use a complete sentence to explain your reasoning.

5. What is the solution of the equation $x^2 = -5$? Use a complete sentence to explain your reasoning.

8

8.6 Kicking a Soccer Ball

Using the Quadratic Formula to Solve Quadratic Equations

Objectives

In this lesson, you will:

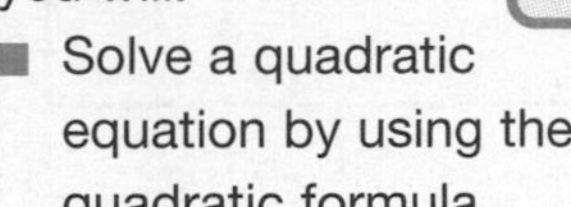

- Solve a quadratic equation by using the quadratic formula.
- Find the value of the discriminant.

Key Terms

- quadratic formula
- discriminant

SCENARIO A friend of yours is working on a project that involves the path of a soccer ball. She tells you that she has collected data for several similar soccer kicks in a controlled environment (with no wind and minimum spin on the ball). She has modeled the general path of the ball using a quadratic function. You are interested in her model because you are studying quadratic functions in your math class.

Problem 1 The Path of a Soccer Ball

Your friend's model is $y = -0.01x^2 + 0.6x$ where x is the horizontal distance that the ball has traveled in meters and y is the vertical distance that the ball has traveled in meters.

A. Complete the table of values that shows the vertical and horizontal distances that the ball has traveled. Copy the values into the table on the next page.

Quantity Name	Horizontal distance	Vertical distance
Unit	meters	meters
Expression		

B. Can you approximate from your table how far the ball traveled before it hit the ground? If so, describe the distance. Use a complete sentence in your answer.

Quantity Name	Horizontal distance	Vertical distance
Units	meters	meters
Expression		

8

Problem 1 The Path of a Soccer Ball

C. Create a graph of the path of the ball on the grid below. First, choose your bounds and intervals. Be sure to label your graph clearly.

Variable quantity	Lower bound	Upper bound	Interval

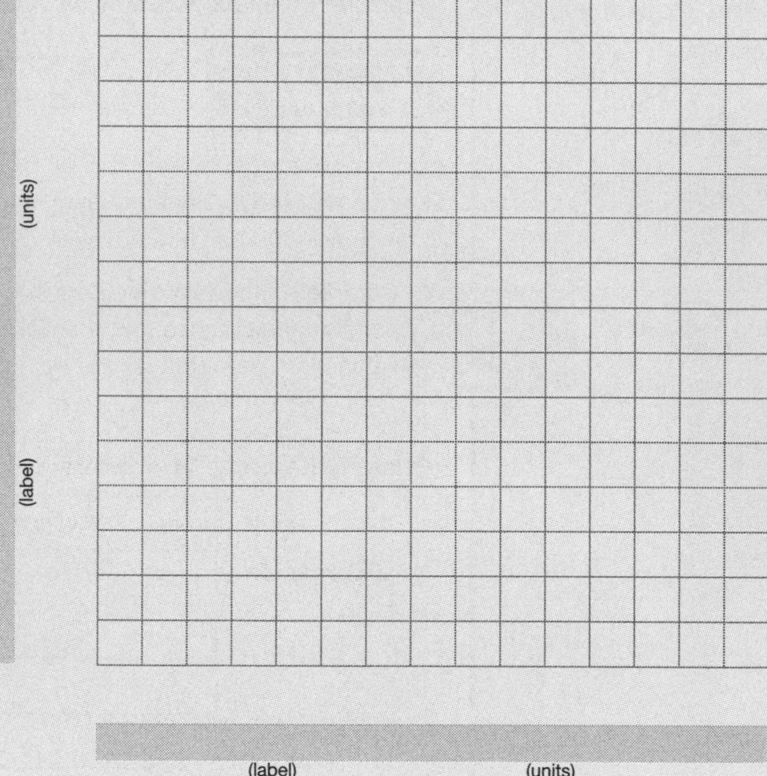

D. Use your graph to determine the maximum height of the ball. Use a complete sentence in your answer.

E. What is the y-intercept of the graph? What does it represent in this problem situation? Use a complete sentence in your answer.

F. How far does the ball travel horizontally before it hits the ground? Use a complete sentence in your answer.

Investigate Problem 1

1. In terms of the graph of the function, how can you interpret your answer to part (F)? Use a complete sentence in your answer.

2. Write an equation that you can use to algebraically find the answer to the question in part (F).

   Can you visually determine the solutions to this equation?

   Can you solve this equation by using the methods that you learned in the previous lesson?

3. **Just the Math: Quadratic Formula** To solve the equation in Question 2, we can use the *quadratic formula*. The **quadratic formula** states that the solutions to the equation $ax^2 + bx + c = 0$ when $a \neq 0$ are given by

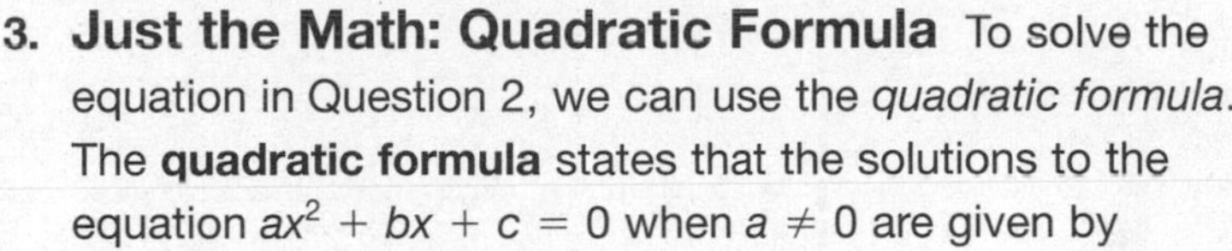

$$x = \frac{-b \pm \sqrt{b^2 - 4ac}}{2a}.$$

You will see where this formula comes from in Chapter 13.

For instance, consider the equation $2x^2 - 3x + 1 = 0$.

What are the values of a, b, and c in this equation? Write your answer using a complete sentence.

To find the solutions of the equation, substitute the values for a, b, and c into the quadratic formula and simplify:

$$x = \frac{-(\square) \pm \sqrt{(\square)^2 - 4(\square)(\square)}}{2(\square)}$$

$$= \frac{\square \pm \sqrt{\square - \square}}{\square}$$

$$= \frac{3 \pm \sqrt{\square}}{4}$$

$$= \frac{3 \pm \square}{4}$$

So, the solutions are $x = \frac{3+1}{4} = \frac{4}{4} = 1$ and $x = \frac{3-1}{4} = \frac{2}{4} = \frac{1}{2}$.

Take Note

The symbol $\pm$ means "plus or minus" and is a compact way to write a solution. For instance, $x = m \pm n$ is the compact notation for $x = m + n$ and $x = m - n$.

Take Note

Remember that you must have zero on one side of the equation in order to use the quadratic formula.

8

Investigate Problem 1

For each quadratic equation below, find the values of *a*, *b*, and *c*.

$5x^2 + 6x + 1 = 0$ $8x^2 + 4x - 6 = 0$

$10x^2 - 1 = 0$ $-x^2 + 8x = 2$

4. Use the quadratic formula to find the horizontal distance that the ball travels before it hits the ground. Show all your work. Use a complete sentence to describe the answers that you find.

5. Write an equation that you can use to find the horizontal distance the ball has traveled when it reaches a height of five meters.

Solve the equation. Show all your work and use a complete sentence in your answer.

Investigate Problem 1

Does your answer make sense? Use complete sentences to explain your reasoning.

6. For each quadratic equation below, find the value of $\sqrt{b^2 - 4ac}$. Show all your work. Write your answer as a radical.

$x^2 + 7x - 2 = 0$

$-3x^2 + 4x - 8 = 0$

$8x^2 + 8x + 2 = 0$

$3x^2 - 5x + 2 = 0$

What can you conclude about the number of solutions of each of the quadratic equations above? Use complete sentences in your answer.

The expression $b^2 - 4ac$ is called the **discriminant** of the quadratic formula.

8

Summary Solving Quadratic Equations

In this lesson and the previous lesson, you explored three different methods for solving a quadratic equation, depending on its form:

- An equation in the form $(x - a)(x - b) = 0$ is solved by determining the value of x that makes each factor zero. This method is called **factoring.**
- An equation in the form $x^2 = b$ is solved by recognizing that $x = \sqrt{b}$ and $x = -\sqrt{b}$ satisfy the equation $x^2 = b$. This method is called **extracting square roots.**
- An equation in the form $ax^2 + bx + c = 0$ is solved by using the **quadratic formula:** $x = \dfrac{-b \pm \sqrt{b^2 - 4ac}}{2a}$.

8

8.7 Pumpkin Catapult

Using a Vertical Motion Model

Objective

In this lesson, you will:

- Write and use a vertical motion model.

Key Term

- vertical motion model

SCENARIO Every year, the city of Millsboro, Delaware, holds a competition called the World Championship Punkin Chunkin, which is a pumpkin throwing competition. Participants build a pumpkin catapult that hurls a pumpkin. The catapult that hurls the pumpkin the farthest is the winner.

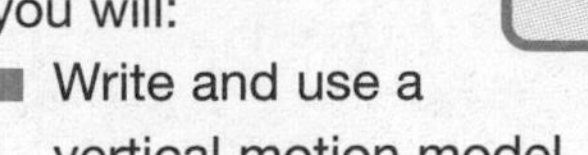

Take Note

Often, in a model, when the independent variable represents time, the variable t is used instead of x.

Problem 1 A Pumpkin Catapult

You can model the motion of a pumpkin that is released by a catapult by using the **vertical motion model** $y = -16t^2 + vt + h$, where t is the time that the object has been moving in seconds, v is the initial velocity (speed) of the object in feet per second, h is the initial height of the object in feet, and y is the height of the object in feet at time t seconds.

A. Suppose that a catapult is designed to hurl a pumpkin from a height of 30 feet at an initial velocity of 212 feet per second. Write a quadratic function that models the height of the pumpkin in terms of time.

B. Write an equation that you can use to determine when the pumpkin will hit the ground. Then solve the equation. Show all your work.

Do both solutions have meaning in the problem situation? Use complete sentences to explain your reasoning.

8

Problem 1 A Pumpkin Catapult

When does the pumpkin hit the ground? Use a complete sentence in your answer.

C. Complete the table of values that shows the height of the pumpkin in terms of time.

Quantity Name	Time	Height
Unit		
Expression		
	0	
	2	
	5	
	10	
	12	
	13	
	15	

D. Create a graph of the model to see the path of the pumpkin on the grid on the next page. First, choose your bounds and intervals. Be sure to label your graph clearly.

Variable quantity	Lower bound	Upper bound	Interval

Problem 1 A Pumpkin Catapult

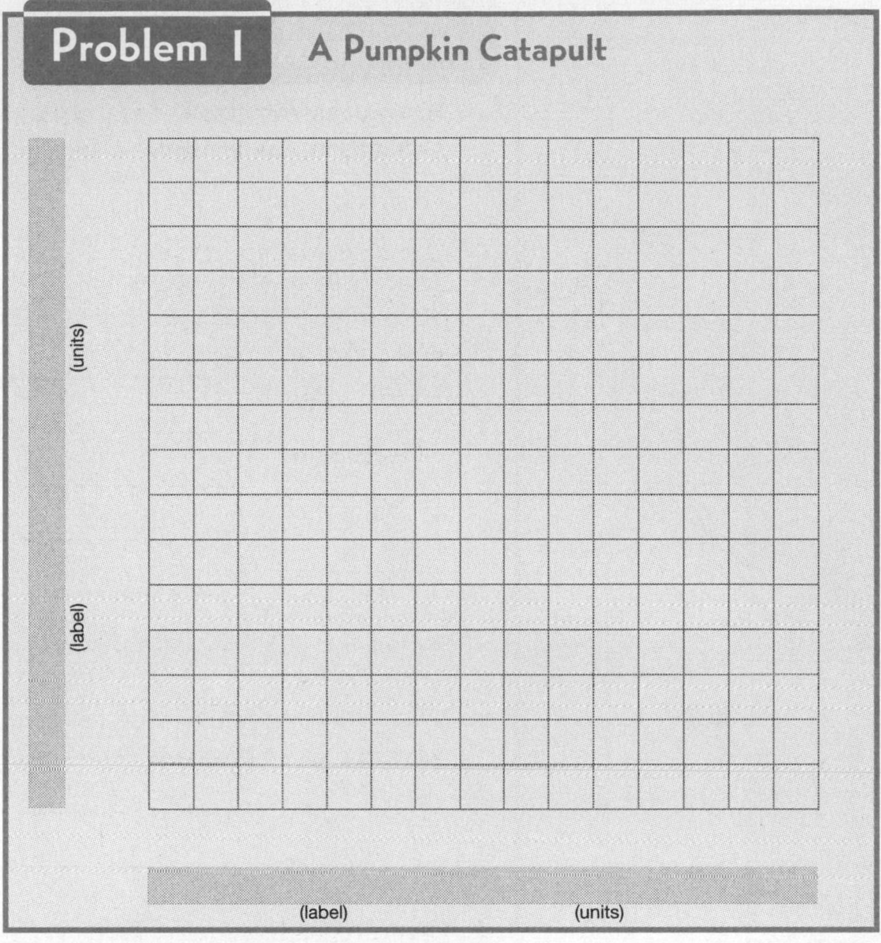

8

Investigate Problem 1

1. Does your answer to part (B) make sense in terms of the graph? Write your answer using a complete sentence.

2. What is the height of the pumpkin three seconds after it is launched from the catapult? Show all your work and use a complete sentence in your answer.

   What is the height of the pumpkin eight seconds after it is launched from the catapult? Show all your work and use a complete sentence in your answer.

   What is the height of the pumpkin 20 seconds after it is launched from the catapult? Show all your work and use a complete sentence in your answer.

Investigate Problem 1

Do all of your answers to Question 2 make sense? Use a complete sentence to explain your reasoning.

3. When is the pumpkin at its highest point? Show all your work and use a complete sentence in your answer.

4. What is the maximum height of the pumpkin? Show all your work and use a complete sentence in your answer.

5. When is the pumpkin at a height of 500 feet? Show all your work and use a complete sentence in your answer.

Is your answer confirmed by your graph?

8

Problem 2 How Far Can the Pumpkin Go?

In 2005, the winner in the catapult division of the World Championship Punkin Chunkin hurled a pumpkin 2862.28 feet.

A. A model for the path of a pumpkin being launched from the catapult described in Problem 1 is $y = -0.00036x^2 + x + 30$, where x is the horizontal distance of the pumpkin in feet and y is the vertical distance of the pumpkin in feet. According to the model, what is the pumpkin's height when it has traveled 500 feet horizontally? Show all your work and use a complete sentence in your answer.

B. What is the pumpkin's height when it has traveled 1000 feet horizontally? Show all your work and use a complete sentence in your answer.

C. What is the pumpkin's height when it has traveled 2500 feet horizontally? Show all your work and use a complete sentence in your answer.

D. What is the pumpkin's height when it has traveled 3000 feet horizontally? Show all your work and use a complete sentence in your answer.

E. Do you think that this catapult has a chance of beating the 2005 catapult winner? Use complete sentences to explain your reasoning.

8

Investigate Problem 2

1. Algebraically determine the horizontal distance the pumpkin travels before it hits the ground. Does it beat the winner? Show all your work and use a complete sentence in your answer.

2. Create a graph of the model to see the path of the pumpkin on the grid below. First, choose your bounds and intervals.

Variable quantity	Lower bound	Upper bound	Interval

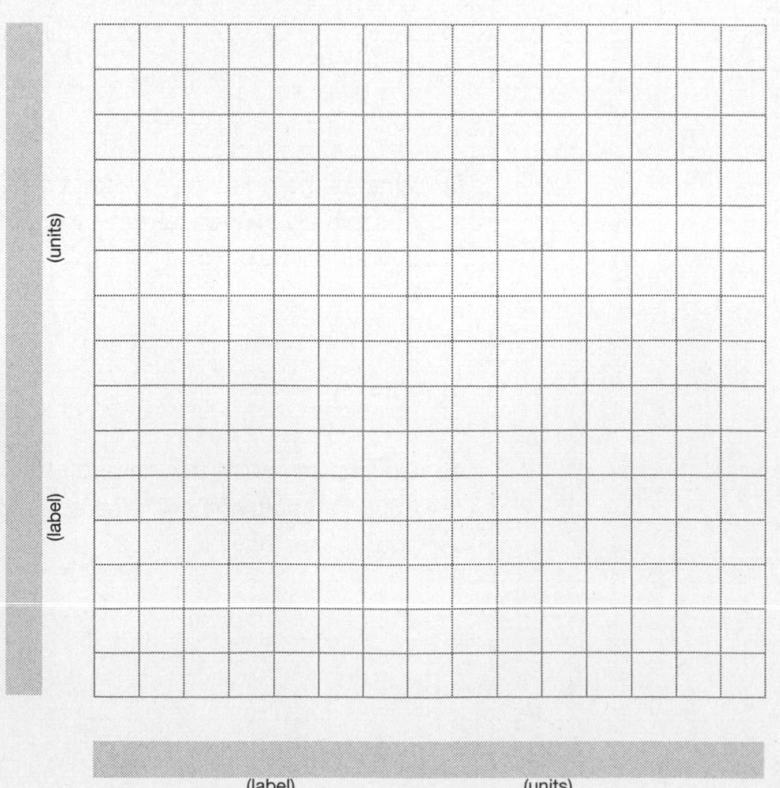

Investigate Problem 2

3. Use the information from Problem 1 and this problem to find the *horizontal* distance the pumpkin travels after 10 seconds. Show all your work and use a complete sentence in your answer.

8

8

8.8

Viewing the Night Sky

Using Quadratic Functions

Objective

In this lesson, you will:

- Analyze a quadratic function that models the shape of an object.

Key Terms

- axis of symmetry
- vertex
- domain
- range

SCENARIO A telescope uses two lenses, an objective lens and an eyepiece, to enable you to magnify stars, planets, and other objects in the night sky. The objective lens is shaped like a parabola.

Telescopes are described by the *aperture* (pronounced ăpər-chər) and the *focal length*. The aperture is the width of the objective lens. The focal length is a bit more complicated. It is the distance from the *vertex* (the lowest point) of the lens to a point, called the focal point, on the *axis of symmetry*. The focal point is the point at which light rays coming into the telescope meet after they bounce off the lens.

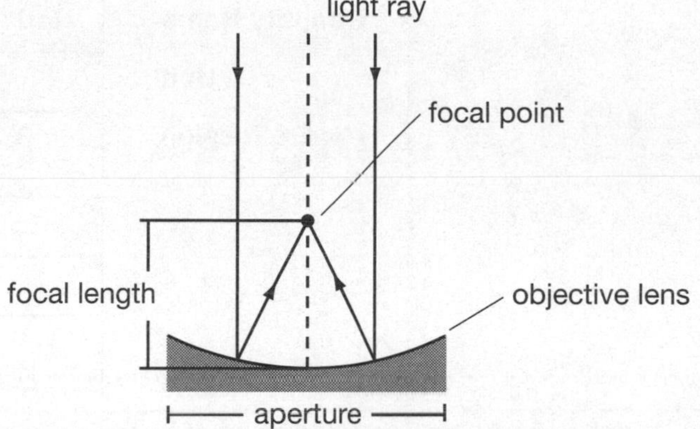

The shape of the lens can be described by the quadratic function $y = \frac{1}{4p}x^2$, where x is the number of units to the right of the axis of symmetry, y is the height of the lens, and p is the focal length.

Problem 1 Size of the Lens

A. The aperture of one telescope model is 6 inches and the focal length of the objective lens is 48 inches. Write the function that represents the shape of the lens.

B. What is the **axis of symmetry** of the graph of the lens? Use a complete sentence in your answer.

C. What point is the *vertex* of the lens? Use a complete sentence in your answer.

Problem 1 Size of the Lens

D. What is the *domain* of this function in the problem situation? Use a complete sentence in your explanation.

Investigate Problem 1

8

1. Complete the table of values that shows the shape of the lens. Use your domain as a guide for choosing the x-values. If necessary, round your answers to the nearest hundredth.

Quantity Name	Horizontal position	Height
Unit		
Expression		

2. What is the *range* of the function? Show all your work and use a complete sentence in your answer.

Use complete sentences to explain how you found your answer to Question 2.

3. What is the maximum height of this lens? If necessary, round your answer to the nearest thousandth. Use a complete sentence to explain how you found your answer.

8

Investigate Problem 1

4. Create a graph of the quadratic function on the grid below. First, choose your bounds and intervals. Be sure to label your graph clearly.

Variable quantity	Lower bound	Upper bound	Interval

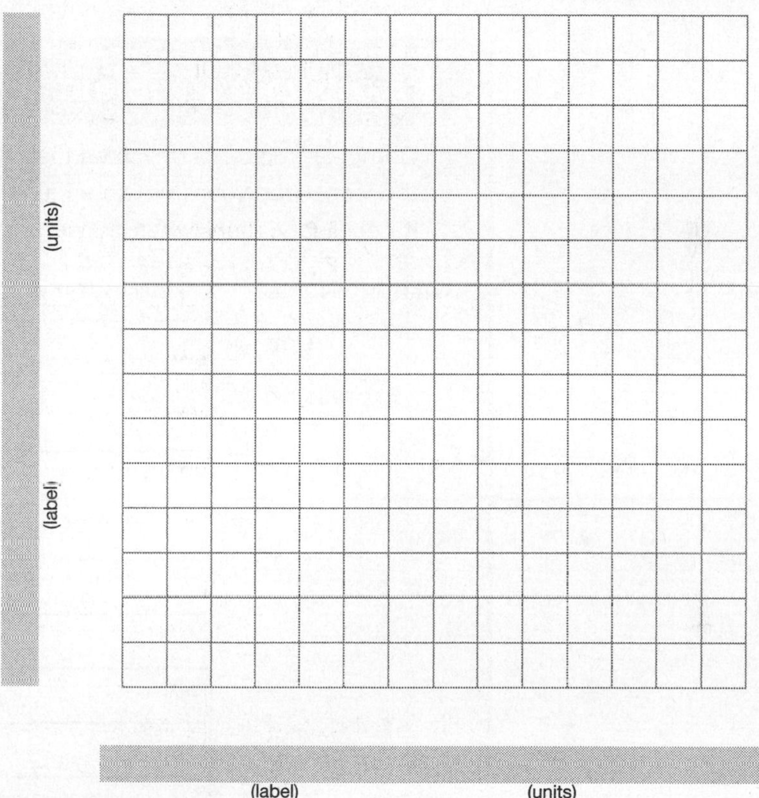

Problem 2 Increase the Focal Length

A. Now consider a different telescope. This telescope has the same aperture as the one in part (A), but its focal length is 56 inches. Write the function that represents the lens shape.

B. What is the axis of symmetry of the graph of the lens? Use a complete sentence in your answer.

Problem 2 Increase the Focal Length

C. What is the vertex of the lens? Use a complete sentence in your answer.

D. What is the domain of this function in the problem situation? Use a complete sentence in your explanation.

8

Investigate Problem 2

1. Complete the table of values that shows the shape of the lens. Use your domain as a guide for choosing the *x*-values. If necessary, round your answers to the nearest thousandth.

	Horizontal position	Height
Quantity Name		
Unit		
Expression		

2. What is the range of the function? Show all your work and use a complete sentence in your answer.

Use complete sentences to explain how you found your answer to Question 2.

Investigate Problem 2

3. What is the maximum height of this lens? If necessary, round your answer to the nearest thousandth. Use a complete sentence to explain how you found your answer.

4. Create a graph of the quadratic function on the grid below. First, choose your bounds and intervals. Be sure to label your graph clearly.

Variable quantity	Lower bound	Upper bound	Interval

(label) (units)

(label) (units)

8

Investigate Problem 2

5. What is the difference in the widths of the lenses? What is the difference in the heights of the lenses? Use complete sentences in your answer.

6. How does the focal length affect the shape of the lens? Use a complete sentence in your answer.

Use complete sentences to explain how you found your answer to Question 6.

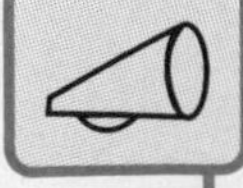

8

8

Looking Ahead to Chapter 9

Focus In Chapter 9, you will learn how to identify prime and composite numbers, factor composite numbers by using prime factorizations, and write numbers in scientific notation. You will also work with powers and learn properties of powers, as well as different forms of *n*th roots of numbers.

Chapter Warm-up

Answer these questions to help you review skills that you will need in Chapter 9.

Use mental math to find the value of *x*.

1. $3x = 81$

2. $5x = 105$

3. $17x = 85$

Write each expression as a power.

4. (8)(8)(8)(8)

5. 11 • 11 • 11 • 11 • 11 • 11

6. (–13)(–13)(–13)

Evaluate each power.

7. 2^6

8. 5^2

9. 10^4

Read the problem scenario below.

You work for a cooking supply manufacturer and you are in charge of making circular pizza pans. Your boss would like to know the area of each circular pan to get an idea of the amount of material that will be needed for each of the pizza pans. Note that the area of a circle is $A = \pi r^2$, where r is the radius of the circle. Use 3.14 for π.

10. What is the area of a pizza pan that has a radius of 3 inches?

11. What is the area of a pizza pan that has a radius of 6 inches?

12. One pizza pan has a radius of 7 inches. Another pizza pan has a radius of 5 inches. How much more area does the first pizza pan have than the second pizza pan?

Key Terms

factors ■ p. 422
prime number ■ p. 423
composite number ■ p. 423
prime factorization ■ p. 423
power ■ p. 425
exponent ■ p. 425
product ■ p. 425
quotient ■ p. 425
positive exponent ■ p. 429
negative exponent ■ p. 430
zero exponent ■ p. 430
standard form ■ p. 433
scientific notation ■ p. 433
cube root ■ p. 444
index ■ p. 444
*n*th root ■ p. 445
radicand ■ p. 445
rational exponent ■ p. 447
radical ■ p. 447

CHAPTER

9

Properties of Exponents

In 2004, Steve Fossett set a world record for the fastest trip around the world in a sailboat. He and his crew of thirteen made the journey in 58 days and 9 hours. In Lesson 9.6, you will examine the capsize factor of a boat by using its weight and width.

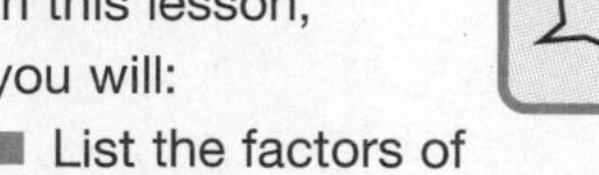

9.1 The Museum of Natural History

Powers and Prime Factorization

Objectives

In this lesson, you will:

- List the factors of numbers.
- Identify prime and composite numbers.
- Write the prime factorizations of numbers.

Key Terms

- factor
- prime number
- composite number
- prime factorization

SCENARIO Some of the students at an elementary school are going on a field trip to a museum of natural history. Some adults are also going on the trip to serve as guides. The school principal wants to divide the students and adults into groups so that each group has the same number of students and the same number of adults.

Problem 1 Splitting Up

Suppose that there are 12 students and 4 adults going on the trip.

A. Can there be two groups of students and adults? Use complete sentences to explain your reasoning.

B. Can there be three groups of students and adults? Use complete sentences to explain your reasoning.

C. Can there be four groups of students and adults? Use complete sentences to explain your reasoning.

D. Can there be five groups of students and adults? Use complete sentences to explain your reasoning.

E. What are the different-sized groups that are possible for this number of students and adults? Describe the number of groups, and the numbers of students and adults in each group. Use complete sentences in your answer.

Investigate Problem 1

1. Now, suppose that there are 30 students and 6 adults going on the trip. What are the different-sized groups that are possible for this number of students and adults? Describe the number of groups, and the numbers of students and adults in each group. Use complete sentences to explain your reasoning.

2. Now suppose that there are 29 students and 5 adults going on the trip. What are the different-sized groups that are possible for this number of students and adults? Describe the number of groups, and the number of students and adults in each group. Use complete sentences to explain your reasoning.

3. How does the number of groups relate to the number of students and the number of adults going on the trip? Use complete sentences in your answer.

4. How did you determine the answers to part (E) and Questions 1 and 2? Use complete sentences to explain your method.

5. **Just the Math: Factors of a Number** The **factors** of a given number are the numbers that evenly divide the given number. For each pair of numbers, list all the factors.

   4 and 12　　　6 and 30　　　5 and 29

Investigate Problem 1

In part (E) and in Questions 1 and 2, you were finding all the *common* factors of the numbers of students and adults. List the common factors of each pair of numbers in Question 5.

In part (E) and in Questions 1 and 2, did you find all the different-sized groups? How do you know? Use complete sentences in your answer.

6. **Just the Math: Prime Numbers** What do you notice about the factors of 5 and 29?

The numbers 5 and 29 are called *prime numbers*. A **prime number** is a number greater than 1 that has exactly two whole number factors, 1 and itself. The numbers 4, 12, 6, and 30 are **composite numbers,** or numbers greater than 1 that have more than two whole number factors. Make a list of the first 10 prime numbers after the prime number 2.

9

7. **Just the Math: Prime Factorization** Every composite number can be written as a product of prime numbers. This is called the **prime factorization** of a number. For instance, write 36 as the product of prime factors.

36 = _____ • _____ • _____ • _____

You can use your knowledge of powers from Lesson 1.2 to write this prime factorization as products of powers: $2^2 \cdot 3^2$. Write the prime factorization of each of the numbers in Question 5. Write your answers as products of powers.

8. Use complete sentences to explain how you can use the prime factorization of a number to help you determine the common factors of a pair of numbers.

Investigate Problem 1

9. Use prime factorizations to find the common factors of each pair of numbers. Show all your work and use a complete sentence in your answer.

9 and 12

21 and 42

36 and 40

54 and 24

31 and 50

10. Suppose that 126 students and 48 adults are going on the trip. What are the different-sized groups that are possible for this number of students and adults? Describe the number of groups, and the numbers of students and adults in each group. Show all your work and use a complete sentence in your answer.

11. Which of the groupings would you choose from Question 10? Use complete sentences to explain your answer.

Take Note

Whenever you see the share with the class icon, your group should prepare a short presentation to share with the class that describes how you solved the problem. Be prepared to ask questions during other groups' presentations and to answer questions during your presentation.

9

9.2 Bits and Bytes

Multiplying and Dividing Powers

Objectives

In this lesson, you will:

- Write numbers as powers.
- Multiply powers.
- Divide powers.

Key Terms

- power
- exponent
- product
- quotient

SCENARIO The amount of memory available on CDs, hard drives, zip drives, and so on are measured in bytes. A byte is a basic unit of measurement of size for computer information, but the most basic unit is a bit. There are 8 bits contained in one byte.

Problem 1 Kilobytes, Megabytes, and Gigabytes

The most common units of measurement for computer data storage are kilobytes, megabytes, and gigabytes.

A. One kilobyte is the same as 1024 bytes. Write the prime factorization of the number of bytes in one kilobyte.

B. One megabyte is the same as 1,048,576 bytes. Write the prime factorization of the number of bytes in one megabyte.

C. One gigabyte is the same as 1,073,741,824 bytes. Write the prime factorization of the number of bytes in one gigabyte.

D. What do the prime factorizations in parts (A) through (C) have in common? Use a complete sentence in your answer.

Investigate Problem 1

1. Divide the number of bytes in one megabyte by the number of bytes in one kilobyte. Show all your work.

What does this number represent? Use a complete sentence in your answer.

2. Write the numerator, denominator, and quotient from Question 1 as powers of 2.

9

Investigate Problem 1

3. Divide the number of bytes in one gigabyte by the number of bytes in one kilobyte. Show all your work and use a complete sentence in your answer.

What does this number represent? Use a complete sentence in your answer.

4. Write the numerator, denominator, and quotient from Question 3 as powers of 2.

5. In Question 2, how do the bases of all the powers compare? In Question 4, how do the bases of all the powers compare? In each division problem, how does the exponent in the quotient relate to the exponents in the numerator and the denominator? Use complete sentences in your answer.

6. Write a rule that you can use to find the quotient of two powers that have the same base. Use a complete sentence in your answer.

7. Use your rule from Question 6 to simplify each expression. Show all your work and write your answer as a power.

$\frac{4^9}{4^8}$ $\frac{5^6}{5^3}$ $\frac{10^{12}}{10^8}$

Problem 2 Storage Options

External (outside) storage for a computer comes in different forms: CD, DVD, external hard drive, flash drive, and so on. The sizes for these different options vary and get larger as new technologies develop.

A. One model of hard drive can store up to 4 gigabytes of data. Find the number of bytes that this hard drive can store. Remember that 1 gigabyte = 1,073,741,824 bytes. Show all your work and use a complete sentence in your answer.

B. One model of flash drive can store up to 128 megabytes of data. Find the number of bytes that this flash drive can store. Remember that 1 megabyte = 1,048,576 bytes. Show all your work and use a complete sentence in your answer.

C. Use complete sentences to explain how you found your answers to parts (A) and (B).

9

Investigate Problem 2

1. Write the multiplication problem that you used in part (A) to find the number of bytes of storage for the hard drive.

Write each factor in the product as a power of 2. Then write the result as a power of 2. What do you notice about the exponents? Use a complete sentence in your answer.

2. Write the multiplication problem that you used in part (B) to find the number of bytes of storage for the hard drive.

Investigate Problem 2

Write each factor in the product as a power of 2. Then write the result as a power of 2. What do you notice about the exponents? Use a complete sentence in your answer.

3. How do the bases of the powers in Question 1 compare? How do the bases of the powers in Question 2 compare? Use a complete sentence in your answer.

4. Write a rule that you can use to find the product of two powers that have the same base. Use a complete sentence in your answer.

5. Use your rule from Question 4 to simplify each expression. Show all your work and write your answer as a power.

$5^6 \cdot 5^8$ $\qquad$ $2^3 \cdot 2^5$ $\qquad$ $1^9 \cdot 1^7$

6. Simplify each expression, if possible. Show all your work and write your answer as a power.

$4^5 \cdot 4^5$ $\qquad$ $\dfrac{8^{10}}{8^3}$ $\qquad$ $2^3 \cdot 3^2$

$\dfrac{6^4}{5^4}$ $\qquad$ $10^5 \cdot 10^1$ $\qquad$ $8^4 \cdot 3^4$

7. Describe the situations in which you would use powers to multiply and divide. Use complete sentences in your answer.

9.3 As Time Goes By

Zero and Negative Exponents

Objectives

In this lesson, you will:

- Write a number as a power.
- Evaluate powers with positive, negative, and zero exponents.

Key Terms

- positive exponent
- negative exponent
- zero exponent

SCENARIO Computer operations and communications between electronic equipment happen so fast that they need to be measured in units of time that are smaller than seconds. Three units of time that are smaller than seconds are milliseconds, microseconds, and nanoseconds.

Problem 1 Faster and Faster

A. One millisecond is the same as $\frac{1}{1000}$ second. Complete the statement below to determine the number of seconds that there are in 10,000 milliseconds.

$$10{,}000\ \cancel{\text{milliseconds}}\left(\frac{1\text{ second}}{1000\ \cancel{\text{milliseconds}}}\right) = \frac{\square\text{ seconds}}{\square}$$

$$= \square\text{ seconds}$$

There are ______ seconds in 10,000 milliseconds.

B. Complete the statement below to determine the number of seconds there are in 1000 milliseconds.

$$1000\ \cancel{\text{milliseconds}}\left(\frac{1\text{ second}}{1000\ \cancel{\text{milliseconds}}}\right) = \frac{\square\text{ seconds}}{\square}$$

$$= \square\text{ second}$$

There is ______ second in 1000 milliseconds.

C. Complete the statement below to determine the number of seconds there are in 100 milliseconds.

$$100\ \cancel{\text{milliseconds}}\left(\frac{1\text{ second}}{1000\ \cancel{\text{milliseconds}}}\right) = \frac{\square\text{ seconds}}{\square}$$

$$= \square\text{ second}$$

There is ______ second in 1000 milliseconds.

D. How does the numerator compare to the denominator in each problem in parts (A) through (C)? Use complete sentences in your answer.

9

Investigate Problem 1

1. Show how you could use powers to find the answer to part (A). Show all your work.

2. Write the numerator and denominator from the statement in part (B) as a quotient of powers.

   According to your answer in part (B), what is the value of this quotient?

   Use the rule for finding a quotient of powers to simplify the quotient of powers above. Show your work and write your answer as a power.

9

3. Consider the quotient $\frac{2^4}{2^4}$. What is the value of this quotient? Use a complete sentence to explain your reasoning.

   Write your answer as a power of 2. Show your work.

4. What is the value of any number raised to the power of zero? Use a complete sentence in your answer.

5. Write the numerator and denominator from the statement in part (C) as a quotient of powers.

   Use the rule for finding a quotient of powers to write the quotient as a power of 10.

   According to your answer to part (C), what is the value of this power of 10?

   So, $10^{-1} = \frac{1}{10^1}$.

Investigate Problem 1

6. Complete the table below that shows small units of time.

Unit	**Number of seconds**	**Number of seconds as a power with a positive exponent**	**Number of seconds as a power with a negative exponent**
Millisecond	$\frac{1}{1000}$	$\frac{1}{10^{\square}}$	$10^{\square}$
Microsecond	$\frac{1}{1,000,000}$	$\frac{1}{10^{\square}}$	$10^{\square}$
Nanosecond	$\frac{1}{1,000,000,000}$	$\frac{1}{10^{\square}}$	$10^{\square}$

7. Use complete sentences to explain how you can write a power with a negative exponent as a power with a positive exponent.

8. Rewrite the power so that the exponent is positive.

5^{-3} $\qquad$ 4^{-6} $\qquad$ 3^{-10}

9. Suppose that you are given a fraction that has a power in the denominator. How can you rewrite the value so that the power is no longer in the denominator? Use complete sentences in your answer.

10. Rewrite the fraction so that there is no power in the denominator.

$\frac{1}{8^3}$ $\qquad$ $\frac{1}{1^5}$ $\qquad$ $\frac{1}{6^7}$

Investigate Problem 1

11. What can you conclude about the value of a power when the exponent is greater than zero? Use a complete sentence in your answer.

What can you conclude about the value of a power when the exponent is less than zero? Use a complete sentence in your answer.

What can you conclude about the value of a power when the exponent is zero? Use a complete sentence in your answer.

12. Use what you have learned so far in this chapter to simplify each expression completely. Show all your work.

$\frac{8^3}{8^5}$

$6^{-3} \cdot 6^2$

$10^0 \cdot 10^{-3}$

$\frac{2^0}{2^4}$

$\frac{2^{-3}}{2^2}$

$5^4 \cdot 5^{-2}$

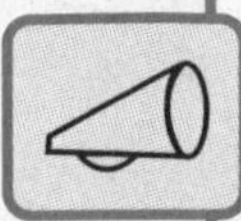

9.4 Large and Small Measurements

Scientific Notation

Objectives

In this lesson, you will:

- Write numbers in scientific notation.
- Write numbers in standard form.

Key Terms

- standard form
- scientific notation

SCENARIO In our universe, we encounter very large numbers, such as the diameter of Earth, the distances to Mars, other planets and stars, and so on. We also encounter very small numbers, such as the weight of a butterfly, the length of a blood cell, the width of a grain of sand, and so on. **Scientific notation** is a shorthand notation that is used to write these numbers so that they can be more easily used in computations.

Problem 1 The Big Stuff

Scientific notation uses powers of ten to represent large and small numbers. A number is written in scientific notation if it is the product of a number greater than or equal to one and less than 10 and a power of 10. You can use scientific notation to describe the distances from the sun to planets in the solar system.

A. Earth's average distance from the sun is 1.496×10^8 kilometers. Complete the statement below to write this distance in standard form.

1.496×10^8 kilometers = ______ kilometers

Take Note

To write a number in *standard form* means to write the number as a numeral.

B. Mercury's average distance from the sun is 5.8×10^7 kilometers. Complete the statement below to write this distance in standard form.

5.8×10^7 kilometers = ______ kilometers

C. What happens to the value of a power of ten as the exponent gets larger? Use a complete sentence in your answer.

D. Mars' average distance from the sun is 227,900,000 kilometers. Complete the statement below to write this distance in scientific notation.

227,900,000 kilometers = $2.279 \times$ ______ kilometers

E. Saturn's average distance from the sun is 1,433,000,000 kilometers. Complete the statement below to write the diameter in scientific notation.

1,433,000,000 kilometers = ______ $\times 10^9$ kilometers

Investigate Problem 1

1. The following numbers represent the closest distance of a comet to the sun during the comet's orbit. Which distances are *not* written in scientific notation? How do you know? Use complete sentences in your explanation.

   Comet Halley: 8.78×10^7 kilometers

   Comet Encke: 50×10^6 kilometers

   Comet Wild 2: 2.368×10^8 kilometers

   Comet Hale-Bopp: 136×10^6 kilometers

2. Write the distances that you identified in Question 1 in scientific notation.

9

Take Note

Note that when you compare two numbers written in scientific notation that have the same exponent, the number that is larger is the number with the larger value between 1 and 10. For instance, the number 3.4×10^5 is greater than the number 3.2×10^5.

3. Without writing the distances in standard form, list the comets in order from shortest distance from the sun to longest distance from the sun.

4. Use a complete sentence to explain how to compare two large numbers that are in scientific notation.

5. Write each of the distances from Question 1 in standard form.

   Comet Halley: ____________________

   Comet Encke: ____________________

   Comet Wild 2: ____________________

   Comet Hale-Bopp: ____________________

Problem 2 The Small Stuff

You can also use scientific notation to write very small numbers.

A. The diameter of a large grain of sand is 2.0×10^{-1} centimeter. Complete the statement below to write the diameter in standard form.

   2.0×10^{-1} centimeter = ☐ centimeter

Problem 2 The Small Stuff

B. The diameter of a red blood cell is 8.4×10^{-4} centimeter. Complete the statement below to write this diameter in standard form.

8.4×10^{-4} centimeter = ☐ centimeter

C. What happens to the value of a number as the absolute value of the exponent of a power of ten gets larger? Use a complete sentence in your answer.

D. The diameter of a bacterium is 0.00002 centimeter. Complete the statement below to write this diameter in scientific notation.

0.00002 centimeter = 2.0 × ☐ centimeter

E. The diameter of a human hair is 0.0025 centimeter. Complete the statement below to write the diameter in scientific notation.

0.0025 centimeter = ☐ $\times 10^{-3}$ centimeter

9

Investigate Problem 2

1. The following numbers represent the diameters of the nucleus (inside) of different kinds of atoms. Which diameters are *not* written in scientific notation? How do you know? Use complete sentences in your explanation.

   Aluminum atom nucleus: 7.2×10^{-13} centimeter

   Cobalt atom nucleus: 0.93×10^{-15} centimeter

   Gold atom nucleus: 14×10^{-11} centimeter

   Sodium atom nucleus: 6.8×10^{-13} centimeter

2. Write the diameters that you identified in Question 1 in scientific notation.

3. Without writing the diameters in standard form, list the atoms by diameter from least to greatest.

Investigate Problem 2

4. Use a complete sentence to explain how to compare two small numbers that are in scientific notation.

5. Write each of the diameters from Question 1 in standard form.

Aluminum atom nucleus: ____________________

Cobalt atom nucleus: ____________________

Gold atom nucleus: ____________________

Sodium atom nucleus: ____________________

6. Complete the table that shows measurements for different objects.

Object	Measurement	Measurement in standard form	Measurement in scientific notation
Jupiter	average distance from sun (kilometers)	778,600,000	
Water molecule	diameter (centimeters)		2.82×10^{-8}
Comet Hyakutake	nearest distance to the sun (kilometers)		3.4×10^{7}
Atom	diameter (centimeters)	0.00000005	
Dust speck	diameter (centimeters)		3.0×10^{-5}
Saturn's E ring	inner radius (kilometers)	300,000	

7. What happens to the decimal point in a number after you multiply the number by a power of ten with an exponent that is an integer greater than zero?

What happens to the decimal point in a number after you multiply the number by a power of ten with an exponent that is an integer less than zero?

9

9.5 The Beat Goes On

Properties of Powers

Objectives

In this lesson, you will:

- Use the power of a power property.
- Use the power of a product property.
- Use the power of a quotient property.

Key Terms

- power
- product
- quotient

SCENARIO A basic drum is made of a cylindrical frame and one or two circular drumheads that are stretched over the frame. The sound that a drum makes depends on the amount that the drumhead is stretched, as well as the size of the drumhead.

Problem 1 Area of a Drumhead

A. A snare drum's drumhead is 8 inches. This measurement describes the diameter of the drumhead. Find the area of the drumhead by using the formula for the area of a circle: $A = \pi r^2$, where r is the radius and A is the area. Show all your work and use a complete sentence in your answer. Leave your answer in terms of π.

Take Note

In a circle, the radius is half the length of the diameter.

B. A bass drum's drumhead is 18 inches. Find the area of the drumhead. Show all your work and use a complete sentence in your answer. Leave your answer in terms of π.

Take Note

Recall that π is an irrational number whose value is approximately 3.14.

C. A tom-tom's drumhead is 16 inches. Find the area of the drumhead. Show all your work and use a complete sentence in your answer. Leave your answer in terms of π.

9

Investigate Problem 1

1. For each answer in parts (A) through (C), write the prime factorization of the number that is multiplied by π.

Area of 8-inch drumhead: $A = \square\pi$

Area of 18-inch drumhead: $A = \square\pi$

Area of 16-inch drumhead: $A = \square\pi$

Take Note

The plural of radius is *radii.*

Take Note

Recall that a *conjecture* is a possible explanation that can be tested by further investigation.

9

Investigate Problem 1

2. What do you notice about the radii of the drumheads in parts (A) through (C)? Use a complete sentence in your answer.

3. Write each radius from the problem situation as a power.

Radius of 8-inch drumhead: $r = \square$

Radius of 18-inch drumhead: $r = \square$

Radius of 16-inch drumhead: $r = \square$

4. In finding each drumhead area, you squared the radius of the drumhead. Review your work in Questions 1 and 3. What is the result of squaring a power? Use a complete sentence in your answer.

5. What do you think is the result of cubing a power? Write an example that demonstrates your conjecture. Use a complete sentence in your answer.

6. Write a rule using a complete sentence that explains how to simplify a power that has a base that is a power, such as:

$(2^4)^5$. ← exponent

↖ base is a power

Problem 2 More Bass Drum Drumheads

A. Bass drum drumheads come in a multitude of sizes. Another size of a bass drum drumhead is 24 inches. Find the area of the drumhead. Show all your work and use a complete sentence in your answer. Leave your answer in terms of π.

B. Write the prime factorization of the radius of the drumhead in part (A).

$r = \square$

Now write the prime factorization of the area.

$A = \square\,\pi$

Problem 2 More Bass Drumheads

How are the prime factorizations related? Use a complete sentence in your answer.

C. Another bass drum drumhead size is 36 inches. Find the area of the drumhead. Show all your work and use a complete sentence in your answer. Leave your answer in terms of π.

D. Write the prime factorization of the radius of the drumhead in part (C).

$r =$ ☐

Now write the prime factorization of the area.

$A =$ ☐ π

How are the prime factorizations related? Use a complete sentence in your answer.

9

Investigate Problem 2

1. Use a complete sentence to explain how you can simplify a power that has a product as its base without first simplifying the base.

2. Now consider a power that has a quotient as its base, such as: $\left(\frac{3}{4}\right)^{10}$.

   Write a conjecture for a method of how to simplify this kind of power. Write an example that demonstrates your conjecture. Use a complete sentence in your answer.

9

Investigate Problem 2

3. Use your properties of powers to simplify each expression. Show all your work.

$(3^2)^3$

$(15 \cdot 12)^2$

$\left(\frac{2}{3}\right)^4$

$(4^5)^0$

4. A summary of the rules for powers that you have learned so far in this chapter is shown below. Complete each property.

Product rule of powers: $a^b a^c = a^{\square}$

Quotient rule of powers: $\frac{a^b}{a^c} = a^{\square}$

Negative exponents: $\frac{1}{a^b} = a^{\square}$

Zero exponents: $a^0 = \square$

Power of a power rule: $(a^b)^c = a^{\square}$

Power of a product rule: $(ab)^c = a^{\square}b^{\square}$

Power of a quotient rule: $\left(\frac{a}{b}\right)^c = \frac{a^{\square}}{b^{\square}}$

5. All the properties that you have used so far apply to algebraic expressions too. Simplify each expression. Show all your work.

$(x^3)^3$

$(2p)^2$

y^3y^7

$\left(\frac{x}{4}\right)^3$

Investigate Problem 2

6. For each problem below, identify the property that is used in each step to simplify the expression. The first problem is done as an example.

$$\left(\frac{x^3}{y^2z}\right)^4 = \frac{(x^3)^4}{(y^2z)^4}$$ Power of a quotient rule

$$= \frac{(x^3)^4}{(y^2)^4z^4}$$ Power of a product rule

$$= \frac{x^{12}}{y^8z^4}$$ Power of a power rule

$(2ab^2)^3(-3b)^2 = 2^3a^3(b^2)^3(-3)^2b^2$ ____________________

$= 8a^3(b^2)^3(9)b^2$ ____________________

$= 8a^3b^6(9)b^2$ ____________________

$= 8(9)a^3b^6b^2$ ____________________

$= 72a^3b^6b^2$ ____________________

$= 72a^3b^8$ ____________________

Take Note

Recall that in Lesson 4.5 you learned other properties of real numbers.

$\left(\frac{x^2}{2y^3}\right)^4\left(\frac{xy^2}{3}\right)^3 = \frac{(x^2)^4}{(2y^3)^4} \cdot \frac{(xy^2)^3}{3^3}$ ____________________

$= \frac{(x^2)^4}{2^4(y^3)^4} \cdot \frac{x^3(y^2)^3}{3^3}$ ____________________

$= \frac{x^8}{2^4y^{12}} \cdot \frac{x^3y^6}{3^3}$ ____________________

$= \frac{x^8x^3y^6}{2^4y^{12}(3^3)}$ ____________________

$= \frac{x^{11}y^6}{2^4y^{12}(3^3)}$ ____________________

$= \frac{x^{11}}{2^4y^6(3^3)}$ ____________________

$= \frac{x^{11}}{16y^6(27)}$ ____________________

$= \frac{x^{11}}{432y^6}$ ____________________

9.6 Sailing Away

Radicals and Rational Exponents

Objectives

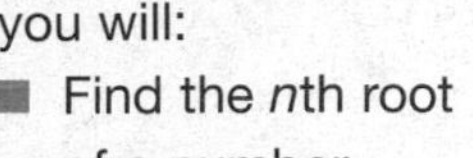

In this lesson, you will:

- Find the nth root of a number.
- Write an expression in radical form.
- Write an expression in rational exponent form.

Key Terms

- cube root
- index
- nth root
- radicand
- rational exponent
- radical

SCENARIO Some boats move by skimming across the surface of the water, while other boats move by pushing through the water. The boats that push through the water have a body, or hull, that is called a displacement hull. Sailboats are boats with displacement hulls. Important measurements of a boat that can be used to determine the boat's speed and stability are labeled on the figure below.

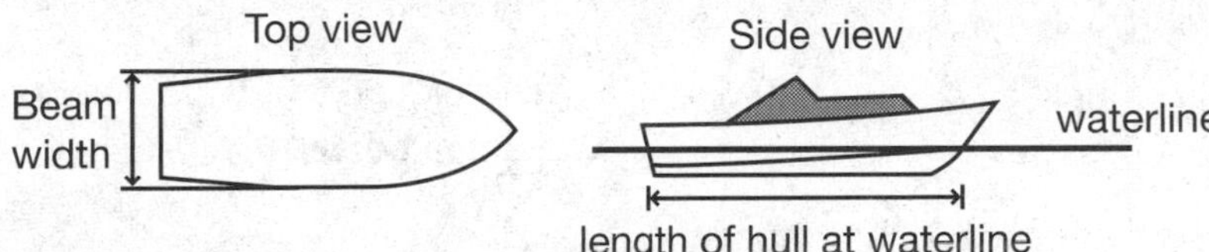

Problem 1 Boat Stability

The weight of a boat depends on its beam width. An equation that relates a boat's weight to its beam width is $w = 64\left(\frac{b}{c}\right)^3$, where w is the boat's weight in pounds, b is the beam width in feet, and c is the capsize factor. When the capsize factor c is less than 2, the boat is less likely to capsize, or turn over.

A. Suppose that a boat has a capsize factor of three and a beam width of six feet. What is the weight of the boat? Show your work and use a complete sentence in your answer.

B. Suppose that a boat has a capsize factor of three and a beam width of nine feet. What is the weight of the boat? Show your work and use a complete sentence in your answer.

Take Note

When a power has an exponent of 3, it is called the third power. When you evaluate a third power, you are *cubing* the base.

9

Problem 1 Boat Stability

C. Use complete sentences to explain how you found your answers to parts (A) and (B).

D. Suppose that a boat has a capsize factor of 2 and weighs 1000 pounds. Write an equation that you can use to find the beam width of the boat.

In the equation that you wrote, get the power by itself on one side of the equation. Show your work.

9

E. To find the value of *b*, you need to find the number that when multiplied by itself three times is equal to 125. What is this number? Use a complete sentence in your answer.

F. What is the boat's beam width? Use a complete sentence in your answer.

Investigate Problem 1

1. Just the Math: Cube Root Your answer to part (E) is the *cube root* of 125. You can say that a number *b* is a **cube root** of a number *a* if $b^3 = a$.

So, 5 is a cube root of 125 because $5^3 = 125$.

Is there another number whose cube is 125?

A cube root is designated by using the symbol $\sqrt[3]{\ }$. The number 3 is called the **index** of the radical. So, $\sqrt[3]{125} = 5$.

Complete each statement below.

$\sqrt[3]{8} = \square$ $\sqrt[3]{-27} = \square$

Take Note

Finding the cube root of a number is the *inverse operation* of finding the cube of a number.

Investigate Problem 1

2. **Just the Math: *n*th Roots** You can extend the idea of square roots and cube roots. Use n to represent a positive number. Then a number b is the ***n*th root of *a*** if $b^n = a$. For instance, 2 is the fourth root of 16 because $2^4 = 16$.

   Complete each statement below.

   3 is the fifth root of 243 because $\square = 243$.

   -2 is the cube root of -8 because $(-2)^3 = \square$.

   4 is the $\square$ root of 4096 because $4^6 = 4096$.

   The nth root of a number a is designated as $\sqrt[n]{a}$, where n is the index of the radical and a is the *radicand*.

Take Note

It is understood that $\sqrt{}$ and $\sqrt[2]{}$ indicate a square root.

3. Complete each statement below.

   $\sqrt{100} = \square$ because $\square^2 = 100$.

   $\sqrt[3]{216} = \square$ because $\square^3 = 216$.

   $\sqrt[4]{81} = \square$ because $\square^4 = 81$.

   $\sqrt[5]{-32} = \square$ because $(\square)^5 = -32$.

4. Notice that a power can be positive or negative, depending on the base and the exponent. When the exponent of a power is an even number and the base is a positive number, is the value of the power a positive number or a negative number? How do you know? Use a complete sentence to explain.

   When the exponent of a power is an even number and the base is negative, Is the value of the power a positive number or a negative number? Use a complete sentence to explain.

5. When the exponent of a power is an odd number and the base is a positive number, is the value of the power a positive number or negative number? Use a complete sentence to explain.

   When the exponent of a power is an odd number and the base is negative, is the value of the power a positive number or negative number? Use a complete sentence to explain.

9

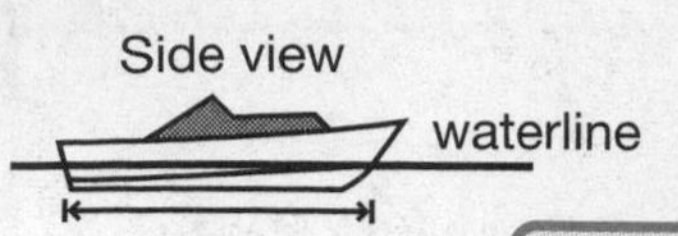

Problem 2 Boat Speed

The speed of a boat depends on the length of the hull at the waterline. An equation that relates the speed s in knots and the length ℓ in feet of the hull at the waterline is $s = 1.34\sqrt{\ell}$.

A. What is the speed of a boat that has a length of 16 feet at the waterline? Show your work and use a complete sentence in your answer.

B. Write an equation that you can use to find the length of a boat at its waterline if the boat's speed is 6.7 knots.

C. In the equation that you wrote, get the radical by itself on one side of the equation. Show your work.

D. What is the length of the boat at the waterline? How do you know? Use complete sentences in your answer.

Your answer is the value of which variable? Use a complete sentence in your answer.

9

Investigate Problem 2

1. In the problem above, you found that the solution of the equation $\sqrt{\ell} = 5$ is $\ell = 25$. Complete the steps below.

$\ell = 25$ Given

$\ell = \square$ Write 25 as a power.

$\ell = \square$ Replace 5 by $\sqrt{\ell}$.

Investigate Problem 2

2. Because the definition of the nth root involves powers, it would be nice if we could write an nth root of a number as a power of the number. Consider your equation from Question 1:

$\ell^1 = (\sqrt{\ell})^2$.

If we could write the square root of ℓ as a power of ℓ, we would have $\ell^1 = (\ell^?)^2$. You know that when you find the power of a power, you multiply the exponents: $(a^b)^c = a^{\square}$.

Represent the square root as an exponent so the exponent times 2 is equal to 1. Use complete sentences to explain.

3. **Just the Math: Radicals and Rational Exponents**
A **rational exponent** is an exponent that is a rational number. We can write each nth root as a rational exponent in the following way: If n is an integer greater than 1, then $\sqrt[n]{a} = a^{1/n}$. Write each radical as a power.

$\sqrt[3]{7}$ $\qquad$ $\sqrt[5]{x}$ $\qquad$ $\sqrt{y}$

Write each power as a *radical*.

$8^{1/4}$ $\qquad$ $z^{1/5}$ $\qquad$ $m^{1/3}$

Take Note

Remember that a *rational number* is a number of the form $\frac{a}{b}$ where $b \neq 0$.

4. Write the equation in Problem 2 in rational exponent form.

5. Another nautical equation can be used to determine how fast a sailboat can travel in light wind. This equation is $s = \frac{a}{d^{2/3}}$ where a is the sail area and d is the boat's displacement. You can write this equation in radical form by using the properties you know about powers. Use the properties of powers to write the equation in radical form.

Take Note

A boat's *displacement* is the volume of water that is moved by the weight of the boat in the water.

$s = \frac{a}{d^{2/3}}$ $\qquad$ Given equation

$s = \frac{a}{\square}$ $\qquad$ Write power as a product.

$s = \frac{a}{\square}$ $\qquad$ Power of a power property

$s = \frac{a}{\square}$ $\qquad$ Definition of rational exponent

Investigate Problem 2

6. The equation in Question 5 gives you s, the *sail area to displacement ratio.* Use the equation to find s for a boat that has a sail area of 600 square feet and a displacement of 125 cubic feet. Show your work and use a complete sentence in your answer.

7. Write each expression in radical form. Show your work and simplify your answer, if possible.

$4^{3/2}$ $\quad$ $5^{3/4}$

$x^{4/5}$ $\quad$ $y^{2/3}$

8. Write each expression in rational exponent form. Show your work and simplify your answer, if possible.

$(\sqrt[4]{2})^3$ $\quad$ $(\sqrt{5})^4$

$(\sqrt[5]{x})^8$ $\quad$ $(\sqrt[5]{y})^{10}$

9

Looking Ahead to Chapter 10

Focus In Chapter 10, you will learn about polynomials, including how to add, subtract, multiply, and divide polynomials. You will also learn about polynomial and rational functions.

Chapter Warm-up

Answer these questions to help you review skills that you will need in Chapter 10.

Solve each two-step equation.

1. $5x + 3 = 2x - 12$

2. $4x = 7 - 3x$

3. $\frac{x}{5} + 3 = \frac{x}{10}$

Simplify each expression.

4. $(3^2)^5$

5. $x^7 \cdot x^{-5}(x^2)^{-3}$

6. $\left(\frac{xy^5}{y^{-2}}\right)^{-1}$

Read the problem scenario below.

You have just planted a flower bed in a 3-foot wide by 5-foot long rectangular section of your yard. After planting some flowers, you decide that you would like to add to the width of your garden so that there is more space to plant flowers. Let x represent the amount added to the length of your garden.

10

7. Represent the area of your expanded garden with an expression in two ways by using the distributive property.

8. What is the area of your garden if you expand the width by 4 feet?

Key Terms

polynomial ■ p. 454
term ■ p. 454
coefficient ■ p. 454
degree of a term ■ p. 454
degree of the polynomial ■ p. 454
monomial ■ p. 455
binomial ■ p. 455
trinomial ■ p. 455
standard form ■ p. 455
Vertical Line Test ■ p. 457
combine like terms ■ p. 460
distributive property ■ p. 460
area model ■ p. 464
divisor ■ p. 468
dividend ■ p. 468
remainder ■ p. 468
FOIL pattern ■ p. 472
square of a binomial sum ■ p. 473
square of a binomial difference ■ p. 475
rational expression ■ p. 483
domain ■ p. 483
restrict the domain ■ p. 485

CHAPTER

10

Polynomial Functions and Rational Expressions

Stained glass windows have been used as decoration in homes, religious buildings, and other buildings since the 7th century. In Lesson 10.4, you will find the area of a stained glass window.

10

10

10.1 Water Balloons

Polynomials and Polynomial Functions

Objectives

In this lesson, you will:

- Identify terms and coefficients of polynomials.
- Classify polynomials by the number of terms.
- Classify polynomials by degree.
- Write polynomials in standard form.
- Use the Vertical Line Test to determine whether equations are functions.

Key Terms

- polynomial
- term
- coefficient
- degree
- monomial
- binomial
- trinomial
- standard form
- Vertical Line Test

Take Note

The *vertical motion model* is $y = -16t^2 + vt + h$, where t is the time in seconds that the object has been moving, v is the initial velocity (speed) in feet per second of the object, h is the initial height in feet of the object, and y is the height in feet of the object at time t.

SCENARIO On a calm day, you and a friend are tossing water balloons in a field trying to hit a boulder in the field. The balloons travel in a path that is in the shape of a parabola.

Problem 1 Ready, Set, Launch

A. On your first throw, the balloon leaves your hand 3 feet above the ground at a velocity of 20 feet per second. Use what you learned in Chapter 8 about vertical motion models to write an equation that gives the height of the balloon in terms of time.

B. What is the height of the balloon after one second? Show your work and use a complete sentence to explain your answer.

C. What is the height of the balloon after two seconds? Show your work and use a complete sentence in your answer.

D. On your second throw, the balloon leaves your hand at ground level at a velocity of 30 feet per second. Write an equation that gives the height of the balloon in terms of time.

E. What is the height of the balloon after one second? Show your work and use a complete sentence in your answer.

F. What is the height of the balloon after two seconds? Show your work and use a complete sentence in your answer.

10

Investigate Problem 1

1. How are your models the same? Use a complete sentence in your answer.

   How are your models different? Use a complete sentence in your answer.

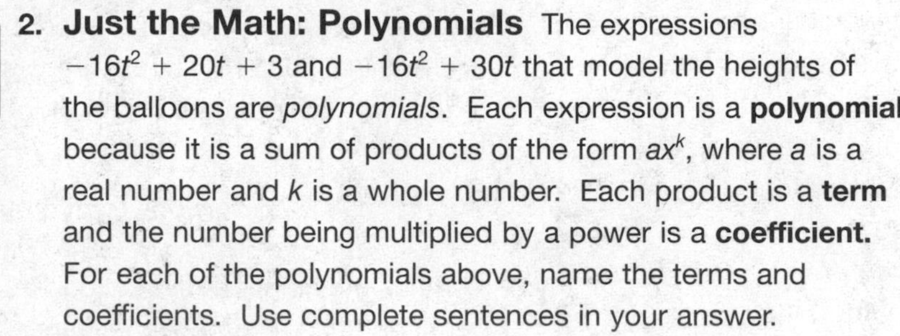

2. **Just the Math: Polynomials** The expressions $-16t^2 + 20t + 3$ and $-16t^2 + 30t$ that model the heights of the balloons are *polynomials*. Each expression is a **polynomial** because it is a sum of products of the form ax^k, where a is a real number and k is a whole number. Each product is a **term** and the number being multiplied by a power is a **coefficient.** For each of the polynomials above, name the terms and coefficients. Use complete sentences in your answer.

Take Note

Whole numbers are the numbers 0, 1, 2, 3, and so on.

10

3. For each of your polynomial models, what is the greatest exponent? Use a complete sentence in your answer.

   The **degree of a term** in a polynomial is the exponent of the term. The greatest exponent in a polynomial determines the **degree of the polynomial.** For instance, in the polynomial $4x + 3$, the greatest exponent is 1, so the degree of the polynomial is 1. What is the degree of each of your polynomial models? Use a complete sentence in your answer.

4. What kind of expression is a polynomial of degree 0? Give an example and use a complete sentence to explain your reasoning.

   What kind of expression is a polynomial of degree 1? Give an example and use a complete sentence to explain.

Investigate Problem 1

What kind of expression is a polynomial of degree 2? Give an example and use a complete sentence to explain your reasoning.

A polynomial of degree 3 is a called a cubic polynomial. Write an example of a cubic polynomial.

5. For each of your polynomial models in parts (A) and (D), find the number of terms in the model. Use a complete sentence in your answer.

Polynomials with only one term are **monomials.** Polynomials with exactly two terms are **binomials.** Polynomials with exactly three terms are **trinomials.** Classify each polynomial model in parts (A) and (D) by its number of terms. Use a complete sentence in your answer.

6. Give an example of a monomial of degree 3.

Give an example of a trinomial of degree 5.

10

7. Just the Math: Standard Form of a Polynomial

Later in this chapter, we will be adding, subtracting, multiplying, and dividing polynomials. To make this process easier, it is helpful to write polynomials in *standard form*. A polynomial is written in **standard form** by writing the terms in *descending* order, starting with the term with the greatest degree and ending with the term with the least degree. Write each polynomial in standard form.

$6 + 5x$ $\qquad$ $7 - x^2$

$4 + 3x + 4x^2$ $\qquad$ $4 + 3x^2 + 9x - x^3$

$5 - 6x^4$ $\qquad$ $x^6 - 4x^3 + 16$

Investigate Problem 1

8. Determine whether each algebraic expression is a polynomial. If the expression is a polynomial, classify it by its degree and number of terms. If the expression is not a polynomial, use a complete sentence to explain why it is not a polynomial.

$4x^2 + 3x - 1$ $\qquad$ $3x^{-2} + 4x - 1$

$4x^6 + 1$ $\qquad$ $10 - x^4$

$2\sqrt{x} + 3x - 4$ $\qquad$ 25

Problem 2 The Balloon's Path

It is now your friend's turn to throw water balloons at the boulder.

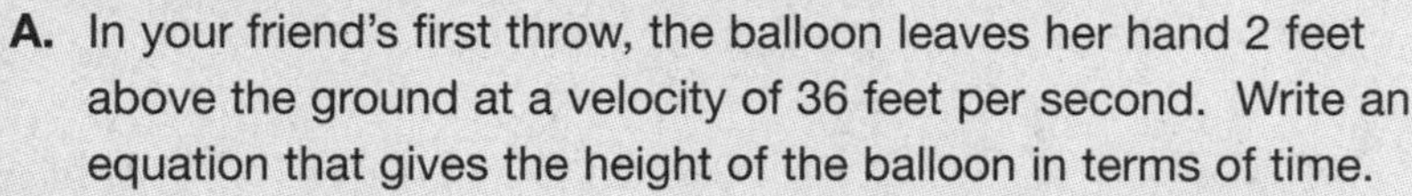

A. In your friend's first throw, the balloon leaves her hand 2 feet above the ground at a velocity of 36 feet per second. Write an equation that gives the height of the balloon in terms of time.

B. Complete the table of values that shows the height of the balloon in terms of time.

Quantity Name	Time	Height
Unit		
Expression		
	0.0	
	0.5	
	1.0	
	2.0	
	2.5	
	3.0	

10

Problem 2 The Balloon's Path

C. Create a graph of the model to see the path of the balloon on the grid below. First, choose your bounds and intervals. Be sure to label your graph clearly.

Variable quantity	Lower bound	Upper bound	Interval

10

Investigate Problem 2

1. Is the equation that you wrote in part (A) a function? How do you know? Use a complete sentence in your answer.

2. **Just the Math: Vertical Line Test** You can use a graph to determine whether an equation is a function. The **Vertical Line Test** states that an equation is a function if you can pass a vertical line through any part of the graph of the equation and the line intersects the graph, at most, one time. Consider your graph in part (C). Does your graph pass the Vertical Line Test?

Investigate Problem 2

3. Consider each equation and its graph. Use the Vertical Line Test to determine whether the equation is a function.

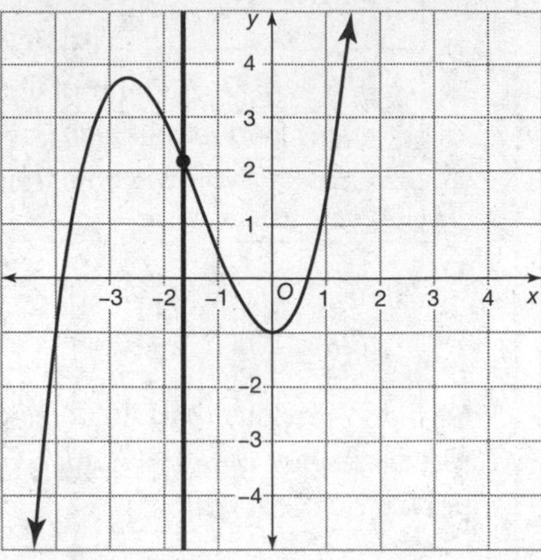

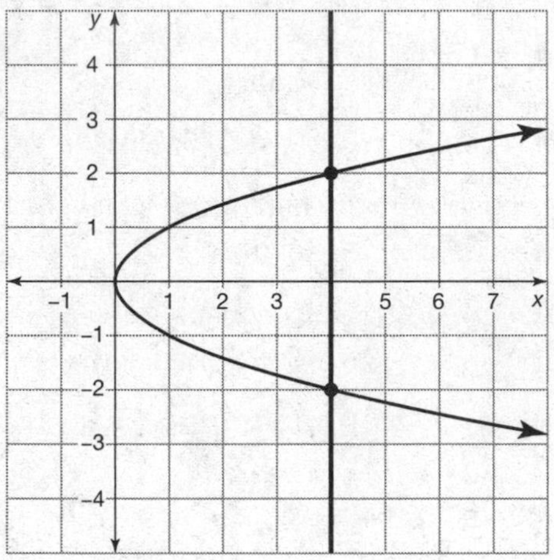

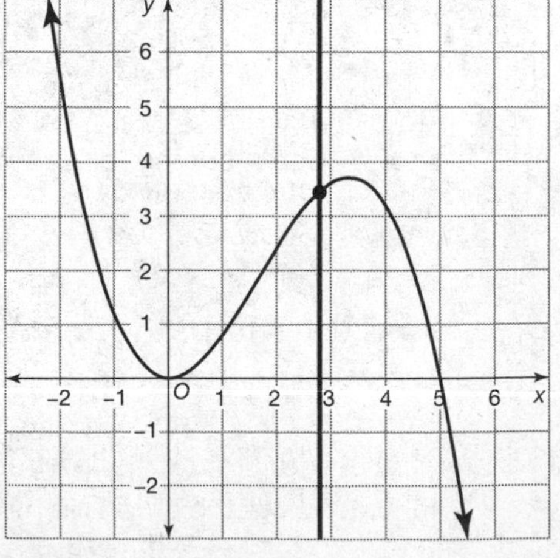

10

Take Note

Whenever you see the share with the class icon, your group should prepare a short presentation to share with the class that describes how you solved the problem. Be prepared to ask questions during other groups' presentations and to answer questions during your presentation.

10.2 Play Ball!

Adding and Subtracting Polynomials

Objectives

In this lesson, you will:

- Add polynomials.
- Subtract polynomials.

Key Terms

- combine like terms
- distributive property
- add
- subtract

SCENARIO A friend of yours loves baseball and plans to visit every major league baseball park in the country. The major league is made up of two divisions, the National League and the American League.

Problem 1 Batter Up

Your friend recently read an article that stated that the attendance at National League baseball games from 1990 through 2001 can be modeled by the function

$y = -86{,}584x^3 + 1{,}592{,}363x^2 - 5{,}692{,}368x + 24{,}488{,}926$

where x is the number of years since 1990 and y is the number of people who attended. The article also stated that the attendance at American League baseball games from 1990 through 2001 can be modeled by the function

$y = -56{,}554x^3 + 1{,}075{,}426x^2 - 4{,}806{,}571x + 30{,}280{,}751$

where x is the number of years since 1990 and y is the number of people who attended.

A. Find the attendance for each league in 1995. Show your work and use a complete sentence in your answer.

B. Find the total attendance at all games in major league baseball in 1995. Show your work and use a complete sentence in your answer.

How did you find your answer to part (B)? Use a complete sentence in your answer.

10

Problem 1 Batter Up

C. Find the attendance for each league in 2000. Show your work and use a complete sentence in your answer.

D. Find the total attendance at all games in major league baseball in 2000. Show your work and use a complete sentence in your answer.

How did you find your answer to part (D)? Use a complete sentence in your answer.

10

Investigate Problem 1

1. How would you write a function that you could use to find the total attendance at all major league baseball games? Use a complete sentence in your answer.

Take Note

Remember that you use a **distributive property** to combine like terms:

$$4x + 10x = x(4 + 10)$$
$$= x(14)$$
$$= 14x$$

2. You can add or subtract two polynomials by **combining like terms**. What are the like terms in the attendance polynomial models?

Find the sum of each group of like terms. What is the model for total attendance at all major league baseball games?

Investigate Problem 1

3. Use your model to find the total attendance in 1995 and 2000. Show your work and use a complete sentence in your answer.

How do these answers compare to those in Problem 1 parts (B) and (D)? Use a complete sentence in your answer.

When is it useful for you to find the sum of two functions first, and then evaluate the function rather than evaluating each function separately and then finding the sum? Use a complete sentence in your answer.

4. You can also write a function that shows how many more people attended National League games each year than attended American League games. Describe how you can find this function. Use a complete sentence in your answer.

10

Complete the statement below that gives the function described above.

$y =$ ______________________________

Because you are subtracting one function from another function, you must subtract *each term* of the second function from the first function. To do this, use the distributive property to distribute the negative sign to each term in the second function.

$y = -86{,}584x^3 + 1{,}592{,}363x^2 - 5{,}692{,}368x + 24{,}488{,}926$

____

Investigate Problem 1

Now combine like terms and simplify.

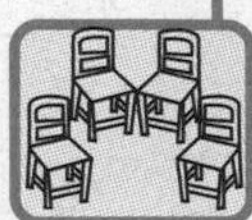

5. What was the difference in attendance between the leagues in 1998? Which league had more people attending games in 1998? How do you know? Show your work and use complete sentences in your answer.

What was the difference in attendance between the leagues in 1992? Which league had more people attending games in 1992? How do you know? Show your work and use a complete sentence in your answer.

10

6. Simplify each expression by finding the sum or difference. Show your work.

$(4x^2 + 3x - 5) + (x^2 - 8x + 4)$

$(2x^2 + 3x - 4) - (2x^2 + 5x - 6)$

$(4x^3 + 5x - 2) + (7x^2 - 8x + 9)$

$(9x^4 - 5) - (8x^4 - 2x^3 + x)$

10.3 Se Habla Español

Multiplying and Dividing Polynomials

Objectives

In this lesson, you will:

- Use an area model to multiply polynomials.
- Use distributive properties to multiply polynomials.
- Use long division to divide polynomials.

Key Terms

- area model
- distributive property
- divisor
- dividend
- remainder

SCENARIO Your high school is trying to decide whether to offer more foreign language classes. The guidance counselor finds a model for the percent of high school students that were in a foreign language class in high school during the years from 1985 to 2000, which is

$$y = -0.0005t^2 + 0.02t + 0.23$$

where t represents the number of years since 1980 and y is the percent (in decimal form) of all high school students who were in a foreign language class. The guidance counselor also finds that the total number of students in high school during the years from 1985 to 2000 can be modeled by

$$y = -3t^3 + 134t^2 - 1786t + 18{,}398$$

where t represents the number of years since 1980 and y is the number of students in thousands.

Problem 1 Learning a Foreign Language

A. What percent of high school students were in a foreign language class in 1990? Show your work and use a complete sentence in your answer.

B. Find the total number of students in high school in 1990. Show your work and use a complete sentence in your answer.

C. In 1990, how many students were in a foreign language class? Show your work and use a complete sentence in your answer.

D. Use complete sentences to explain how you found your answer to part (C).

Take Note

In Lesson 3.3, you learned how to use the percent equation. The *percent equation* is an equation of the form $a = pb$ where p is the percent in decimal form and the numbers that are being compared are a and b.

10

Investigate Problem 1

1. Use a complete sentence to explain how you can use the functions given in Problem 1 to write a function that gives the number of students that were in a foreign language class during the years from 1985 to 2000.

2. Just the Math: Area Model You can use an **area model** to multiply two polynomials. Suppose that you want to find the product of $3x$ and $4x + 1$. Consider these polynomials to be the length and width of a rectangle as shown below. The area of the rectangle is the product of the polynomials.

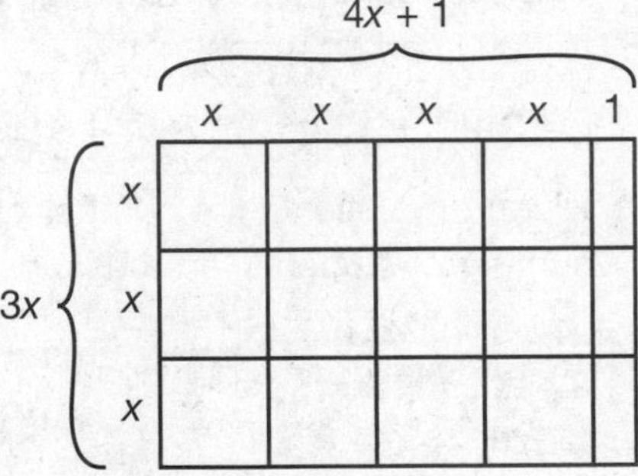

What is the area of each square in the model? Use a complete sentence in your answer.

What is the area of each small rectangle in the model? Use a complete sentence in your answer.

What is the area of the entire rectangle? Show your work and use a complete sentence in your answer.

10

Take Note

Recall the distributive properties of multiplication from Lesson 4.4:

$a(b + c) = ab + ac$
$a(b - c) = ab - ac$

Two other related distributive properties are:

$(b + c)a = ba + ca$
$(b - c)a = ba - ca$

3. Just the Math: Multiplying Polynomials To multiply two polynomials, you need to use the distributive properties of multiplication and the properties of exponents. The number of times that you need to use a distributive property depends on the number of terms in the polynomials. For instance, to multiply the polynomials $3x$ and $4x + 1$ from Question 2 above, you only need to use the distributive property once. Use the distributive property to complete the first step below.

$(3x)(4x + 1) = (\_\_\_\_)(\_\_\_\_) + (\_\_\_\_)(\_\_\_\_)$

Investigate Problem 1

To simplify each product, remember that multiplication is commutative (you can multiply numbers in any order) and use the properties of exponents that you learned in Chapter 9. For instance, $(2x)(5x) = 2(5)(x)(x) = 10x^2$. Complete the product of $3x$ and $4x + 1$ below.

$(3x)(4x + 1) = (3x)(4x) + (3x)(1) =$ _____ + _____

To multiply the polynomials $x + 1$ and $x^2 - 3x + 2$, you need to use the distributive property twice. First, use a distributive property to multiply each term of $x + 1$ by the polynomial $x^2 - 3x + 2$. Complete the first step below.

$(x + 1)(x^2 - 3x + 2) = (x)($ __________ $) + (1)($ __________ $)$

Now, distribute x to each term of $x^2 - 3x + 2$ and distribute 1 to each term of $x^2 - 3x + 2$. Complete the second step below:

$(x + 1)(x^2 - 3x + 2)$

$= (x)(x^2) + ($ ____ $)($ ____ $) + ($ ____ $)($ ____ $) + ($ ____ $)($ ____ $)$

$+ ($ ____ $)($ ____ $) + ($ ____ $)($ ____ $)$

Now multiply and collect like terms. Show your work and write your answer as a polynomial in standard form.

4. What do you notice about the products of the terms in Question 3 when you used a distributive property the second time? Use a complete sentence in your answer.

10

5. Find each product. Show all your work.

$2x(x + 3)$

$5x^2(7x - 1)$

$(x + 1)(x + 3)$

$(x^2 - 4)(2x + 3)$

$(x - 5)(x^2 + 3x + 1)$

Investigate Problem 1

6. Use multiplication to find the function that gives the number of students in thousands that were in a foreign language class during the years from 1985 to 2000.

$(-0.0005t^2 + 0.02t + 0.23)(-3t^3 + 134t^2 - 1786t + 18,398)$

First, distribute each term of the polynomial for the percent to each term of the polynomial for the total number of students.

$-0.0005t^2(-3t^3 + 134t^2 - 1786t + 18,398) +$
$0.02t(-3t^3 + 134t^2 - 1786t + 18,398) +$
$0.23(-3t^3 + 134t^2 - 1786t + 18,398)$

Complete the steps below. Show your work.

$-0.0005t^2(-3t^3 + 134t^2 - 1786t + 18,398)$

= ______________________________

____

= ______________________________

$0.02t(-3t^3 + 134t^2 - 1786t + 18,398)$

= ______________________________

____

= ______________________________

$0.23(-3t^3 + 134t^2 - 1786t + 18,398)$

= ______________________________

____

= ______________________________

Now combine like terms and simplify. Show your work.

What is your function?

7. How many students were in a foreign language class in 2000? Show all your work and use a complete sentence in your answer.

10

Problem 2 Spanish, Anyone?

A model for the number of high school students that were in a Spanish class in high school during the years from 1985 to 2000 is $y = 4t^2 + 14t + 2137$, where t represents the number of years since 1980 and y is the number of high school students in thousands that were in a Spanish class.

A. Find the number of students that were in a Spanish class in 1990. Show your work and use a complete sentence in your answer.

B. Find the total number of students in high school in 1990. You can use the function $y = -3t^3 + 134t^2 - 1786t + 18{,}398$ from Problem 1. Show your work and use a complete sentence in your answer.

C. In 1990, what percent of all high school students were in a Spanish class? Show your work and use a complete sentence in your answer.

D. Use complete sentences to explain how you found your answer to part (C).

10

Investigate Problem 2

1. Use a complete sentence to explain how you can use the functions given in Problem 2 to write a function that gives the percent of students that were in a Spanish class during the years from 1985 to 2000.

Take Note

In the *quotient* $a \div b$, a is the *dividend* and b is the *divisor*.

Investigate Problem 2

2. You can divide two polynomials just like you divide numbers by using long division. For instance, consider the quotient of $10x^3 + 13x^2 + 2x - 4$ and $2x + 1$ shown near the bottom of the page. Begin by finding the quotient of the first terms. In this case, what is $10x^3$ divided by $2x$?

This is the first term of the quotient. Write this term in the quotient below. Then multiply this expression by the polynomial $2x + 1$. Subtract the result from $10x^3 + 13x^2$ to get $8x^2$ (see Step 1).

Bring down the next term, $2x$, from the **dividend**. You need to do this because the product of $2x + 1$ and the second term of the quotient will have two terms. Now, we have to divide $8x^2$ by the $2x$ in the **divisor**. What is the result? This is the second term of the quotient.

Write this term in the quotient below. Then multiply this expression by the polynomial $2x + 1$. Subtract the result from $8x^2 + 2x$ (see Step 2 below).

Bring down the last term, –4, from the dividend. Finally, we have to divide $-2x$ by $2x$. What is the result? This is the last term of the quotient.

Write this term in the quotient below. Then multiply this expression by the polynomial $2x + 1$. Subtract the result from $-2x - 4$ (see Step 3 below).

Because the difference –3 is a term whose degree is less than the degree of the divisor ($2x$), we are done. This number –3 is the **remainder**. Write the remainder over the divisor below.

$$\underline{\quad} + \underline{\quad} + \underline{\quad} + \frac{\underline{\quad}}{2x + 1}$$

$$2x + 1\overline{)10x^3 + 13x^2 + 2x - 4}$$

$$\underline{-(10x^3 + 5x^2)} \qquad \text{Step 1}$$

$$8x^2 + 2x$$

$$\underline{-(8x^2 + 4x)} \qquad \text{Step 2}$$

$$-2x - 4$$

$$\underline{-(-2x - 1)} \qquad \text{Step 3}$$

$$-3$$

Take Note

Whenever you divide two polynomials, it is important to write the polynomials in *standard form*.

Investigate Problem 2

You can check your answer by multiplying the divisor and quotient and adding the remainder:

Divisor	Quotient	Remainder	Dividend

$(2x + 1)(\_\_\_\_\_\_\_\_\_\_) + (\_\_\_) \stackrel{?}{=} 10x^3 + 13x^2 + 2x - 4$

$\_\_\_\_\_\_\_\_\_\_\_\_\_\_\_\_\_\_\_\_\_\_\_\_ \stackrel{?}{=} 10x^3 + 13x^2 + 2x - 4$

$\_\_\_\_\_\_\_\_\_\_\_\_\_\_ = 10x^3 + 13x^2 + 2x - 4$

3. Find each quotient. Show all your work.

$(x^2 + 6x + 5) \div (x + 1) =$ ________

Take Note

When the dividend and divisor polynomials are in standard form and the difference between consecutive exponents is greater than 1, you should write in a placeholder for the missing terms. For instance, you should write $x^3 + 4x - 1$ as $x^3 + 0x^2 + 4x - 1$.

$(2x^2 + 5x - 12) \div (2x - 3) =$ ________

10

Investigate Problem 2

$(x^3 + 2x - 6) \div (x + 1) =$ ____________________

4. Complete the division problem below to find the function that represents the percentage of the total number of high school students that are enrolled in a Spanish class.

$(-3t^3 + 134t^2 - 1786.00t + 18{,}398) \div (4t^2 + 14t + 2137)$

$= \_\_\_\_\_ + \_\_\_\_\_ + \dfrac{\_\_\_\_\_\_\_\_}{4t^2 + 14t + 2137}$

$4t^2 + 14t + 2137\overline{)-3t^3 + 134t^2 - 1786.00t + 18{,}398}$

10

10.4 Making Stained Glass

Multiplying Binomials

Objectives

In this lesson, you will:

- Use the FOIL pattern to multiply binomials.
- Use formulas to find special products.

Key Terms

- FOIL pattern
- square of a binomial sum
- square of a binomial difference

SCENARIO An artist creates designs in stained glass. One of the artist's more popular designs is a rectangle in which the ratio of the length to the width of the stained glass is 7:5. The artist also surrounds the stained glass with a two-inch wide carved wooden frame.

Problem 1 Stained Glass Design

A. Complete the diagram below that models the stained-glass design in its frame.

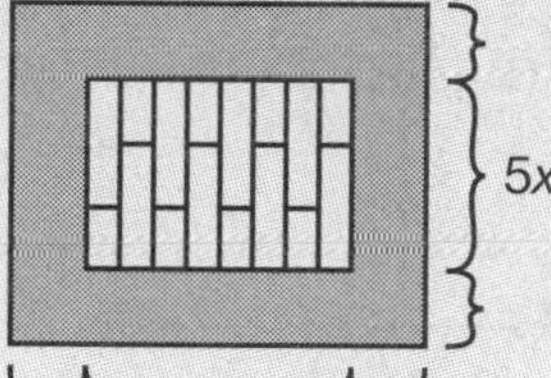

B. Write an expression for the total length of the stained-glass design with its frame.

C. Write an expression for the total width of the stained-glass design with its frame.

D. Write a function for the area of the stained-glass design with the frame.

E. Use a distributive property to simplify the function in part (D). Show your work.

F. What type of function is in part (E)? Use a complete sentence in your answer.

10

Investigate Problem 1

1. What is the value of writing the function in standard form in part (E)? Show your work and use a complete sentence in your answer.

2. In part (E), you found the product of two binomials by using the distributive property. Consider the product after two uses of the distributive property:

   $(2x + 3)(x + 8) = (2x + 3)(x) + (2x + 3)(8)$ First use of distributive property

   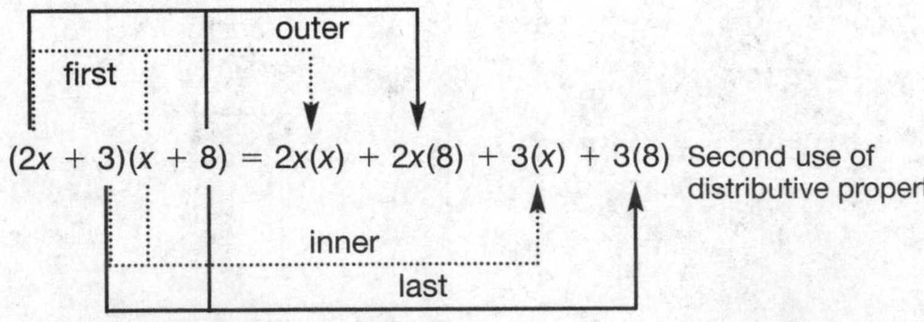

   $(2x + 3)(x + 8) = 2x(x) + 2x(8) + 3(x) + 3(8)$ Second use of distributive property

   You can quickly find the product of two binomials by remembering the word FOIL. FOIL stands for multiplying the **f**irst terms, the **o**uter terms, the **i**nner terms, and the **l**ast terms. Then the products are added together as shown above. Finish finding the product of $2x + 3$ and $x + 8$.

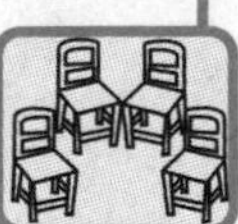

3. Use the FOIL pattern to find each product. Show your work.

   $(x + 2)(x + 9)$ $(x - 1)(x + 7)$

   $(x - 3)(x - 6)$ $(4x + 3)(x + 5)$

   $(3x - 4)(x + 2)$ $(5x + 1)(3x - 2)$

Problem 2 New Stained Glass Design

The stained glass artist is working on a new design that is square with a carved wood frame that is three inches wide.

A. Draw a diagram that models the stained-glass design with its frame. Let x be the width of the stained glass without the frame.

B. Write a function for the area of the stained-glass design with its frame.

C. Use the FOIL pattern to simplify your function in part (B). Show all your work.

D. Suppose that the artist changes the width of the frame to five inches wide. Write and simplify a new function for the area of the stained glass with the frame. Show all your work.

10

Investigate Problem 2

1. Use complete sentences to describe the similarities and differences between the functions in parts (C) and (D).

2. **Just the Math: Square of a Binomial Sum** In Problem 2, you wrote and simplified the square of a binomial. In each simplified product, the middle term related to the product of the linear term and the constant term in the binomial. For instance, the square of $(x + 3)$ is $x^2 + 6x + 9$. How is the middle term $6x$ related to x and 3? Use a complete sentence to explain.

Investigate Problem 2

Does this relationship hold true for the square of the binomials in parts (C) and (D)? Use complete sentences to explain.

In $(x + 3)(x + 3)$, which is $x^2 + 6x + 9$, how is the last term 9 related to the constant term 3? Use a complete sentence to explain.

Does this relationship hold true for the square of the binomials in parts (C) and (D)? Use complete sentences to explain.

Complete the formula below for simplifying the square of a binomial sum of the form $(a + b)^2$. Then use the FOIL pattern to check your answer.

$(a + b)^2 = \square^2 + 2\square + \square^2$

FOIL:

3. Use the FOIL pattern to find the products $(x - 4)^2$ and $(4x - 3)^2$. Show your work.

Investigate Problem 2

4. Complete the formula for simplifying the **square of a binomial difference** of the form $(a - b)^2$. Then use the FOIL pattern to show that your formula works.

   $(a - b)^2 = \square^2 - 2\square + \square^2$

   FOIL:

5. Use the FOIL pattern to find the products $(x - 3)(x + 3)$ and $(2x - 5)(2x + 5)$. Show your work.

6. Write a formula for simplifying the product of a sum and a difference of the form $(a - b)(a + b)$. Then use the FOIL pattern to show that your formula works.

   FOIL:

7. Find each product. Show your work.

   $(x + 5)(x + 3)$

   $(x - 6)^2$

   $(3x + 4)(x - 2)$

   $(2x + 1)^2$

   $(x + 9)(x - 9)$

   $(3x + 2)(3x - 2)$

10

10

10.5 Suspension Bridges

Factoring Polynomials

Objectives

In this lesson, you will:

- Factor a polynomial by factoring out a common factor.
- Factor a polynomial of the form $x^2 + bx + c$.
- Factor a polynomial of the form $ax^2 + bx + c$.

Key Terms

- factor
- linear factor
- trinomial
- FOIL pattern

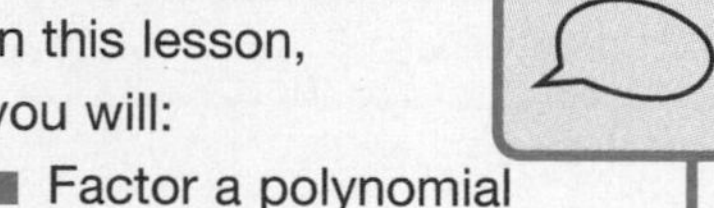

SCENARIO In your science class, you have to make a presentation on a "feat of engineering." You have decided to make your presentation on suspension bridges, such as the one shown below. During the research for the presentation, you have discovered that the cables that are used to carry the weight on a bridge form the shape of a parabola. Because you have recently studied parabolas in your math class, you decide to use what you know about parabolas in your presentation.

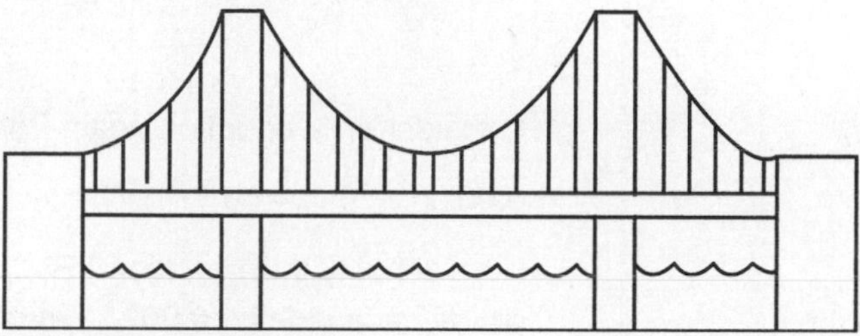

Problem 1 Modeling the Cable Shape

You have modeled the main cable's shape of a particular suspension bridge by using the function $y = 0.002x^2 - 0.4x + 96$, where x is the distance in meters from the left tower and y is the height in meters of the cable above the high water level.

A. Write and simplify an equation that you can use to find the cable's horizontal distance from the left tower at 96 meters above the high water level. Show your work.

B. How can you solve the equation in part (A)? Use a complete sentence in your answer.

C. Solve the equation in part (A). Show all your work.

Problem 1 Modeling the Cable Shape

D. Interpret your solutions from part (C) in the problem situation. Use a complete sentence in your answer.

Investigate Problem 1

1. In the last lesson, you multiplied polynomials. The product of what kinds of polynomials gives you a quadratic (second-degree) polynomial? Use a complete sentence in your answer.

Consider your equation again from part (A):

$0.002x^2 - 0.4x = 0$

Let's simplify this equation. Because 0.002 evenly divides 0.4, divide each side by 0.002. What is the new equation?

If we could write the polynomial $x^2 - 200x$ as the product of two linear polynomials, how would this help us be able to solve the equation $x^2 - 200x = 0$? Use complete sentences in your answer.

10

What expression do the terms of $x^2 - 200x$ have in common?

Rewrite your equation so that each term is written as a product with this common expression as a factor.

The product of what two linear expressions gives you $x^2 - 200x$?

So now you have the following.

$$x^2 - 200x = 0$$

$$x(x) - x(200) = 0$$

$$x(x - 200) = 0$$

What are the solutions of the equation?

Investigate Problem 1

You have just solved the equation by *factoring* the polynomial. How do these solutions compare to the solutions from part (C)? Use a complete sentence in your answer.

Which method of finding the solutions was easier? Why? Use a complete sentence in your answer.

2. **Just the Math: Factoring Out a Common Factor** In Question 1, you solved the equation by **factoring out a common factor** of x. Which mathematical rule was used to factor the polynomial? Use a complete sentence to explain your reasoning.

Take Note

Recall the Symmetric Property from Lesson 4.5: For any real numbers a and b, if $a = b$, then $b = a$.

So, because the equality is *symmetric*, you can write your multiplicative distributive properties as follows:

$ab + ac = a(b + c)$ $\quad$ $ab - ac = a(b - c)$

$ba + ca = (b + c)a$ $\quad$ $ba - ca = (b - c)a$

When the distributive properties are used in this manner, you are *factoring* expressions.

Take Note

An expression is *factored completely* when none of the factors of the expression can be factored further.

Factor each expression completely. Show your work.

$x^2 + 12x$ $\quad$ $x^3 - 5x$

$3x^2 - 9x$ $\quad$ $10x^2 - 6$

3. What is the domain of the function in Problem 1? Use complete sentences to explain your reasoning.

Problem 2 Using the Cable Shape Model

A. Write and simplify an equation that you can use to find the cable's horizontal distance from the left tower at 81 meters above the high water level. Show your work.

Now divide each side by 0.002.

B. How is this equation the same as or different from the equation in Problem 1? Use a complete sentence in your answer.

C. Can you factor out a common factor?

Investigate Problem 2

1. If we want to factor the polynomial from part (A) as the product of two linear expressions $(x + a)$ and $(x + b)$, what must be true about the product ab? Explain your reasoning. Use a complete sentence in your answer.

What must be true about the sum $a + b$? Explain your reasoning. Use a complete sentence in your answer.

Make a list of pairs of negative integers whose product is 7500. Then find the sum of each pair of numbers. Stop when you find the pair of numbers that has a sum of –200.

10

Investigate Problem 2

Which pair of numbers has a product of 7500 and a sum of –200?

Complete the factorization of $x^2 - 200x + 7500$.

$x^2 - 200x + 7500 = (x + \square)(x + (\square)$

What are the solutions of the equation $x^2 - 200x + 7500 = 0$? Show your work.

What is the cable's horizontal distance from the left tower at 81 meters above high water level? Use a complete sentence in your answer.

2. Factor each trinomial as a product of linear factors. Then use the FOIL pattern to verify your answer. Show your work.

$x^2 + 4x + 3$ $\qquad$ $x^2 - 4x - 5$

$x^2 - x - 6$ $\qquad$ $x^2 - 9x + 20$

$x^2 + 18x + 81$ $\qquad$ $x^2 - 36$

3. How does the sign of the constant in the trinomial determine the signs of the constants in the linear factors? Use complete sentences in your answer.

Take Note

Your special product rules from Lesson 10.4 can help you factor special products:

$a^2 + 2ab + b^2 = (a + b)^2$

$a^2 - 2ab + b^2 = (a - b)^2$

$a^2 - b^2 = (a + b)(a - b)$

Investigate Problem 2

4. In Questions 1 and 2, what do all the trinomials have in common? How are they different? Use complete sentences in your answer.

5. Consider the trinomial $2x^2 + 11x + 9$. If we want to factor this expression as a product of linear factors, what must be true about the coefficients of the x-terms of the linear factors? Use complete sentences to explain your reasoning.

   What must be true about the constants of the linear factors? Use complete sentences to explain your reasoning.

   Now that you have identified all the possible coefficients of the x-terms and the constants for the linear factors, list the possible pairs of linear factors below that could result from the different positions of the numbers in the factors. The first one is listed.

   $(2x + 3)(1x + 3) =$ ____________

10

   Now find the product of each pair of linear factors and write your answer above. Which pair of linear factors gives the factorization of $2x^2 + 11x + 9$?

6. Factor each trinomial as a product of linear factors. Then use the FOIL pattern to verify your answer. Show your work.

   $3x^2 + 7x + 2 =$ ____________

   $5x^2 + 17x + 6 =$ ____________

   $6x^2 + 19x + 10 =$ ____________

10.6 Swimming Pools

Rational Expressions

Objectives

In this lesson, you will:

- Find domains of rational expressions.
- Simplify rational expressions.
- Add, subtract, multiply, and divide rational expressions.

Key Terms

- rational expression
- domain
- excluded value
- restricting the domain

Take Note

Recall that the *domain* of an expression is all possible numbers that *x* can be so that either the expression is a real number or the value of *x* makes sense in a real-life problem situation.

Also remember that division by zero does not result in a real number. To express this, we say that division by zero is "undefined."

SCENARIO A swimming pool company designs and installs custom in-ground swimming pools. A swimming pool design is based on the location, the amount of area available, and client preferences. In-ground swimming pools can have any shape and can be covered in tiles, fabric, or a concrete coating.

Problem 1 Pool Length and Area

A. The company's designer is studying how the change in the length of a pool affects the change in the area of the top surface of the pool. A rectangular pool that is being designed is 20 feet longer than it is wide. Write expressions for the width and the length of the pool. Use the variable *x* to represent the width of the pool.

B. Write a proportion that compares the length of the pool to the area of the surface of the pool.

C. What is the domain of the expression in part (B)? Do not consider the problem situation when finding the domain. Use complete sentences to explain your reasoning.

D. How are the numerator and denominator of your expression the same? How are they different? Use complete sentences in your answer.

E. **Just the Math: Rational Expressions** The proportion that you wrote in part (B) is a *rational expression*. A **rational expression** is a fraction in which the numerator and denominator are both polynomials. What are the polynomials, in standard form, of your rational expression in part (B)? What is the degree of each polynomial? Use a complete sentence in your answer.

Investigate Problem 1

1. Use your work from Problem 1 to describe how to find the domain of any rational expression. Use a complete sentence in your answer.

2. What is the form of the polynomials in your rational expression in part (B)? Use a complete sentence in your answer.

3. Do you think that it is easier to identify the domain of a rational expression when the numerator and denominator are in standard form or in factored form? Use a complete sentence to explain your reasoning.

4. Factor the numerator and denominator of each rational expression, if possible. Then identify the domain of the rational expression.

$\frac{4}{x + 1}$ $\frac{x + 3}{x^2 - 5x}$

$\frac{x - 3}{x^2 + 5x + 4}$ $\frac{x - 1}{x^2 + x - 6}$

5. Can you simplify your rational expression in part (B)? If so, what is your simplified expression? Explain how you found your answer. Use complete sentences in your answer.

10

Investigate Problem 1

6. Complete the table of values that compares your expression from part (B) to your expression from Question 5.

Expression	x	$\frac{x + 20}{x(x + 20)}$	$\frac{1}{x}$
	−25		
	−20		
	−10		
	0		
	10		
	20		

What do you notice about the values in the table? Use a complete sentence in your answer.

7. What is the domain of your simplified expression in Question 5? Is this domain different from the domain in part (C)? If so, how is it different? Use complete sentences in your answer.

10

In order for the original expression and the simplified expression to be equivalent, we must **restrict the domain** of the simplified expression so that it is the same as the original expression.

What value must be excluded from the domain of $\frac{1}{x}$ so that its domain is the same as the domain of $\frac{x + 20}{x(x + 20)}$?

We indicate that the expressions are equal by writing $\frac{x + 20}{x(x + 20)} = \frac{1}{x}, x \neq -20$.

Investigate Problem 1

8. Simplify each rational expression. Then restrict the domain so that the simplified expression is equivalent to the original expression. Show your work.

$\frac{x}{x^2 - 3x}$

$\frac{x + 2}{x^2 + 3x + 2}$

$\frac{x - 6}{2x^2 - 11x - 6}$

$\frac{x^2 - 1}{x + 1}$

$\frac{x^2 + x}{x^2 - 6x - 7}$

$\frac{x^2 - 5x}{x^2 - 25}$

9. Just the Math: Multiplying Rational Expressions
You multiply rational expressions in the same way that you multiply fractions of numbers. For instance, to find the product of $\frac{x + 1}{x - 3}$ and $\frac{x}{x + 1}$, you multiply numerators and you multiply denominators, and then simplify. Complete the steps below to find the product.

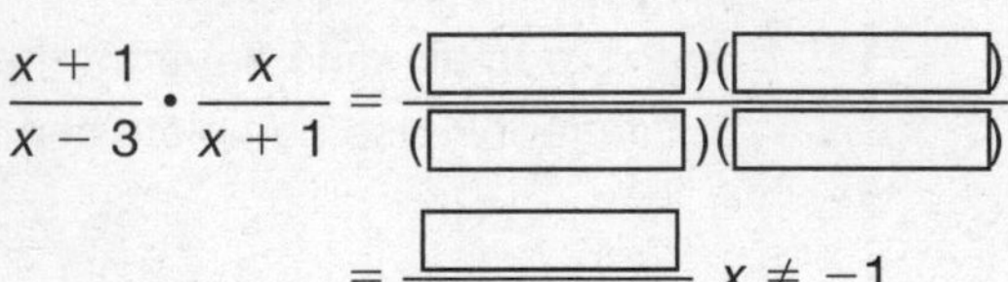

$\frac{x + 1}{x - 3} \cdot \frac{x}{x + 1} = \frac{(\quad)(\quad)}{(\quad)(\quad)}$ Multiply numerators and multiply denominators.

$= \frac{\quad}{\quad}, x \neq -1$ Simplify.

10. Just the Math: Dividing Rational Expressions
You divide rational expressions in the same way that you divide fractions of numbers. For instance, to find the quotient of $\frac{x}{x - 5}$ and $\frac{x^2}{x + 2}$, you multiply the dividend by the reciprocal of the divisor. Complete the steps below to find the quotient.

$\frac{x}{x - 5} \div \frac{x^2}{x + 2} = \frac{x}{x - 5} \cdot \frac{\quad}{\quad}$ Multiply by reciprocal of divisor.

$= \frac{(\quad)(\quad)}{(\quad)(\quad)}$ Multiply numerators and multiply denominators.

$= \frac{\quad}{\quad}, x \neq -2$ Simplify.

Take Note

Unless you are specifically instructed, you should leave your rational expressions in factored form. The factored form makes it easier for you to see the domain of the expression. Later on, when you study rational functions, you will see that it is easier to graph the functions when the rational expressions are left in factored form.

Take Note

In the *quotient* $a \div b$, a is the *dividend* and b is the *divisor*.

10

Investigate Problem 1

11. Find the product or quotient. Show your work and leave your answer in simplified form. Remember to restrict the domain, if necessary.

$\frac{x + 6}{x} \cdot \frac{x}{x - 5}$

$\frac{x + 3}{x - 2} \div \frac{x}{x - 4}$

$\frac{x^2 + 3x}{x - 4} \cdot \frac{x + 5}{x + 3}$

$\frac{x - 1}{x^2 - 4x} \div \frac{x + 1}{x}$

$\frac{x^2 - 7x}{x + 3} \cdot \frac{x^2 + 4x + 3}{x - 7}$

12. Do you think that it matters whether you factor your expressions before you multiply or divide? Use complete sentences to explain your reasoning.

10

Problem 2 Installing a Pool

Two workers are responsible for cutting and placing steel reinforcement bars (rebar) on the bottom and sides of a standard size pool.

A. It takes one of the workers nine hours to cut and place the rebar for a standard-sized pool by himself. Write a fraction that represents the amount of the job that is completed by this worker in one hour if the worker is doing the job by himself.

B. It takes the other worker an unknown number of hours to cut and place the rebar for a standard-sized pool by herself. Write a fraction that represents the amount of the job that is completed by this worker in one hour if the worker is doing the job by herself. Use t to be the number of hours it takes this worker to complete the job by herself.

C. Use your answers from parts (A) and (B) to write an expression that shows the amount of the job that is completed in one hour by the workers if they are doing the job together.

D. Suppose that it takes the second worker eight hours to complete the job by herself. If the workers work together, what fraction of the job is completed in one hour? Show your work and use a complete sentence in your answer.

E. Use complete sentences to explain the steps that you took to find your answer to part (D).

Investigate Problem 2

1. You can add and subtract rational expressions in the same way that you add and subtract fractions. Consider your sum in part (C). Before you can add numerators, what must you do first? Use a complete sentence in your answer.

Take Note

The *least common denominator* (LCD) of a pair of fractions is the least of the common multiples of the denominators of the fractions. For instance, the common multiples of the denominators of $\frac{3}{4}$ and $\frac{5}{6}$ are 12, 24, 36, … . The least of these multiples is 12, so the LCD of $\frac{3}{4}$ and $\frac{5}{6}$ is 12.

What is the least common denominator (LCD) of the rational expressions in part (C)? Use a complete sentence to explain how you found your answer.

By what expression do you have to multiply $\frac{1}{t}$ so that the denominator is the LCD?

By what expression do you have to multiply $\frac{1}{9}$ so that the denominator is the LCD?

Simplify the sum from part (C) by completing each step below.

$\frac{1}{9} + \frac{1}{t} = \frac{1}{9} \cdot \frac{\square}{\square} + \frac{1}{t} \cdot \frac{\square}{\square}$ Multiply each expression by an appropriate form of 1.

$= \frac{\square}{\square} + \frac{\square}{\square}$ Multiply.

$= \frac{\square}{\square}$ Add.

2. Find each sum or difference. Show your work and write your answer in simplified form.

$\frac{4}{x} + \frac{2}{3x}$

$\frac{1}{3} - \frac{8}{x - 2}$

10

Looking Ahead to Chapter 11

Focus In Chapter 11, you will be introduced to probability, including theoretical and experimental probabilities, making predictions by using probabilities, independent and dependent events, and geometric probabilities. You will also learn about counting techniques.

Chapter Warm-up

Answer these questions to help you review skills that you will need in Chapter 11.

Simplify each expression. Write your answers in simplest form.

1. $\frac{2}{3} + \frac{4}{5}$
2. $\frac{7}{18} - \frac{1}{6}$
3. $\frac{2}{9} + \frac{12}{15} - \frac{3}{5}$

Solve each proportion.

4. $\frac{5}{x} = \frac{14}{350}$
5. $\frac{x}{12} = \frac{4}{16}$
6. $\frac{9}{22} = \frac{63}{x}$

Read the problem scenario below.

You are conducting a survey at your school to see what everyone's favorite subject is. You take a random sample of 50 students in your school. Eighteen students say that math is their favorite subject; thirteen students say that psychology is their favorite subject; eleven students say that English is their favorite subject, and eight students say that art is their favorite subject. Assume that there are 2700 students in your school.

7. Based on your sample, how many students would you expect to say that math is their favorite subject?

8. Based on your sample, how many students would you expect to say that English is their favorite subject?

11

Key Terms

outcomes ■ p. 493
sample space ■ p. 493
event ■ p. 493
probability ■ p. 493
probability of the event ■ p. 494
favorable outcome ■ p. 494
odds in favor ■ p. 497
complementary events ■ p. 497
odds against ■ p. 498
theoretical probability ■ p. 500
experimental probability ■ p. 500
experiment ■ p. 500
trial ■ p. 500
success ■ p. 500
line plot ■ p. 507
tree diagram ■ p. 513
Fundamental Counting Principle ■ p. 517
permutation ■ p. 517
factorial ■ p. 518
permutation of *n* distinct objects taken *r* at a time ■ p. 522
combinations ■ p. 526
combinations of *n* distinct objects taken *r* at a time ■ p. 522
compound events ■ p. 528
independent events ■ p. 528
dependent events ■ p. 528
triangle ■ p. 533
parallelogram ■ p. 533
trapezoid ■ p. 533
congruent ■ p. 533
area ■ p. 533
geometric probability ■ p. 536
fair game ■ p. 542

CHAPTER

11

Probability

The word *sock* is derived from the Latin word *soccus*. A soccus was a shoe made of matted animal hair that was worn by Greek and Roman comedians. In Lesson 11.7, you will find the probability of picking two socks of the same color from a drawer.

11

11.1 Your Best Guess

Introduction to Probability

Objectives

In this lesson, you will:

- Find the probability of an event.
- Find the odds in favor of an event.
- Find the odds against an event.

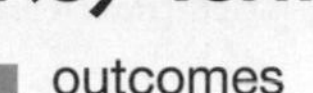

Key Terms

- outcomes
- sample space
- event
- probability
- favorable outcome
- odds in favor
- complementary events
- odds against

SCENARIO You and your friends are studying together for an upcoming test and are wondering whether you have a better chance of guessing the correct answer to a true-or-false question or of guessing the correct answer to a multiple-choice question with six possible answers. The chance, or *probability*, is the likelihood that getting a correct answer will occur.

Problem 1 Toss and Roll

A. Choosing true or choosing false are the **outcomes** of answering a true-or-false question. The collection of possible outcomes is called a **sample space.** An **event** consists of one or more outcomes. For instance, choosing true and being correct is an event. The chance that the event will happen is the **probability** of the event.

Because the sample space consists of two outcomes, you can model guessing the answer to a true-or-false question by tossing a coin. The coin landing heads up can represent choosing true and the coin landing tails up can represent choosing false. Suppose that a multiple-choice question has six possible answers: A, B, C, D, E, and F. What is the sample space for the multiple choice question? Use a complete sentence in your answer.

Because the sample space consists of six outcomes, you can model guessing the answer to this multiple-choice question by rolling a six-sided number cube. Rolling the number 1 can represent choosing A, rolling the number 2 can represent choosing B, and so on.

B. Choose one of the outcomes from a coin toss. Toss a coin 12 times and keep track of the number of times that a toss results in heads and the number of times that the toss results in tails in the table below. How many times did your choice of outcome appear during the 12 tosses? Use a complete sentence in your answer.

Possible outcomes	
Heads	**Tails**

Problem 1 Toss and Roll

C. Choose a possible outcome from rolling a number cube. Circle your choice in the table below. Roll a number cube 12 times and record the results in the table below. How many times did the number that you chose appear out of the 12 rolls? Use a complete sentence in your answer.

Possible outcomes					
1	**2**	**3**	**4**	**5**	**6**

Based on your results from parts (B) and (C), would you have a better chance of correctly guessing the outcome of a coin toss or the roll on a number cube? Use a complete sentence to explain your reasoning.

Investigate Problem 1

1. **Just the Math: Probability** The chance that an event will occur is the **probability of the event.** You can find the probability of an event by finding the ratio of the number of **favorable outcomes** (the outcomes that you want) to the number of possible outcomes.

$$\text{Probability} = \frac{\text{Number of favorable outcomes}}{\text{Number of possible outcomes}}$$

You guess that a coin toss will result in heads. What is the probability that your guess is correct? Use complete sentences to explain.

You guess that a roll of a six-sided number cube will result in 1. What is the probability that your guess is correct? Use complete sentences to explain.

11

Investigate Problem 1

You guess that a roll of a six-sided number cube will result in an odd number. What is the probability that your guess is correct? Use complete sentences to explain.

You guess that a roll of a six-sided number cube will result in a number that is evenly divisible by three. What is the probability that your guess is correct? Use complete sentences to explain.

2. In general, which is greater, the number of favorable outcomes or the number of possible outcomes? Use complete sentences to explain your reasoning.

Can the number of favorable outcomes and the number of possible outcomes be the same? If so, what would the probability be? Use complete sentences to explain your reasoning.

What is the largest probability? What is the smallest probability? Give an example of each situation. Use complete sentences to explain.

Problem 2 What are the Odds?

You and your friends are still thinking about the likelihood of answering a multiple-choice question correctly. Again, suppose that the multiple-choice question has six possible answers: A, B, C, D, E, and F.

A. What is the probability that you would guess the answer to this multiple-choice question correctly? Use a complete sentence in your answer.

B. What is the probability that you would guess the answer to this multiple-choice question incorrectly? Explain how you found the probability. Use complete sentences in your answer.

C. Compare the probabilities in parts (A) and (B) by writing the ratio of the probability that you would correctly answer the question to the probability that you would incorrectly answer the question. Simplify your ratio and use a complete sentence in your answer.

This ratio tells you that for every one chance that you would *correctly* answer the question, there are five chances that you would *incorrectly* answer the question. What does this ratio tell you about the likelihood of you answering the question correctly? Use a complete sentence in your answer.

11

Investigate Problem 2

1. **Just the Math: Odds in Favor** The ratio that you wrote in part (C) represents your *odds in favor* of correctly answering the question. The **odds in favor** of an event occurring can be defined as the ratio of the number of favorable outcomes to the number of unfavorable outcomes:

$$\text{Odds in favor} = \frac{\text{Number of favorable outcomes}}{\text{Number of unfavorable outcomes}}.$$

What can you conclude about the sum of the number of favorable outcomes and the number of unfavorable outcomes? Use a complete sentence in your answer.

The event that consists of the favorable outcomes and the event that consists of the unfavorable outcomes are *complementary events*. Two events are **complementary events** when one event or the other event must occur, but not both. What is the sum of the probabilities of two complementary events? Use complete sentences to explain your reasoning.

2. You guess that the roll of a six-sided number cube will result in an even number. What are the odds in favor of your guess being correct? Show your work and use a complete sentence in your answer.

3. You guess that the roll of a six-sided number cube will result in a number that is divisible by three. What are the odds in favor of your guess being correct? Show your work and use a complete sentence in your answer.

Investigate Problem 2

4. Another ratio that is used to compare probabilities is the **odds against** an event occurring. For instance, the odds against your correctly guessing the answer to the multiple-choice question is the ratio of the probability that you will guess the answer incorrectly to the probability that you will guess the answer correctly. Write a rule for the odds against an event occurring in terms of the number of favorable and unfavorable outcomes. Use complete sentences to explain your reasoning.

Take Note

Composite numbers are numbers that are greater than 1 that have more than two whole number factors.

5. You guess that the roll of a six-sided number cube will result in a composite number. What are the odds against you being correct? Show your work and use a complete sentence in your answer.

Take Note

Whenever you see the share with the class icon, your group should prepare a short presentation to share with the class that describes how you solved the problem. Be prepared to ask questions during other groups' presentations and to answer questions during your presentation.

6. You guess that the roll of a six-sided number cube will result in an even number. What are the odds against your guess being correct? Show your work and use a complete sentence in your answer.

Does this answer surprise you? Use complete sentences to explain your reasoning.

11

11.2 What's in the Bag?

Theoretical and Experimental Probabilities

Objectives

In this lesson, you will:

- Find theoretical probabilities.
- Find experimental probabilities.
- Compare theoretical and experimental probabilities.

Key Terms

- theoretical probability
- experimental probability
- experiment
- trial
- success

SCENARIO You decide to learn about and apply probabilities in your own hands-on experiment. Take 30 slips of paper that are all the same size and mark an "X" on 10 of the slips, mark an "O" on 10 of the slips, and leave the last 10 slips blank. Then put these slips into a paper bag (or some other bag or container that you cannot see inside of) and shake up the bag.

Problem 1 What Will Come Out of the Bag?

A. If you choose a slip of paper from the bag, how many different outcomes are possible? What are the possible outcomes? Use a complete sentence in your answer.

B. Determine the probability of each outcome in part (A). Write each probability in simplest form. Use a complete sentence in your answer.

C. What do you notice about the probabilities? Why is this so? Use complete sentences in your answer.

D. Which kind of slip are you most likely to choose? Use complete sentences to explain your reasoning.

E. Suppose that the bag contains 16 "X" slips, 6 "O" slips, and 8 blank slips. Would your answer to part (D) change? If your answer would change, what would your new answer be? Use a complete sentence to explain your reasoning.

Investigate Problem 1

1. Perform an experiment by choosing a slip from the bag that you used in part (A). Record the kind of slip that you choose in the table below and put the slip back into the bag. Repeat this process 9 more times.

Slip	X	O	blank
Number of times slip was chosen			

2. **Just the Math: Theoretical and Experimental Probabilities** The probabilities that you found in Lesson 11.1 and in Problem 1 are *theoretical probabilities*. A **theoretical probability** is a probability that is based on knowing all of the possible outcomes that are equally likely to occur.

$$\text{Theoretical probability} = \frac{\text{Number of favorable outcomes}}{\text{Number of possible outcomes}}$$

An **experimental probability** is based on running an **experiment** in the same way many times; each run is called a **trial.** Each time that the desired event occurs is called a **success.** You can find the experimental probability by finding the ratio of the number of successes to the number of trials:

$$\text{Experimental probability} = \frac{\text{Number of successes}}{\text{Number of trials}}.$$

Use your data from Question 1 to find the experimental probability of each possible outcome. Use complete sentences in your answer.

How do the experimental probabilities compare to the theoretical probabilities in part (B)? Use complete sentences in your answer.

3. Would your experimental probabilities have been different if you had not replaced the slips of paper? Use complete sentences to explain your reasoning.

11

Investigate Problem 1

4. Gather the class results from the experiment in Question 1 and record the results in the table below.

	Your results	Class results
X		
O		
Blank		
Total		

5. Find the experimental probabilities of each outcome by using the results of the class. Use complete sentences in your answer.

How do these experimental probabilities compare to the theoretical probabilities in part (B)? Use a complete sentence in your answer.

6. Are the experimental probabilities in Question 5 closer to the theoretical probabilities than the experimental probabilities in Question 2? What can you conclude about experimental and theoretical probabilities? Explain your reasoning. Use complete sentences in your answer.

11

11.3 A Brand New Bag

Using Probabilities to Make Predictions

Objective

In this lesson, you will:

- Use experimental probabilities to make predictions.

Key Terms

- trial
- experimental probability

SCENARIO Now you are ready to use probabilities. Have a friend take 30 slips of paper that are all the same size. Your friend can divide the slips up any way he or she likes by marking an "X" on some of the slips, an "O" on some of the slips, and leaving the rest of the slips blank. Then have your friend put the slips into a paper bag (or some other bag or container that you cannot see inside of) and shake up the bag.

Problem 1 What's in Your Bag?

A. Perform an experiment by choosing a slip from the bag. Record the kind of slip you choose in the table below and put the slip back into the bag. Repeat this process 9 more times.

Slip	X	O	blank
Number of times slip was chosen			

B. What is the experimental probability of choosing each kind of slip? Use a complete sentence in your answer.

C. What fraction of the slips in the bag do you think are "X" slips? Use complete sentences to explain your reasoning.

What fraction of the slips in the bag do you think are "O" slips? Use complete sentences to explain your reasoning.

11

Problem 1 What's in Your Bag?

What fraction of the slips in the bag do you think are blank slips? Use complete sentences to explain your reasoning.

D. How many of each kind of slip do you think is in the bag? Show your work and use a complete sentence in your answer.

Investigate Problem 1

1. How accurate do you think your prediction from part (D) is? Use a complete sentence to explain your reasoning.

2. Could you increase the accuracy of your prediction without looking in the bag? If so, explain how you would increase the accuracy. Use a complete sentence in your answer.

3. Run 40 more trials of the experiment and combine these results with the results from part (A) in the table below.

Slip	X	O	Blank
Number of times slip was chosen			

4. Can you use the results from Question 3 to predict the number of each kind of slip that is in the bag? Why or why not? Use complete sentences in your answer.

11

Investigate Problem 1

5. Use your results from Question 3 to predict the number of each kind of slip that is in the bag. Show your work and use complete sentences in your answer.

6. Do you think that the prediction in Question 5 is better than the prediction in part (D)? Why or why not? Use complete sentences in your answer.

7. Open the bag and count each kind of slip. Compare the actual numbers to the predicted numbers from part (D) and Question 5. How close were the predictions? Which prediction was better? Use complete sentences in your answer.

8. What could account for any differences between the predicted numbers and the actual numbers? Use complete sentences to explain your reasoning.

9. If you are using experimental probabilities to make predictions, how do you think you should determine the number of trials that are necessary to get a fairly accurate outcome? Use complete sentences to explain your reasoning.

11

11

11.4 Fun with Number Cubes

Graphing Frequencies of Outcomes

Objectives

In this lesson, you will:

- Use a line plot to graph frequencies of outcomes.
- Find and compare probabilities.

Key Term

- line plot

SCENARIO In this chapter, you have found that number cubes can be used to model problem situations. So, let's run an experiment that uses number cubes.

Problem 1 One Number Cube Experiment

In this experiment, you will roll a six-sided number cube and record the result. However, this time we will use a data display called a *line plot* to record the results.

A **line plot** displays the frequency of numerical data on a number line. To make a line plot of your results, first draw a number line that includes all the possible outcomes of rolling a six-sided number cube. Then draw an X above the number line for the outcome of each roll. If there is more than one occurrence of an outcome, draw another X above the first occurrence.

A. Before you perform the experiment, guess what your line plot will look like after recording the results of 30 rolls of a six-sided number cube. Create a line plot of your guess. Use a complete sentence to explain why the results will turn out this way.

B. Perform the experiment and record the results of 30 rolls on the line plot below.

11

Investigate Problem 1

1. Does the shape of your line plot in part (B) agree with your prediction in part (A)? Use a complete sentence in your answer.

   Compare your line plot in part (B) with the line plots of other students in your class. What do you notice? Use a complete sentence in your answer.

2. Now consider a line plot of the results of the class. How does the class line plot compare to your line plot in part (B)? Use complete sentences in your answer.

3. Suppose that you perform this experiment again. Do you think that your results will be the same as or different from the results in Problem 1? Use complete sentences to explain your reasoning.

11

Problem 2 Number Cube Pair Experiment

In this next experiment, you will roll a pair of six-sided number cubes and record the sum of the results of the roll on a line plot.

A. What are the possible sums? How many possible sums are there? Use complete sentences in your answer.

Problem 2 Number Cube Pair Experiment

B. Before you perform the experiment, guess what your line plot will look like after recording the results of 50 rolls of a pair of number cubes. Draw the rough shape of the line plot. Use complete sentences to explain why the results will turn out this way.

C. Perform the experiment and record the results of 50 rolls on the line plot below.

Investigate Problem 2

1. Describe the shape of your line plot. Use a complete sentence in your answer.

How does the shape of your line plot compare with your prediction in part (B)? Use complete sentences in your answer.

2. Now consider a line plot of the results of the entire class. How does the class line plot compare to your line plot in part (C)? Use complete sentences in your answer.

11

Investigate Problem 2

3. Complete the table below that shows all of the possible rolls of pairs of six-sided number cubes and the sums of the results.

		First number cube					
		1	2	3	4	5	6
Second number cube	1						
	2						
	3						
	4						
	5						
	6						

4. Describe a possible outcome of one run of the experiment. Use a complete sentence in your answer.

5. How many possible outcomes are there? Note: It is important which number cube is first and which is second. Use a complete sentence in your answer.

6. For each sum, find the number of different ways in which the sum can occur.

Sum is 2: _______ Sum is 3: _______ Sum is 4: _______

Sum is 5: _______ Sum is 6: _______ Sum is 7: _______

Sum is 8: _______ Sum is 9: _______ Sum is 10: _______

Sum is 11: _______ Sum is 12: _______

7. Are there any patterns in the number of ways that each sum can occur? Use complete sentences in your answer.

11

Investigate Problem 2

8. For each sum, find the probability that the sum will occur.

Probability that sum is 2: ☐ Probability that sum is 3: ☐

Probability that sum is 4: ☐ Probability that sum is 5: ☐

Probability that sum is 6: ☐ Probability that sum is 7: ☐

Probability that sum is 8: ☐ Probability that sum is 9: ☐

Probability that sum is 10: ☐ Probability that sum is 11: ☐

Probability that sum is 12: ☐

9. Which sums(s) are you most likely to roll? Which sum(s) are you least likely to roll? Use complete sentences in your answer.

10. Is a sum of 5 or a sum of 8 more likely? Why? Use a complete sentence in your answer.

11. Is an even sum or an odd sum more likely? Why? Show your work and use complete sentences to explain your reasoning.

11

12. Does the information that you gathered in Questions 3 through 11 help you explain the shape of your line plot in Problem 2? If so, how? Use complete sentences in your answer.

11

11.5 Going to the Movies

Counting and Permutations

Objectives

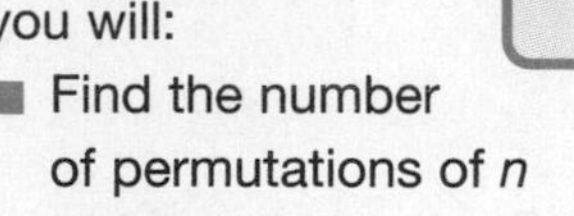

In this lesson, you will:

- Find the number of permutations of *n* objects.
- Simplify expressions that involve factorials.

Key Terms

- tree diagram
- Fundamental Counting Principle
- permutation
- factorial

SCENARIO You and your four friends, Alex, Chris, Daryl, and Kelly, are going to see a movie. You and Daryl are in the same science class. You wonder how likely it is that you will sit next to Daryl. In order to determine this, you must first find out how many different seating orders there are if you all sit in a row together.

Problem 1 Making a List

A. Begin an organized list that shows the different seating orders that can occur. In your list, use the first letter of each person's name and use "Y" for yourself to list the orders. Hint: Start your list by considering the orders that occur if you are sitting in the first seat. Your teacher will tell you when you can stop working on the list.

B. Another way you can list the seating orders is by completing a *tree diagram*. A **tree diagram** is a visual display of an ordering. A tree diagram is started for you below. Begin to complete the diagram. Your teacher will tell you when you can stop working on the diagram.

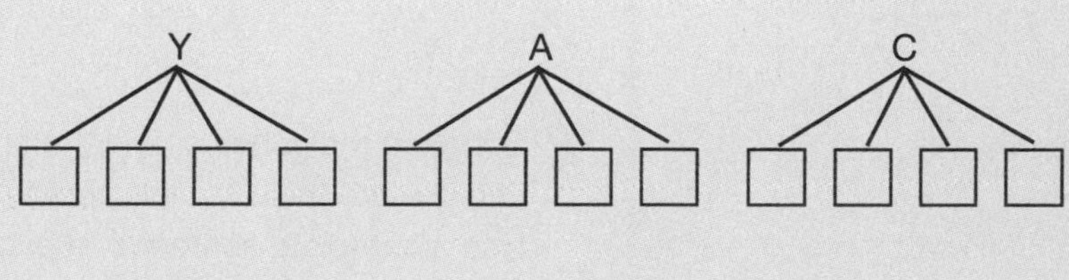

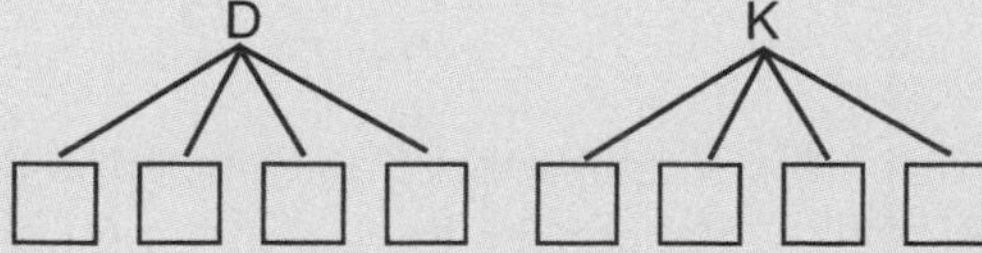

11

Investigate Problem 1

1. Were you able to find all of the possible seating orders by using a list or a tree diagram? If so, how many seating orders are possible? If not, why were you not able to complete the list or tree diagram and what made the task difficult? Use complete sentences in your answer.

If necessary, use the seating chart below to help you answer the following questions.

First seat	Second seat	Third seat	Fourth seat	Fifth seat

2. How many possible choices are there for the person who sits in the first seat? Use a complete sentence to explain your reasoning.

3. Suppose that Alex sits in the first seat. How many possible choices are there for the person who sits in the second seat? Use a complete sentence to explain your reasoning.

4. Suppose that you sit in the first seat. How many possible choices are there for the person who sits in the second seat? Use a complete sentence to explain your reasoning.

5. Suppose that Chris sits in the first seat. How many possible choices are there for the person who sits in the second seat? Use a complete sentence to explain your reasoning.

6. Suppose that Daryl sits in the first seat. How many possible choices are there for the person who sits in the second seat? Use a complete sentence to explain your reasoning.

Investigate Problem 1

7. Suppose that Kelly sits in the first seat. How many possible choices are there for the person who sits in the second seat? Use a complete sentence to explain your reasoning.

8. How many different ways can the first two seats be filled? Use complete sentences to explain your reasoning.

   Write a multiplication problem that represents the number of different ways that the first two seats can be filled. Indicate what each factor represents in the problem situation.

9. Suppose that Alex sits in the first seat and Daryl sits in the second seat. How many possible choices are there for the person who sits in the third seat? Use a complete sentence to explain your reasoning.

10. For each different way that the first two seats can be filled, how many possible choices are there for the person who sits in the third seat? Use a complete sentence to explain your reasoning.

11. Write an expression that represents the number of different ways that the first three seats can be filled. Then simplify your expression. Indicate what the parts of your expression represent in the problem situation.

Investigate Problem 1

12. For each of the 60 different ways that the first three seats can be filled, how many possible choices are there for the person who sits in the fourth seat? Use a complete sentence to explain your reasoning.

13. Write an expression that represents the number of different ways that the first four seats can be filled. Then simplify your expression. Indicate what the parts of your expression represent in the problem situation.

14. For each different way that the first four seats can be filled, how many possible choices are there for the person who sits in the fifth seat? Use a complete sentence to explain your reasoning.

15. Does filling the fifth seat with the person in the group that remains change the number of possible seating orders? Why or why not? Use a complete sentence in your answer.

16. Write an expression that represents the number of different ways that the five seats can be filled. Then simplify your expression. Indicate what the parts of your expression represent in the problem situation.

11

Investigate Problem 1

17. **Just the Math: Fundamental Counting Principle** You used the *Fundamental Counting Principle* to find the answer to Problem 1. The **Fundamental Counting Principle** states that if you have m choices for one event and n choices for another event, then the number of choices for both events is $m \cdot n$. This rule extends to more than two events, as in the case of Problem 1.

You decide to get a beverage and a snack at the movie. The movie theater offers six different beverages and nine different snacks. How many different combinations of beverage and snack could you have? Show your work and use a complete sentence in your answer.

18. **Just the Math: Permutations** In Problem 1, you were finding the number of *permutations* of five objects. A **permutation** is an ordering of a set of objects. In Problem 1, you found the number of possible permutations of five people sitting together in a row. Use a tree diagram or organized list to find all the possible permutations of the numbers 1, 2, and 3. How many permutations are there? Use a complete sentence in your answer.

Use a tree diagram or organized list to find all the possible permutations of the letters D, F, and G. How many permutations are there? Use a complete sentence in your answer.

How does the number of permutations of the numbers 1, 2, and 3 compare to the number of permutations of the letters D, F, and G? Use a complete sentence in your answer.

Does it make any difference whether you are finding the number of permutations of three numbers, three letters, or any other three objects? Use complete sentences to explain your reasoning.

Investigate Problem 1

19. You can find the number of permutations of n objects by using the Fundamental Counting Principle. The number of permutations of n objects is $n! = n \cdot (n - 1) \cdot (n - 2) \cdot \ldots \cdot 3 \cdot 2 \cdot 1$. The expression $n!$ stands for ***n* factorial** and represents the product of the integers between 1 and n. For example, $5! = 5 \cdot 4 \cdot 3 \cdot 2 \cdot 1 = 120$. Write the number of permutations of the numbers 1, 2, and 3 by using factorial notation. Then simplify the expression.

Simplify each expression by first writing each factorial as a product.

$6!$

$8!$

$4!\,2!$

$\frac{5!}{3!}$

$\frac{8!}{2!4!}$

$\frac{2!3!}{4!}$

11

Problem 2 What's the Probability?

A. If you sit in the first seat, where can your friend from science class sit so that you are sitting next to each other? How many seating orders are possible for the other three people? Show your work and use a complete sentence in your answer.

B. If you sit in the second seat, where can your friend from science class sit so that you are sitting next to each other? How many seating orders are possible for the other three people? Show your work and use a complete sentence in your answer.

C. If you sit in the third seat, where can your friend from science class sit so that you are sitting next to each other? How many seating orders are possible for the other three people? Show your work and use a complete sentence in your answer.

D. If you sit in the fourth seat, where can your friend from science class sit so that you are sitting next to each other? How many seating orders are possible for the other three people? Show your work and use a complete sentence in your answer.

E. If you sit in the last seat, where can your friend from science class sit so that you are sitting next to each other? How many seating orders are possible for the other three people? Show your work and use a complete sentence in your answer.

Investigate Problem 2

1. In how many ways can you and your friend sit together? Use a complete sentence in your answer.

2. What is the probability that you and your friend from science class will sit next to each other? Show your work and use a complete sentence in your answer.

   What is the probability that you and your friend from science class will not sit next to each other? Show your work and use a complete sentence in your answer.

3. What is the probability that you will sit in the last seat and your friend from science class will sit in the fourth seat? Show your work and use a complete sentence in your answer.

11

4. What is the probability that you will sit in the second seat and your friend from science class will sit in the third seat? Show your work and use a complete sentence in your answer.

11.6 Going Out for Pizza

Permutations and Combinations

Objectives

In this lesson, you will:

- Find the number of permutations of n objects taken r at a time.
- Find the number of combinations of n objects taken r at a time.

Key Terms

- permutations
- permutation of n distinct objects taken r at a time
- combinations
- combination of n distinct objects taken r at a time

SCENARIO The next time you go to the movies, you are part of a group of six people. Because your group arrives late to the movie, you cannot all sit together. At most, you can find four seats together.

Problem 1 Guessing Again

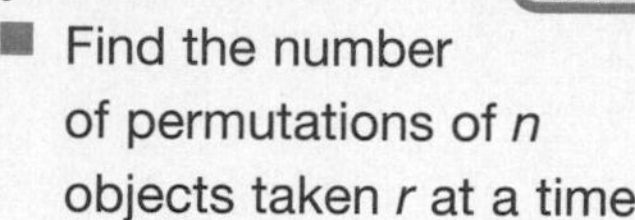

A. In the four seats, how many possible choices are there for the person who sits in the first seat? Use a complete sentence to explain your reasoning.

B. Once the first person is seated, how many possible choices are there for the person who sits in the second seat? Use a complete sentence to explain your reasoning.

C. Once the first and second persons are seated, how many possible choices are there for the person who sits in the third seat? Use a complete sentence to explain your reasoning.

D. Once the first three people are seated, how many possible choices are there for the person who sits in the fourth seat? Use a complete sentence to explain your reasoning.

E. How can you determine the number of seating orders that are possible for the four seats? Use a complete sentence to explain your reasoning.

F. Find the number of different seating orders that are possible for the four seats when six people are present. Show your work and use a complete sentence in your answer.

Investigate Problem 1

1. Do you think that the problem situation uses permutations? Use a complete sentence to explain your reasoning.

2. Is the number of possible seating orders for the four seats equal to 6!? Use a complete sentence to explain your reasoning.

3. What does 6! represent in terms of this problem situation? Use a complete sentence in your answer.

4. How many people in the group did not get seated? Use a complete sentence in your answer.

   How many different seating arrangements do these people represent? Use a complete sentence in your answer.

5. Complete the expression below that gives the number of possible seating orders in four seats when six people are present. Show that this expression will simplify to your answer in part (F).

$$\frac{\square!}{\square!} = \frac{6 \cdot 5 \cdot 4 \cdot 3 \cdot 2 \cdot 1}{2 \cdot 1} = \frac{\square}{\square} = \square$$

11

6. **Just the Math: Permutations of *n* Objects Taken *r* at a Time** In Problem 1, you found the number of permutations of six people taken four at a time. Because choices were not made for two of the people in the group, the last two numbers in 6!, 2 and 1, were not used. A **permutation of *n* distinct objects taken *r* at a time** is a permutation that contains only *r* objects. The number of permutations of *n* distinct objects taken *r* at a time is given by

$${}_nP_r = \frac{n!}{(n-r)!}.$$

Investigate Problem 1

Use the formula to find ${}_6P_4$, which represents the number of different seating orders that can occur if four people from a group of six can sit in a row together. Show your work.

7. What does the expression ${}_6P_6$ represent? Use a complete sentence in your answer.

What might this expression represent in the problem situation? Use a complete sentence in your answer.

Can you write ${}_6P_6$ as a single factorial without using the formula? If so, write the expression.

Consider ${}_6P_6 = \frac{6!}{(6-6)!} = \frac{6!}{0!}$. What must be the value of 0!? Use a complete sentence to explain your reasoning.

8. Consider ${}_nP_r$ when r is n and consider ${}_nP_r$ when r is less than n. How are these situations the same? How are they different? Use complete sentences to explain your reasoning.

9. Find the value of each expression. Show your work.

${}_4P_3$

${}_6P_2$

11

Problem 2 Let's Eat!

After the movie, your group decides to go to a new pizza shop that is becoming known for its tasty pizza crust. The following toppings are available on the menu: peppers, onions, olives, mushrooms, pepperoni, sausage, and ham.

A. Suppose that your group wants to get a pizza with two vegetable toppings. List the possible pizzas that your group could order. Use letters to represent the toppings and identify what each letter stands for. How many pizzas are possible? Use a complete sentence in your answer.

B. Suppose that your group wants to get a pizza with three vegetable toppings. List the possible pizzas that your group could order. Use letters to represent the toppings and identify what each letter stands for. How many pizzas are possible? Use a complete sentence in your answer.

C. Can you count the number of possible pizzas in parts (A) and (B) by using the formula for the permutations of n objects taken r at a time? Why or why not? Use a complete sentence in your answer.

Investigate Problem 2

1. Suppose that order is important; that is, a pepper and onion pizza is different from an onion and pepper pizza. List the possible two-topping vegetable pizzas that your group could order. Use letters to represent the toppings and identify what each letter stands for.

How does this list compare to the list in part (A)? Use a complete sentence in your answer.

11

Investigate Problem 2

2. List the possible three-topping vegetable pizzas that your group could order if the order of the toppings is important. Use letters to represent the toppings and identify what each letter stands for.

How does this list compare to the list in part (B)? Use a complete sentence in your answer.

3. How could you find the number of possible pizzas in part (A) by using the number of pizzas in Question 1? Use a complete sentence in your answer.

How could you find the number of possible pizzas in part (B) by using the number of pizzas in Question 2? Use a complete sentence in your answer.

4. Complete the expression below that gives the number of two-topping vegetable pizzas that can be made from a choice of four vegetable toppings. Then show that this expression will simplify to your answer in part (A).

$$\frac{{}_4P_2}{\square!} =$$

Complete the expression below that gives the number of three-topping vegetable pizzas that can be made from a choice of four vegetable toppings. Then show that this expression will simplify to your answer in part (B).

$$\frac{{}_4P_3}{\square!} =$$

11

Investigate Problem 1

5. **Just the Math: Combinations of *n* Objects Taken *r* at a Time** In Problem 2, you found the number of possible groupings of objects when the order of the objects was *not* important. These groupings that do not need to be ordered are called **combinations.** The number of **combinations of *n* distinct objects taken *r* at a time** is the number of groupings of *n* objects taken *r* at a time and is given by

$${}_nC_r = \frac{n!}{(n-r)!r!}.$$

Use complete sentences to explain how ${}_nC_r$ is related to ${}_nP_r$.

6. Your group wants to get a three-topping pizza and will choose from all of the toppings. Find the number of three-topping pizzas that are possible. Show your work and use a complete sentence in your answer.

When the waiter comes to your table, he tells your group that the shop has a special. The special is that the cost of a five-topping pizza is the same as a three-topping pizza. Find the number of five-topping pizzas that are possible. Show your work and use a complete sentence in your answer.

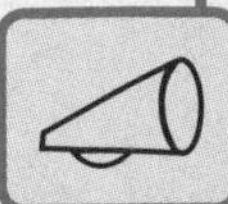

11.7

Picking Out Socks

Independent and Dependent Events

Objectives

In this lesson, you will:

- Find the probability of independent events.
- Find the probability of dependent events.
- Use a tree diagram to find probabilities.

Key Terms

- compound events
- independent events
- dependent events
- tree diagram

SCENARIO It is Monday morning and you are late for school. You did not do any laundry over the weekend, so there are only six socks in your sock drawer. You also do not have the socks combined into pairs. In the drawer there are two black socks and four gray socks.

Problem 1 A Tale of Two Socks

A. You reach into the drawer without looking and pull out a sock. What is the probability that the sock is black?

What is the probability that the sock is gray?

B. Suppose that you pull out a gray sock. Then you pull out another sock without putting the gray sock back. What is the probability that the second sock is gray? Is this probability the same as or different from the probability of pulling out a gray sock in part (A)? Use complete sentences to explain your reasoning.

C. Suppose that instead, you pull out a black sock. Then you pull out another sock, but this time you put the black sock back into the drawer first. What is the probability that the second sock is black? Is the probability the same as or different from the probability of pulling out a black sock from part (A)? Use complete sentences to explain your reasoning.

11

Problem 1 A Tale of Two Socks

D. In part (B), you "sampled without replacement." In part (C), you "sampled with replacement." How is the way in which you found the probability in part (B) different from the way in which you found the probability in part (C)? Use complete sentences in your answer.

Investigate Problem 1

1. **Just the Math: Independent and Dependent Events** Drawing one sock and getting a particular sock and then drawing another sock and getting a particular sock out of a drawer are **compound events.** There are two kinds of compound events. **Independent events** are events in which the occurrence of one event does not affect the probability of the other event. **Dependent events** are events in which the occurrence of one event does affect the probability of the other event.

   Determine whether the compound events are independent or dependent. Use a complete sentence in your answer.

   You spin a spinner and land on red and you roll a six-sided number cube and you get a 5.

   You spin two different spinners and both spinners land on blue.

   You choose one card from a stack of cards that are contained in a board game, then you choose a second card, without replacing the first card and the two cards are the same.

11

2. When you sample a compound event with replacement, are the events independent or dependent? Use a complete sentence in your answer.

   When you sample a compound event without replacement, are the events independent or dependent? Use a complete sentence in your answer.

Investigate Problem 1

3. In part (B) are the events independent or dependent? Use a complete sentence in your answer.

   In part (C) are the events independent or dependent?

4. Create an organized list or tree diagram to show the sample space of pulling two socks out of the drawer when you replace the first sock before pulling out the second sock. If you use letters or symbols for each sock, be sure to indicate what each letter or symbol represents.

5. What is the probability of pulling out two gray socks if you replace the first sock?

   What is the probability of pulling out a gray sock on the first pull?

   What is the probability of pulling out a gray sock on the second pull when you replace the first sock?

   How does the first probability relate to the second probability and the third probability that you wrote above? Use complete sentences in your answer.

6. Use the result of Question 5 to write a rule for finding the probability of two independent events. Use a complete sentence in your answer.

Investigate Problem 1

7. Create an organized list or tree diagram to show the sample space of pulling two socks out of the drawer when you do not replace the first sock. If you use letters or symbols for each sock, be sure to indicate what each letter or symbol represents.

8. What is the probability of pulling out two gray socks if you *do not* replace the first sock? Show your work and use a complete answer in your answer.

   How does this probability of pulling out two gray socks relate to the probability of pulling out a gray sock on the first pull and the probability of pulling out a gray sock on the second pull when you do not replace the first sock? Use complete sentences in your answer.

9. Use the result of Question 8 to write a rule for finding the probability of two dependent events. Use a complete sentence in your answer.

Investigate Problem 1

10. Suppose that you have six blue socks, two black socks, and four gray socks in your sock drawer. You can model the probabilities of drawing two socks by using a tree diagram. The probabilities are given on the "branches" of the tree. Complete the tree diagram below if you pull the first sock and then pull the second sock without replacing the first sock. The probability of drawing a black sock first is already filled in for you.

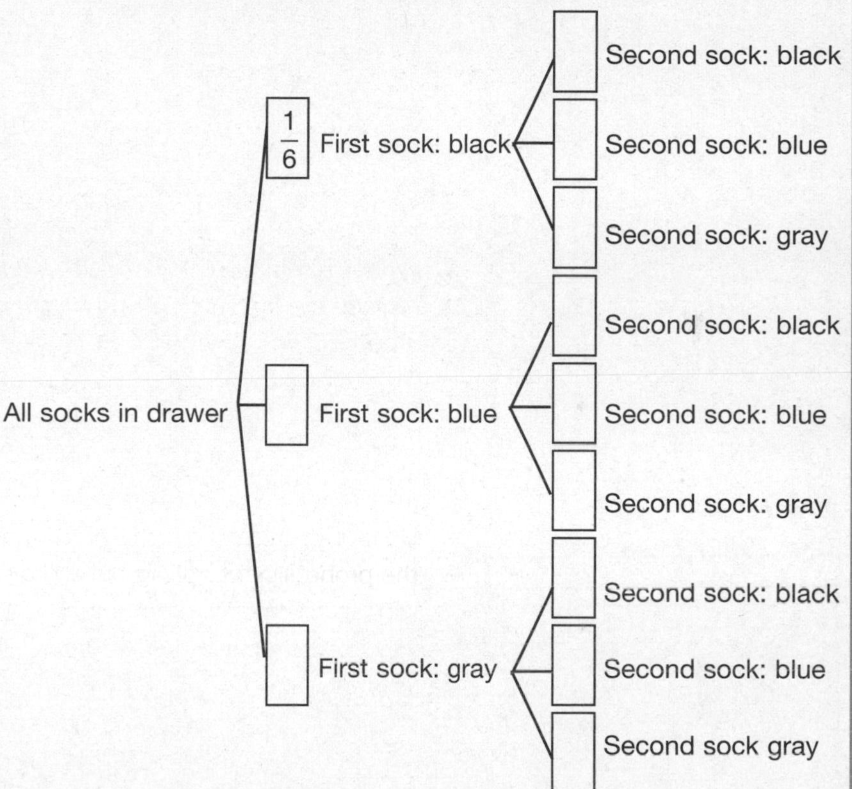

11. What is the probability that you draw two black socks? Use a complete sentence in your answer.

What is the probability that you draw two blue socks? Use a complete sentence in your answer.

12. What is the probability that one sock is gray and one sock is blue? Show your work and use a complete sentence in your answer.

11

11

11.8 Probability on the Shuffleboard Court

Geometric Probabilities

Objective

In this lesson, you will:

- Find and use geometric probabilities.

Key Terms

- triangle
- parallelogram
- trapezoid
- congruent
- area
- geometric probability

Take Note

A trapezoid is a four-sided geometric figure with exactly two parallel sides. A parallelogram is a four-sided geometric figure with its opposite sides parallel.

SCENARIO A local community center often holds shuffleboard tournaments. Shuffleboard is a game in which players use a long stick to push a small disk onto the playing area. Scoring is determined by the part of the playing area on which the disk lands. A diagram of a modified shuffleboard design is shown below.

Problem 1 Where Will the Disk Land?

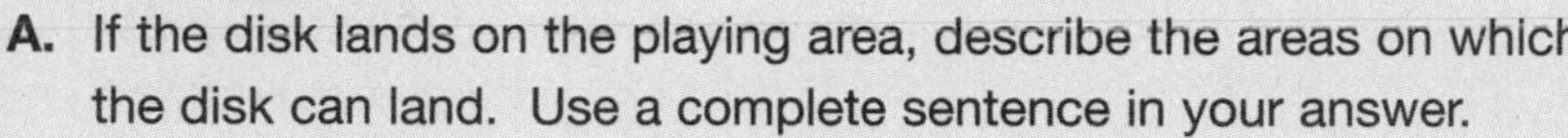

A. If the disk lands on the playing area, describe the areas on which the disk can land. Use a complete sentence in your answer.

B. Do you think that it is more likely for the disk to land on the gray parallelogram or the black trapezoid? Use a complete sentence to explain your reasoning.

C. Do you think that it is more likely for the disk to land on one of the four white triangles or the black trapezoid? Use a complete sentence to explain your reasoning.

D. Do you think that it is more likely for the disk to land on the triangle composed of the parallelogram and the two top white triangles or the trapezoid composed of the black trapezoid and the lower two white triangles? Use a complete sentence to explain your reasoning.

Investigate Problem 1

1. The shuffleboard court in Problem 1 can be divided into nine congruent triangles, as shown below.

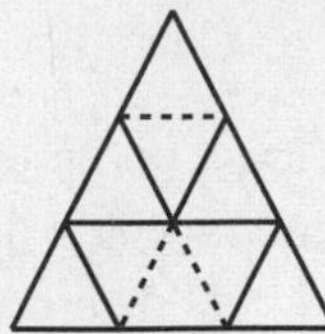

What portion of the shuffleboard is taken up by one white triangle? Use a complete sentence to explain your reasoning.

What portion of the shuffleboard is taken up by the white triangles? Use a complete sentence to explain your reasoning.

What portion of the shuffleboard is taken up by the parallelogram? Use a complete sentence to explain your reasoning.

What portion of the shuffleboard is taken up by the trapezoid? Use a complete sentence to explain your reasoning.

Investigate Problem 1

What portion of the shuffleboard is taken up by the parallelogram and the top two triangles? Use a complete sentence to explain your reasoning.

What portion of the shuffleboard is taken up by the trapezoid and the bottom two triangles? Use a complete sentence to explain your reasoning.

Does your answer to Question 1 change your answers to parts (B) through (D)? If so, explain why. Use complete sentences in your answer.

2. The area of the shuffleboard court is 6.93 square feet. Find the area of one of the nine congruent triangles. Show your work and use a complete sentence in your answer.

Find the area of the gray parallelogram. Show your work and use a complete sentence in your answer.

Find the area of the black trapezoid. Show your work and use a complete sentence in your answer.

Investigate Problem 1

Find the total area of the four white triangles. Show your work and use a complete sentence in your answer.

3. **Just the Math: Geometric Probability** You can find the probability of landing on one of the shapes on the shuffleboard court by using a *geometric probability*. A geometric probability is a ratio of lengths, areas, or volumes. To find the **geometric probability** of landing on one of the shapes on the shuffleboard court, find the ratio of the area of the shape to the total area of the court.

   Find the geometric probability of landing on the gray area. Write your answer as a fraction in simplest form. Show your work and use a complete sentence in your answer.

   Find the geometric probability of landing on any white area. Write your answer as a fraction in simplest form. Show your work and use a complete sentence in your answer.

   Use the probabilities above to find the probability of landing on the black area. Write your answer as a fraction in simplest form. Show your work and use a complete sentence in your answer.

   On which area are you most likely to land? On which area are you least likely to land? Use complete sentences to explain your reasoning.

11.9 Game Design

Geometric Probabilities and Fair Games

Objectives

In this lesson, you will:

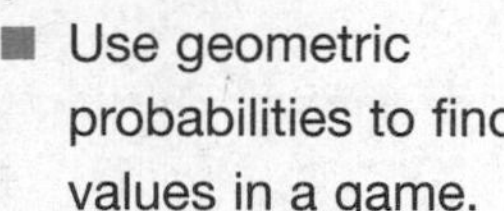

- Use geometric probabilities to find values in a game.
- Determine whether a game is fair.
- Alter the rules of a game so that it is fair.

Key Terms

- geometric probability
- fair game

SCENARIO Every Saturday night, you and your friends get together to make up games to play, and then you play the games. The first game this Saturday night involves spinning a spinner.

Problem 1 Spinning a Spinner

You and your friends create the spinner shown below. You divide the spinner below so that $\frac{1}{2}$ of the spinner is worth 15 points, $\frac{1}{3}$ of the spinner is worth 25 points, and $\frac{1}{6}$ of the spinner is worth 40 points.

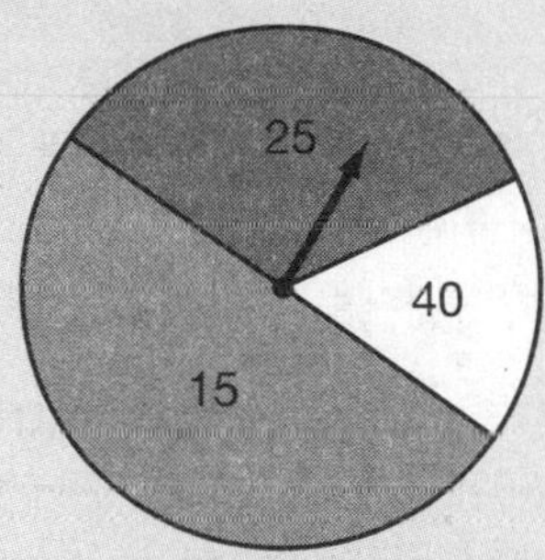

A. If you spin the spinner eight times, what is the greatest number of points that you could earn? Explain your reasoning. Use complete sentences in your answer.

Do you think that it is likely that you could earn this number of points from eight spins? Why or why not? Use complete sentences in your answer.

B. If you spin the spinner eight times, what is the least number of points you could earn? Explain your reasoning. Use complete sentences in your answer.

Problem 1 Spinning a Spinner

Do you think that it is likely that you could earn this number of points from eight spins? Why or why not? Use complete sentences in your answer.

Investigate Problem 1

1. What is the probability of landing on the part worth 15 points? Use a complete sentence to explain your reasoning.

   What is the probability of landing on the part worth 25 points? Use a complete sentence to explain your reasoning.

   What is the probability of landing on the part worth 40 points? Use a complete sentence to explain your reasoning.

2. Suppose that you spin the spinner 18 times. How many times can you expect to land on the part of the spinner that is worth 15 points? Show your work and use a complete sentence in your answer.

   How many points would you earn in the number of spins described above? Show your work and use a complete sentence in your answer.

11

Investigate Problem 1

In 18 spins, how many times can you expect to land on the part of the spinner that is worth 25 points? Show your work and use a complete sentence in your answer.

How many points would you earn in the number of spins described above? Show your work and use a complete sentence in your answer.

In 18 spins, how many times can you expect to land on the part of the spinner that is worth 40 points? Show your work and use a complete sentence in your answer.

How many points would you earn in the number of spins described above? Show your work and use a complete sentence in your answer.

Use complete sentences to explain how you found the total number of points that were likely to be earned from landing on each part of the spinner in 18 spins.

How many total points are you likely to earn from 18 spins? Show your work and use a complete sentence in your answer.

3. How would you make it equally likely to land on each part of the spinner? Use a complete sentence in your answer.

Problem 2 Rolling the Number Cubes

The second game this particular Saturday night involves two six-sided number cubes and is a two-player game. In the first round, one player is the "roller" and the other player is the "recorder." In successive rounds, the players switch roles. At the beginning of the game, each player starts with 12 points. If the sum of the numbers on a roller's roll is 7, then the recorder must give the roller 3 of his or her points. If the sum is not 7, then the roller must give the recorder 1 of his or her points. The winner of the round is the player who has the most points after 12 rolls. If one of the players runs out of points before 12 rolls, then the other player wins.

A. Who do you think is more likely to win a round of the game, the roller or the recorder? Use complete sentences to explain your reasoning.

B. Play two rounds of the game with a person in your class. Record whether or not the sum of the roll is 7 and record the number of points each player has after each roll in the table below.

			Roll 1	Roll 2	Roll 3	Roll 4	Roll 5	Roll 6	Roll 7	Roll 8	Roll 9	Roll 10	Roll 11	Roll 12
Round 1	**Sum of 7?**													
	Roller	12												
	Recorder	12												
Round 2	**Sum of 7?**													
	Roller	12												
	Recorder	12												

C. Identify the winner of each game, the roller or the recorder. Use complete sentences in your answer.

D. How many total games were played in your class? How many rounds were won by the roller? How many rounds were won by the recorder?

Investigate Problem 2

1. Do you think that the roller and the recorder have an equal chance of winning the game in Problem 2? Use complete sentences to explain your reasoning.

2. Complete the table below that shows all of the possible rolls of pairs of six-sided number cubes and the sums of the results.

		First number cube					
		1	2	3	4	5	6
Second number cube	1						
	2						
	3						
	4						
	5						
	6						

What is the probability of rolling the number cubes and the sum is 7? What is the probability of rolling the number cubes and the sum is not 7? Show your work.

In 12 rolls, how many times can you expect to roll numbers that result in a sum of 7? Use a complete sentence in your answer.

11

Investigate Problem 2

In 12 rolls, how many times can you expect to roll numbers that *do not* result in a sum of 7? Use a complete sentence in your answer.

Suppose that the game plays out as you expect during a round. How many points does each player gain or lose? Use complete sentences in your answer.

3. **Just the Math: Fair Game** A game is considered to be a **fair game** if each player has an equally likely chance of winning. Is the game in Problem 2 fair? Use complete sentences to explain your reasoning.

How would you make the game fair? Explain your answer. Use complete sentences in your answer.

11

Looking Ahead to Chapter 12

Focus In Chapter 12, you will learn how to analyze data sets including calculating and comparing different measures of central tendency as well as the sample variance and standard deviation of a data set. You will also learn how to display data using a variety of graphs.

Chapter Warm-up

Answer these questions to help you review skills that you will need in Chapter 12.

Simplify each expression.

1. $\frac{12 + 18}{6}$

2. $\frac{4(25 - 3 \cdot 7)}{5}$

3. $\frac{13 - 25 + 8 \cdot 9}{7 - 4}$

Solve each inequality. Then graph the solution on the number line.

4. $\frac{x}{6} + 3 > -1$

5. $2x - 5 < 3$

6. $-\frac{2}{9}x \geq 4$

Read the problem scenario below.

You arrived 10 minutes late to a basketball game between your favorite teams, the Tigers and the Lions. When you arrived, you were shocked to see that the Tigers had a score of 20 and the Lions had a score of 3. Throughout the rest of the game, the Tigers averaged 3 points per minute and the Lions averaged 4 points per minute.

7. Write an equation for each team that models their score y as a function of the number of minutes you have been at the game x.

8. Which team will be winning 15 minutes after you arrive?

Key Terms

stem-and-leaf plot ■ p. 547
distribution ■ p. 548
mean ■ p. 549
measure of central tendency ■ p. 549
median ■ p. 549
mode ■ p. 550
bimodal ■ p. 550
trimodal ■ p. 550
survey ■ p. 553
sample size ■ p. 556
range ■ p. 557
upper extreme ■ p. 557
lower extreme ■ p. 557
quartile ■ p. 558
box-and-whisker plot ■ p. 559
outlier ■ p. 560
percentile ■ p. 561
interquartile range ■ p. 561
line plot ■ p. 563
deviation ■ p. 564
absolute deviation ■ p. 565
mean absolute deviation ■ p. 565
sample variance ■ p. 567
sample standard deviation ■ p. 567

CHAPTER

12

Statistical Analysis

The game of basketball was created by James Naismith in 1891 in Massachusetts. Basketball was originally designed as an indoor game for college students to play during the winter. Naismith created 13 rules and used a soccer ball and peach baskets for the first game. In Lesson 12.4, you will compare the heights of the players on the home and visiting basketball teams.

12

12.1 Taking the PSAT

Measures of Central Tendency

Objectives

In this lesson, you will:

- Create a stem-and-leaf plot.
- Determine the distribution of a data set.
- Find the mean, median, and mode of a data set.
- Compare the mean and median for different distributions.

Key Terms

- stem-and-leaf plot
- distribution
- mean
- measure of central tendency
- median
- mode

PSAT Scores			
39.3	NV	46.9	IN
41.1	GA	47.3	AR
41.2	FL	47.4	AZ
41.6	ME	47.4	WV
41.7	SC	47.5	AL
42.0	MD	47.8	VT
42.3	DE	47.9	AK
42.3	MS	48.5	UT
42.3	OK	48.9	OR
42.5	RI	49.0	WA
42.8	LA	49.1	TN
43.0	NM	49.7	MI
43.6	TX	49.9	ID
43.9	KY	49.9	KS
44.1	PA	50.2	CO
44.8	CA	50.8	IL
45.0	VA	50.8	MT
45.1	NC	50.8	WY
45.4	CT	51.5	MO
45.9	NY	51.5	NE
46.0	NJ	51.5	WI
46.4	OH	51.7	SD
46.7	MA	52.7	IA
46.8	HI	52.9	MN
46.8	NH	53.2	ND

SCENARIO You and your friends plan to take the PSAT (Preliminary Scholastic Aptitude Test). You learn that this test requires 2 hours and 10 minutes, is usually taken by students during their sophomore or junior years, and includes math, critical reading, and writing questions. You also find out that during the 2004–2005 school year, about 1.2 million sophomores took the PSAT.

Problem 1 How Did Your State Score?

A. The table at the left shows the average PSAT score for each state. To analyze the scores, you can use a *stem-and-leaf plot*. A **stem-and-leaf plot** is a data display that helps you to see how the data are spread out. The *leaves* of the data are made from the digits with the least place value. The *stems* of the data are made from the digits in the remaining place values. Each data value is listed once in the plot. Complete the plot. The first data value, 39.3, is done for you.

Stems	Leaves
39	3
40	
41	
42	
43	
44	
45	
46	
47	
48	
49	
50	
51	
52	
53	

47 | 5 = ______

Be sure to include a key that shows what the stems and leaves indicate. Complete the key in your stem-and-leaf plot.

12

Problem 1 How Did Your State Score?

B. How does the stem-and-leaf plot display the data? Use a complete sentence in your answer.

C. What is the highest average score for a state? What is the lowest average score for a state? Use complete sentences in your answers.

D. Based on your stem-and-leaf plot, what would you estimate is the average PSAT score for the United States?

Investigate Problem 1

1. **Just the Math: Distributions** Rotate the page with your stem-and-leaf plot 90° in a counterclockwise direction so that the leaves go up instead of to the right. The way in which the data are *distributed*, such as being spread out or clustered together, is the **distribution** of the data. Describe the shape of the distribution that you see in your rotated stem-and-leaf plot. Use a complete sentence in your answer.

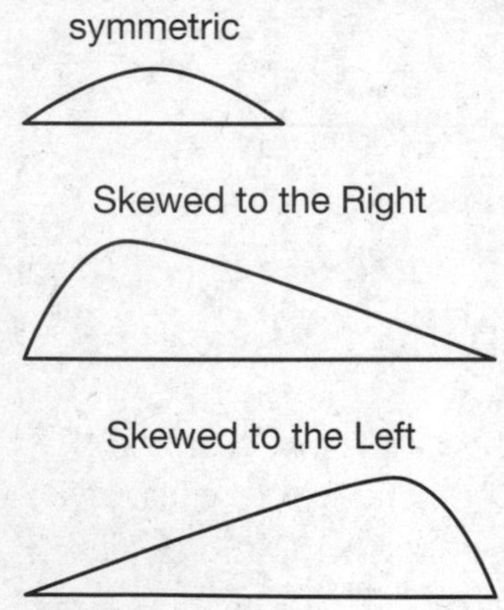

The shape of the distribution can reveal a lot of information about the data. There are many different distributions, but the most common are symmetric, skewed to the right, and skewed to the left, as shown at the left.

2. In your own words, explain how to draw each distribution at the left. Use complete sentences in your answers.

3. What type of distribution does the PSAT score data have? Use a complete sentence in your answer.

Investigate Problem 1

4. Is it easier to see the distribution in the stem-and-leaf plot or the table? Use a complete sentence in your answer.

5. Just the Math: Mean, Median, and Mode

The average PSAT score for each state is shown in order from least to greatest starting from the left. Locate your state's average PSAT score. Did the students that took the PSAT in your state do well? Use a complete sentence to explain your answer.

PSAT Scores			
39.3	NV	46.9	IN
41.1	GA	47.3	AR
41.2	FL	47.4	AZ
41.6	ME	47.4	WV
41.7	SC	47.5	AL
42.0	MD	47.8	VT
42.3	DE	47.9	AK
42.3	MS	48.5	UT
42.3	OK	48.9	OR
42.5	RI	49.0	WA
42.8	LA	49.1	TN
43.0	NM	49.7	MI
43.6	TX	49.9	ID
43.9	KY	49.9	KS
44.1	PA	50.2	CO
44.8	CA	50.8	IL
45.0	VA	50.8	MT
45.1	NC	50.8	WY
45.4	CT	51.5	MO
45.9	NY	51.5	NE
46.0	NJ	51.5	WI
46.4	OH	51.7	SD
46.7	MA	52.7	IA
46.8	HI	52.9	MN
46.8	NH	53.2	ND

One number that is often used to describe a set of data is the **mean** or **arithmetic mean.** The mean is also called the **average.** The mean is the sum of all the data values divided by the number of values in the data set. We write the mean as $\bar{x} = \frac{\Sigma x}{n}$, where Σx is the symbol for the sum of all the x-values (data values) and n is the number of values. What is the mean of the test scores in the table? Round your answer to the nearest hundredth. Use a complete sentence in your answer.

Approximately what percent of the scores are above the mean? Approximately what percent of the scores are below the mean? Use a complete sentence in your answer.

When we talk about a mean score, we are trying to determine a single value that best represents the performance of a group. This single value is a **measure of central tendency.** It is a value that represents a typical value in a data set.

6. Another measure of central tendency is the **median,** the middle score of the data, which is found by listing all the data values in order and finding the value that is exactly in the middle. Use your stem-and-leaf plot to find the median score. Interpret this value in terms of the problem situation. Where does your state fit? Use complete sentences in your answers.

Take Note

When you have an even number of values in a data set, you can find the median by finding the mean of the middle two numbers. For instance, in the data set 12, 13, 15, 16, 18, 19, the median is the mean of 15 and 16, which is $\frac{15 + 16}{2}$, or 15.5

12

Investigate Problem 1

7. A third measure of central tendency is the **mode** of the data. The mode is the value in the data set that appears most often. If two values occur in the data set the same number of times, then each value is a mode and the data set is *bimodal.* If three values occur in the data set the same number of times, then each value is a mode and the data set is *trimodal.* Which test score appears the greatest number of times? Use a complete sentence in your answer.

   What is the mode of the test scores? Use a complete sentence in your answer.

8. **Just the Math: Mean, Median, Mode, and Distributions** When a distribution is symmetric, the mean and median are equal. How do you think the mean compares to the median in a distribution that is skewed to the left? Use a complete sentence in your answer.

   How do you think the mean compares to the median in a distribution that is skewed to the right? Use a complete sentence in your answer.

   Draw representations of two sets of data, one for a distribution that is skewed to the left and one for a distribution that is skewed to the right. Then mark the possible mean and median on each distribution.

Investigate Problem 1

9. The set of data below is a set of PSAT scores from those students in a particular class at your school who took the test. Create a stem-and-leaf plot of the data and determine the distribution of the data. Then analyze the data by finding the mean, median, and mode. Show all your work. Finally, draw a representation of the data and mark the mean and median on the distribution.

   Test scores: 36, 49, 16, 31, 21, 52, 29, 49, 48, 32, 42, 49, 44

Take Note

Whenever you see the share with the class icon, your group should prepare a short presentation to share with the class that describes how you solved the problem. Be prepared to ask questions during other groups' presentations and to answer questions during your presentation.

10. Based on your results in Question 9, decide which measure of central tendency, the median or the mean, is the better representation of the test scores of the class.

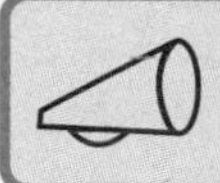

12

12.2 Compact Discs

Collecting and Analyzing Data

Objectives

In this lesson, you will:

- Collect and organize data.
- Find the mean and median of a data set.
- Determine how data values affect the mean and median of a data set.

Key Terms

- survey
- mean
- median
- sample size

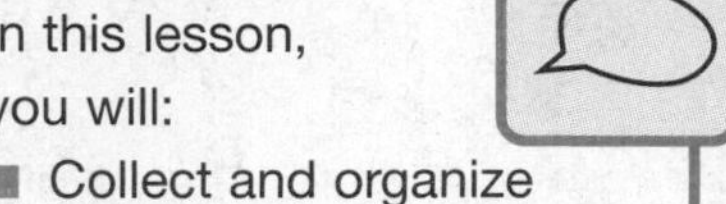

SCENARIO You work at the school newspaper and want to write an article about the CDs that the students at your school think are the most popular. You decide to use a **survey,** which is an investigation of a characteristic of a population (in this case, the students at your school), to gather information for your article.

Problem 1 Rate the CDs

A. To set up the survey, you begin by making a list of five music CDs that are popular. Write your list below.

B. Ask six different people, including at least one adult if possible, to rate each CD based on the following numerical scale:

Excellent: 41–50

Good: 31–40

Fair: 21–30

Poor: 11–20

Awful: 0–10

Record the responses in the table below.

CD	Reviewer 1 rating	Reviewer 2 rating	Reviewer 3 rating	Reviewer 4 rating	Reviewer 5 rating	Reviewer 6 rating

12

Take Note

Remember that when you have an even number of values in a data set, you can find the median by finding the mean of the middle two values. For instance, in the data set 12, 13, 15, 16, 18, 19, the median is the mean of 15 and 16, which is $\frac{15 + 16}{2}$, or 15.5.

Investigate Problem 1

1. Find the mean rating for each CD. Then find the median rating for each CD. Record these measures of central tendency in the table below. Round your answers to the nearest hundredth if necessary.

CD	Mean rating	Median rating

2. Are the mean rating and the median rating close together for any of the CDs? Use a complete sentence in your answer.

3. In each case, which measure of central tendency is more representative of the overall rating of the CD? Why? Use a complete sentence in your answer.

4. With which single reviewer do you agree the most? With which single reviewer do you agree the least? Having identified the reviewer whose ratings you like the least, replace all of his or her ratings with your own ratings in that reviewer's column. (If you agree with every reviewer, pretend that you do not and come up with another set of ratings for one of the reviewers.)

CD	Reviewer 1 rating	Reviewer 2 rating	Reviewer 3 rating	Reviewer 4 rating	Reviewer 5 rating	Reviewer 6 rating

12

Investigate Problem 1

5. Find the new mean rating and new median rating for each CD. Record your results in the table below. Round your answers to the nearest hundredth if necessary.

CD	Mean rating	Median rating

6. Has the relationship between the mean and median changed for any of the CDs? If so, in what way has it changed? Use complete sentences in your answer.

7. How does including your rating instead of the original reviewer's change the distribution? Use a complete sentence in your answer.

8. Identify each rating in the table in part (B) with which you disagree and replace it with your own. (If you agree with every rating, go through the exercise by making up new ratings for some of the original ratings and substituting these new ratings.)

CD	Reviewer 1 rating	Reviewer 2 rating	Reviewer 3 rating	Reviewer 4 rating	Reviewer 5 rating	Reviewer 6 rating

Investigate Problem 1

9. What is the new mean rating for each CD? What is the new median rating for each CD? Record the new measures of central tendency in the table below. Round your answers to the nearest hundredth if necessary.

CD	Mean rating	Median rating

10. Has the relationship between the mean and median changed for any of the CDs? If so, in what way has it changed? Use complete sentences in your answer.

11. How does including your rating instead of the original reviewer's rating change the distribution? Use a complete sentence in your answer.

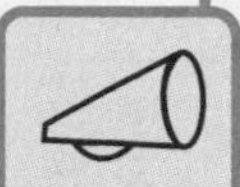

12. Just the Math: Sample Size In your survey, the **sample size,** or the number of people surveyed, was 6. Do you think that the sample size was large enough to accurately represent the opinions of the students at your school? Why or why not? Use complete sentences in your answer.

12.3 Breakfast Cereals

Quartiles and Box-and-Whisker Plots

Objectives

In this lesson, you will:

- Find the range and extremes of a data set.
- Find the first, second, and third quartiles of a data set.
- Represent a data set graphically by using a box-and-whisker plot.
- Identify outliers in a data set.
- Find percentiles of a data set.
- Find the IQR of a data set.

Key Terms

- range
- extreme
- median
- quartile
- box-and-whisker plot
- outlier
- percentile
- interquartile range

SCENARIO Your aunt is a health teacher who is encouraging you to eat a healthier breakfast. She says that the amounts of sugar in different breakfast cereals vary widely. So, you decide to make a trip to the grocery store to see if what your aunt says is true.

Problem 1 How Much Sugar is Too Much?

A. At the store, you write down the amounts of sugar that are in one serving of different kinds of cereal. The table below shows your data. One way we can get a general idea of how the data varies is to find the *range* of the data. The **range** is the difference between the greatest value and the least value in the data set. The greatest value is called the **upper extreme** and the least value is called the **lower extreme.** What is the upper extreme of the amounts of sugar? What is the lower extreme? What is the range?

Cereal	Sugar in one serving (grams)
Cocoa Rounds	13
Flakes of Corn	4
Frosty Flakes	11
Grape Nuggets	7
Golden Nuggets	10
Honey Nut O's	10
Raisin Branola	9
Healthy Living Flakes	9
Wheatleys	8
Healthy Living Crunch	6
Multi-Grain O's	7
All Branola	5
Munch Crunch	12
Branola Flakes	5
Complete Flakes	4
Corn Chrisps	3
Rice Chrisps	4
Sugary Puffs	32
Shredded Wheatleys	1
Fruit Circles	11

12

Problem 1 How Much Sugar is Too Much?

B. In Lesson 12.1, you found that measures of central tendency help us to see what is typical in the data. Other aspects of data are important to identify, such as how the data are spread apart. To see this, we can divide the data into equal parts. Which measure of central tendency divides the data set into two equal parts? Use a complete sentence in your answer.

C. You can further divide a data set by using *quartiles*. The three **quartiles,** called Q_1, Q_2, and Q_3, divide an ordered data set into four equal parts. To find the quartiles of the cereal data, first arrange the values from least to greatest.

Next, find the median. The median is the middle or **second quartile,** Q_2. What is Q_2? Use a complete sentence in your answer. Then, draw a vertical line where Q_2 divides your ordered data.

Now find the median of the values to the left of the line for Q_2. The median of the lower half of the data is the lower or **first quartile,** Q_1. What is Q_1? Use a complete sentence in your answer. Then draw a vertical line where Q_1 divides your ordered data.

Finally, find the median of the values to the right of the line for Q_2. The median of the upper half of the data is the upper or **third quartile,** Q_3. What is Q_3? Use a complete sentence in your answer. Then draw a vertical line where Q_3 divides your ordered data.

D. What fraction of the data falls on or below the first quartile Q_1? Use a complete sentence in your answer.

What fraction of the data falls on or below the second quartile Q_2? Use a complete sentence in your answer.

Problem 1 How Much Sugar is Too Much?

What fraction of the data falls on or below the third quartile Q_3? Use a complete sentence in your answer.

Between which two values does half of the data fall? Use a complete sentence to explain your reasoning.

Investigate Problem 1

1. **Just the Math: Box-and-Whisker Plots** A **box-and-whisker plot** (also known as a box plot) is used to represent a large data set (hundreds or thousands of values). Box-and-whisker plots allow you to easily make comparisons of data sets. The box-and-whisker plot below represents a set of data.

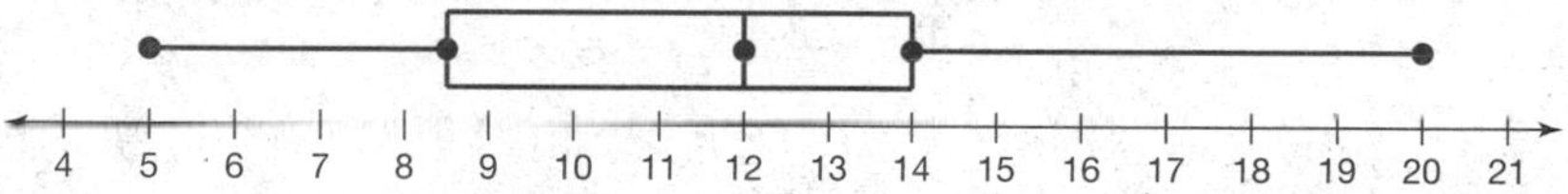

What do you think is the lower extreme of the data set? What do you think is the upper extreme? Use complete sentences in your answer.

The vertical line inside the box represents the second quartile Q_2 of the data. What is the value of Q_2? Use a complete sentence in your answer.

The point in the box directly to the left of the second quartile represents the first quartile Q_1. What is the value of Q_1? Use a complete sentence in your answer.

Similarly, the point in the box directly to the right of the second quartile represents the third quartile Q_3. What is the value of Q_3? Use a complete sentence in your answer.

The horizontal lines on both ends of the box are called *whiskers*. What do the dots at the end of the whiskers represent? Use a complete sentence in your answer.

12

Investigate Problem 1

2. To create a box-and-whisker plot of the cereal data, use the extremes and quartiles that you found in Problem 1. Complete the information below from Problem 1.

Lower extreme	
First quartile, Q_1	
Second quartile, Q_2	
Third quartile, Q_3	
Upper extreme	

Draw a number line below and label it to represent the full range of data values. Locate the second quartile, Q_2 on the number line. About an inch above the number line, draw a dot for Q_2 and label its value.

Repeat this process to draw dots for the first and third quartiles and for the upper and lower extremes.

Now, draw a box with sides at the first and third quartiles. Draw a vertical line through the median. Draw two whiskers from the sides of the box to the extremes.

3. From the box and whisker plot above, why is one whisker longer than the other? What does this mean? Use a complete sentence in your answer.

4. Just the Math: Outliers An **outlier** is a data value that is much greater than or much less than the other values in the set. What is the outlier in the breakfast cereal data? Make a conjecture, or an educated guess, about which quartile would be the most affected by removing the outlier. Write your answer and your conjecture using complete sentences.

Investigate Problem 1

5. Remove the outlier and find the values of the quartiles. Complete the table to see if you were correct.

	Original data	Data with outlier removed
First quartile, Q_1		
Second quartile, Q_2		
Third quartile, Q_3		

6. **Just the Math: Percentiles** Quartiles divide the data set into four parts. **Percentiles** also divide the data set into parts. Based on the root of this word, into how many parts do you think percentiles divide the data set? Use a complete sentence in your answer.

Take Note

Percentiles are often used in health-related fields. For instance, if a 6-year-old child's height is in the 78th percentile, then 78 percent of all 6-year-old children's heights are less than the child's height.

The ***n*th percentile** for a data set is the value for which *n* percent of the numbers in the set are less than that value. For example, the median in a data set often represents the 50th percentile because 50% of the data are less than the median. In the original cereal data set, is the median the 50th percentile? Use a complete sentence in your answer.

What percentile ranking is the first quartile in this data set? Use a complete sentence to explain your reasoning.

The third quartile represents what percentile in this data set? Explain your answer using a complete sentence.

7. **Just the Math: Interquartile Range** The **interquartile range,** or IQR, is the difference between the upper and lower quartiles ($Q_3 - Q_1$) and represents the range of approximately the middle 50% of the data. The IQR indicates the spread between the lower and upper quartiles. If it is a small number, then the middle 50% of the data are consistent. If it is a large number, then the middle 50% of the data are spread apart. Find the IQR for the original cereal data.

12

12.4 Home Team Advantage?

Sample Variance and Standard Deviation

Objectives

In this lesson, you will:

- Use a line plot to represent a data set.
- Find the sample deviation of a data set.
- Find the sample variance of a data set.
- Find the sample standard deviation of a data set.

Key Terms

- line plot
- deviation
- absolute deviation
- mean absolute deviation
- sample variance
- sample standard deviation

SCENARIO Your school's varsity basketball team has its first game of the season on their home court. They are playing a team about which they know very little. The coach does have a record of the heights of the players on the opposing team.

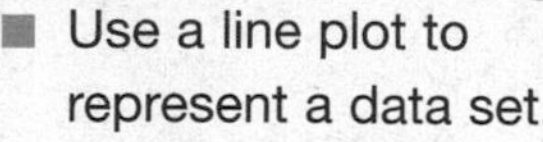

Problem 1 Height Advantage

A. To get a sense of which team may have an advantage, the coach asks you to analyze the heights of the players on both teams.

Home team heights (inches)	69	68	67	68	66	65	70	70	71	71
Visiting team heights (inches)	68	68	68	69	69	67	72	71	66	67

One way to represent this data is to draw a **line plot** for each team's set of heights. To make a line plot of the home team heights, first draw a number line that includes all the heights in both data sets. Then draw an X above the number line for each home team height. If there is more than one occurrence of a height, draw another X above the first occurrence.

Use a similar number line to draw a line plot of the visiting team heights.

B. Compare the two line plots. Describe any difference that you see. Use complete sentences in your answer.

12

Problem 1 Height Advantage

C. You decide that you will try to compare the heights by finding the mean and the range of each data set. Find these statistics. Show your work and use a complete sentence in your answer.

Can you draw any conclusions about who has the advantage from the mean and the range? Why or why not? Use a complete sentence in your answer.

Investigate Problem 1

1. **Just the Math: Deviation** Up until this point, you have observed differences in data sets by visually looking at their distributions, as you did in part (B). Other measures can help us to understand the distribution of a data set. One such measure is *deviation*. The **deviation** of a data value is the difference between the data value and the mean.

   We can use variables to represent the deviation by letting the variable x be the data value and by letting the variable $\bar{x}$, called "x-bar," be the mean. Write an expression for deviation.

2. Complete the table by finding the deviation of each data value.

Home team heights (inches)	Deviation
69	
68	
67	
68	
66	
65	
70	
70	
71	
71	

Visiting team heights (inches)	Deviation
68	
68	
68	
69	
69	
67	
72	
71	
66	
67	

12

Investigate Problem 1

3. Find the mean of the deviations for each team. Show your work and use a complete sentence in your answer.

   Is the mean of the deviations meaningful? Why or why not? Use a complete sentence in your answer.

   Were any of the deviations negative? If so, why? Use a complete sentence in your answer.

4. Although the mean of the deviations was not helpful in determining the spread of the data, you can find the absolute values of the deviations first and then find the mean of the results. These absolute values are called **absolute deviations.** Copy the deviations from the table on the previous page. Then complete the table by finding the absolute value of each deviation.

Home team heights (inches)	Deviation	Absolute value of deviation
69		
68		
67		
68		
66		
65		
70		
70		
71		
71		

Visiting team heights (inches)	Deviation	Absolute value of deviation
68		
68		
68		
69		
69		
67		
72		
71		
66		
67		

   Find the mean of the absolute values of the deviations, called the **mean absolute deviation,** for each team. Does the mean absolute deviation help you to determine the spread of the data? Why or why not? Use complete sentences in your answer.

12

Investigate Problem 1

5. **Just the Math: Sample Variance** Even though the mean absolute deviation is meaningful, it is not commonly used to measure variability, or how the data values within a set differ. Let's consider a more common measure of variability by finding the *sample variance* of each data set. In the table below, copy the deviations that you found in Question 2. Then find the square of each deviation for both the home team and the visiting team.

Home team heights (inches)	Deviation	Square of deviation
69		
68		
67		
68		
66		
65		
70		
70		
71		
71		

Visiting team heights (inches)	Deviation	Square of deviation
68		
68		
68		
69		
69		
67		
72		
71		
66		
67		

Let x_1 be the first data value and let $\bar{x}$ be the mean. Write an expression for the square of the deviation of the first data value.

Let x_1 be the first data value, x_2 be the second data value, x_3 be the third data value, and so on. Write an expression for the sum of the squares of the deviations of a data set with 10 data values.

Another way to write this sum is to use the uppercase Greek letter sigma (Σ) which means "sum":

$$\sum_{i=1}^{n} (x_i - \bar{x})^2$$

The variable n represents the number of data values in the data set. In our problem situation, $n = 10$.

Investigate Problem 1

To find the **sample variance,** or s^2, divide the sum by one less than the number of data values in the data set. This is shown in symbols below.

$$\text{Sample variance: } s^2 = \frac{\sum_{i=1}^{n} (x_i - \bar{x})^2}{n - 1}$$

Find the sample variance for both the home team and the visiting team. Round your answers to the nearest hundredth. Show your work and use a complete sentence in your answer.

6. **Just the Math: Sample Standard Deviation** You can use the sample variance to find the **sample standard deviation,** or s, which is a common measure of the variability of a data set. To find the sample standard deviation, take the square root of the sample variance. This is shown in symbols below.

$$\text{Sample standard deviation: } s = \sqrt{\frac{\sum_{i=1}^{n} (x_i - \bar{x})^2}{n - 1}}$$

Find the sample standard deviation for the both the home team and the visiting team. Round your answers to the nearest hundredth. Use a complete sentence in your answer.

7. Use complete sentences to explain the meaning of the sample standard deviation of the home team and the sample standard deviation of the visiting team.

8. How does finding the sample standard deviation help you to compare the heights of the players on the two teams? Use a complete sentence in your answer.

12

Looking Ahead to Chapter 13

13

Focus In Chapter 13, you will learn how to write quadratic equations in different forms. You will also learn how to work with and graph exponential functions, as well as how to perform transformation of graphs of functions. In addition, you will learn how to use the Pythagorean Theorem and the Midpoint and Distance Formulas.

Chapter Warm up

Answer these questions to help you review skills that you will need in Chapter 13.

Solve each quadratic equation.

1. $x^2 - x - 12 = 0$

2. $2x^2 - 128 = 0$

3. $2x^2 + 10x = 15$

Solve each equation for the indicated variable.

4. $3\pi + tc = h; t$

5. $rs + st = 4; s$

6. $\frac{3x + 4y}{z} = 8; y$

Read the problem scenario below.

The equation that represents the height y of a model rocket in feet as a function of the time t in seconds after it has left the ground is given by $y = -16t^2 + 110t$.

7. When does the rocket reach its maximum height? What is the maximum height of the rocket?

8. What are the x-intercepts of the graph of the function modeling the height of the rocket? What do they represent in the problem situation?

Key Terms

CHAPTER 13

Quadratic and Exponential Functions and Logic

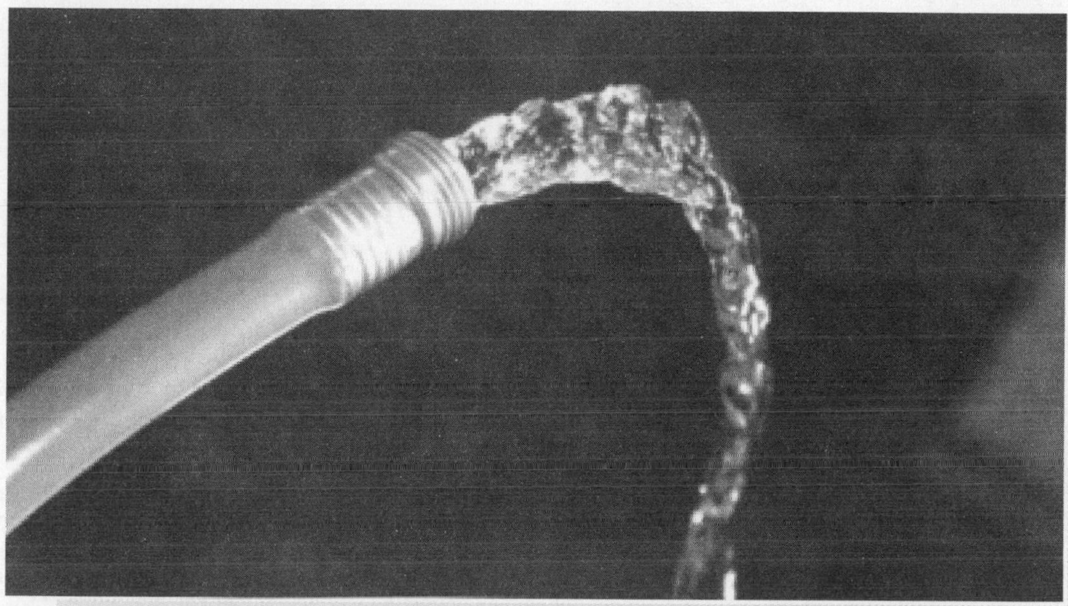

A typical garden hose can deliver between 9 and 17 gallons of water per minute. Most hoses are made from rubber, vinyl, or a rubber-vinyl combination. In Lesson 13.4, you will use quadratic functions to model the path of the water of a garden hose.

13

13.1 Solid Carpentry

The Pythagorean Theorem and Its Converse

13

Objectives

In this lesson, you will:

- Use the Pythagorean Theorem to find the side length of a right triangle.
- Use the converse of the Pythagorean Theorem to determine whether a triangle is a right triangle.

Key Terms

- legs
- hypotenuse
- Pythagorean Theorem
- converse
- converse of Pythagorean Theorem

SCENARIO A carpenter is building a window frame and needs to make sure that the pieces of wood that form the frame meet at a right angle. However, he has dropped his metal square that he uses to check angles and the square has bent, so he needs another method for making sure that the angles are right angles.

Problem 1 Building a Window Frame

The carpenter measures four inches from a corner up the window frame and makes a mark. Then, he measures three inches from the same corner across the bottom of the window frame and makes a mark. Finally, he measures the straight-line distance from each of his marks and finds that this distance is five inches, as shown below. He concludes that this corner is a right angle. How does the carpenter know he is correct?

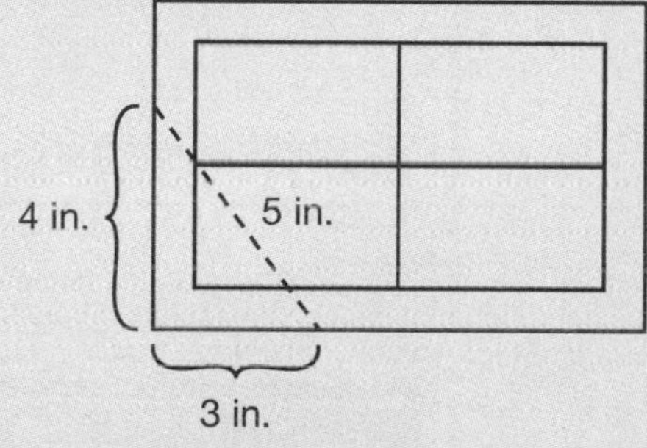

A. You will test the carpenter's method. First, on graph paper, draw a right triangle so that one leg is three units long and the other leg is four units long. Then draw a square on the hypotenuse of the triangle as shown.

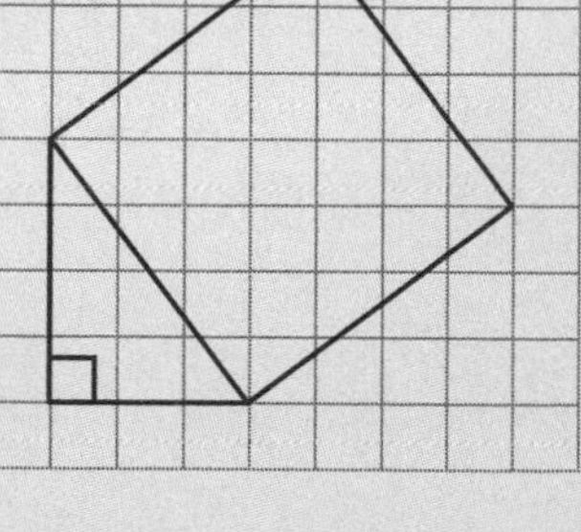

Now cut out a square from the graph paper that has a side length of three blocks. Then cut out another square from the graph paper that has a side length of four blocks. What is the area of each square? Use a complete sentence in your answer.

Cut these squares into strips that are three blocks (or four blocks) long and one block wide. Arrange these strips on top of the square that is along the hypotenuse.

Take Note

In a right triangle, the sides that form the right angle are the legs and the side that is opposite the right angle is the hypotenuse.

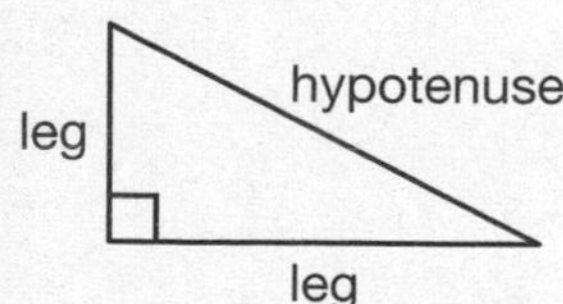

13

Problem 1 Building a Window Frame

B. What is the relationship between the areas of the squares that you cut into strips and the area of the square that is along the hypotenuse? Use a complete sentence in your answer.

C. What is the area of the square that is along the hypotenuse? Show your work and use a complete sentence to explain your reasoning.

D. What is the length of the hypotenuse? Use a complete sentence to explain your reasoning.

E. Write the area of each of the three squares as a power. Then write an equation that relates these powers.

F. Was the carpenter's conclusion correct? Why or why not?

Investigate Problem 1

1. In Problem 1, you demonstrated a consequence of the *Pythagorean Theorem.* The **Pythagorean Theorem** states that if a and b are the lengths of the legs of a right triangle and c is the length of the hypotenuse, then

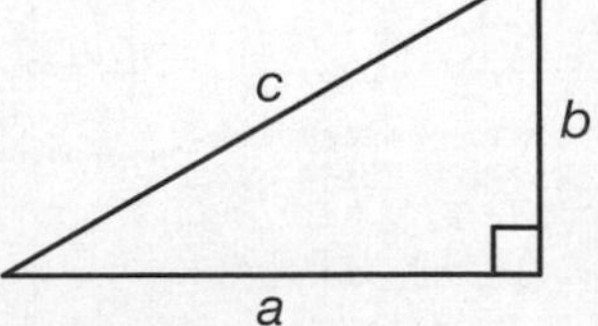

$a^2 + b^2 = c^2$.

Do you think that the Pythagorean Theorem works for triangles that are not right triangles? Use complete sentences to explain your reasoning.

Investigate Problem 1

2. In Problem 1, you used the *converse* of the Pythagorean Theorem. The **converse** of a statement in "if-then" form is created by exchanging the "if" part and the "then" part of the statement. Complete the statement of the converse of the Pythagorean Theorem below by switching the "if" and "then" parts of the Pythagorean Theorem.

Suppose that *a*, *b*, and *c* are the sides of a triangle. The **converse of the Pythagorean Theorem** states that if

_______________, then the triangle is a __________ triangle.

3. The carpenter also has to repair some woodwork on a front porch and needs a ladder to do so. The work needs to be done on an area of the porch that is 12 feet above the ground. There is a bush in front of the porch where he needs to place the ladder, so he needs to place the ladder 5 feet from the porch. What length of ladder does the carpenter need to reach the area of the porch that needs repaired? Show your work and use a complete sentence in your answer.

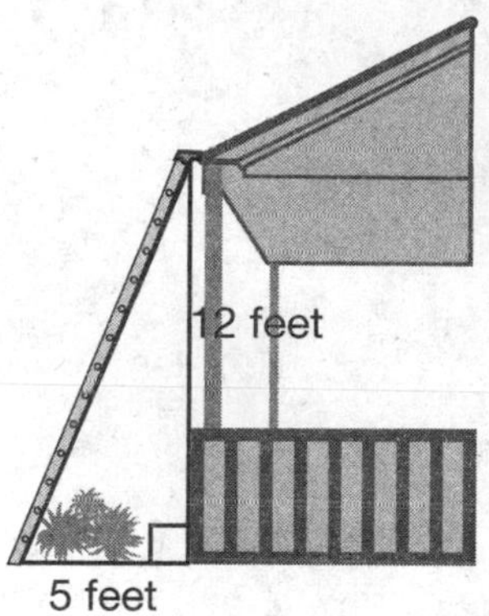

4. The carpenter is installing a door and is checking to see whether the opening in the wall forms a rectangle. The opening is 72 inches tall and 30 inches wide. The diagonal of the opening is 75 inches long. Does the opening form a rectangle? Show your work and use a complete sentence in your answer.

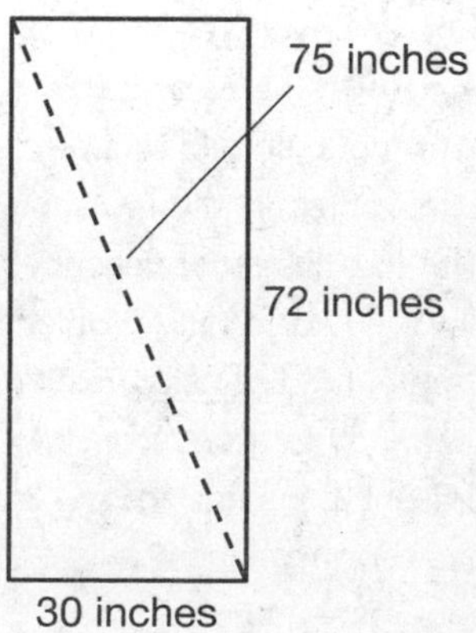

13

Investigate Problem 1

5. The carpenter is on another job building a shed. The roof of the shed will be triangular in shape, as shown. The roof will be ten feet wide and one side of the roof will be six feet long. How tall will the roof be? Show your work and use a complete sentence in your answer. Round your answer to the nearest tenth if necessary.

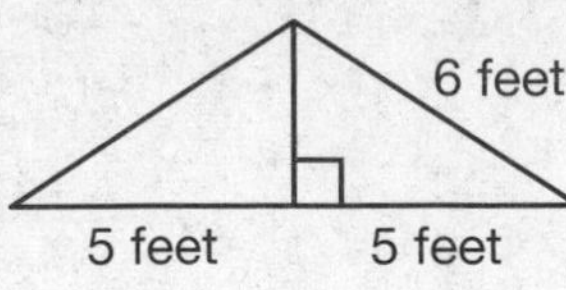

6. In Questions 3 through 5, did you use the Pythagorean Theorem or the converse of the Pythagorean Theorem to answer the question? Use complete sentences to explain your reasoning.

7. Use complete sentences to describe the situations in which you would use the Pythagorean Theorem to solve problems. Then use complete sentences to describe the situations in which you would use the converse of the Pythagorean Theorem to solve problems.

Take Note

Whenever you see the share with the class icon, your group should prepare a short presentation to share with the class that describes how you solved the problem. Be prepared to ask questions during other groups' presentations and to answer questions during your presentation.

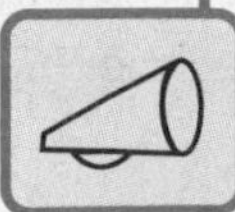

13.2 Location, Location, Location

The Distance and Midpoint Formulas

Objectives

In this lesson, you will:

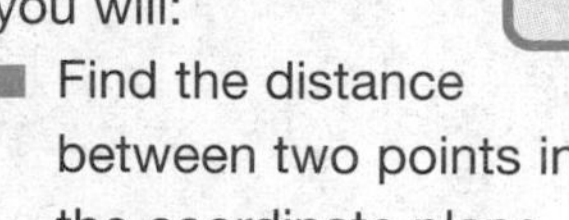

- Find the distance between two points in the coordinate plane.
- Find the midpoint between two points in the coordinate plane.

Key Terms

- Distance Formula
- midpoint
- Midpoint Formula

SCENARIO How many different kinds of maps of Earth do you think there are? The answer is many. You are probably most familiar with the map that is a globe. On this map, Earth is divided into sections by latitude and longitude lines that do not necessarily meet at right angles. Locations on a globe are measured in degrees, minutes, and seconds. Another kind of map is the Universal Transverse Mercator (UTM). This map of Earth uses a rectangular grid and the metric system of measurement.

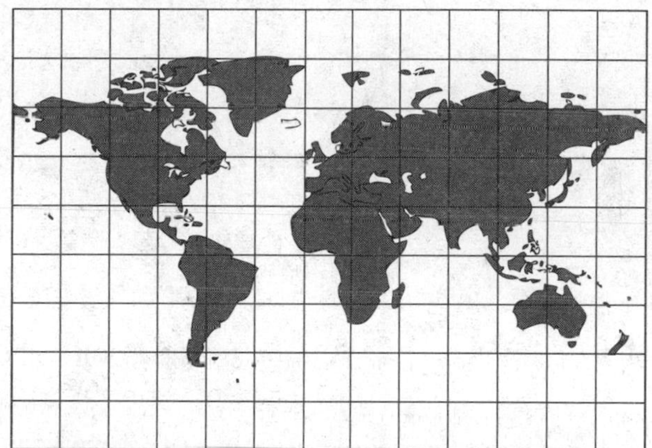

Problem 1 Where on Earth Are You?

Consider the map that shows elevations of an area in UTM coordinates at the right.

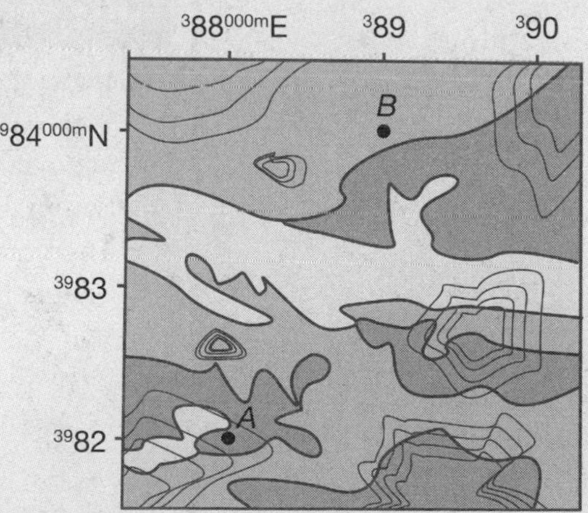

A. On a UTM map, the *x*-coordinate is called an *easting* and is measured in meters. On the top portion of the map, you can see the label $^{3}88^{000\text{m}}$E. This means 388,000 meters east. The label to the right, $^{3}89$, is a shortened notation for $^{3}89^{000\text{m}}$E, or 389,000 meters east. What does the label $^{3}90$ mean?

13

Problem 1 Where on Earth Are You?

B. The *y*-coordinate is called a *northing* and is also measured in meters. On the left portion of the map, you can see the label $^{39}84^{000m}$N. This means 3,984,000 meters north. The next label below, $^{39}83$, is a shortened notation for $^{39}83^{000m}$N, or 3,983,000 meters north. What does the label $^{39}82$ mean?

C. Write the coordinates of points *A* and *B* from the map.

easting of *A*: ____________ meters
northing of *A*: ____________ meters

easting of *B*: ____________ meters
northing of *B*: ____________ meters

D. Now write each set of coordinates in kilometers. Remember that 1 kilometer = 1000 meters.

easting of *A*: ______________________
northing of *A*: ______________________

easting of *B*: ______________________
northing of *B*: ______________________

E. Finally, write each point from part (D) in the coordinate notation (easting, northing).

Investigate Problem 1

1. Label the points with their coordinates in kilometers on the map at the right. Then draw a line that connects the points.

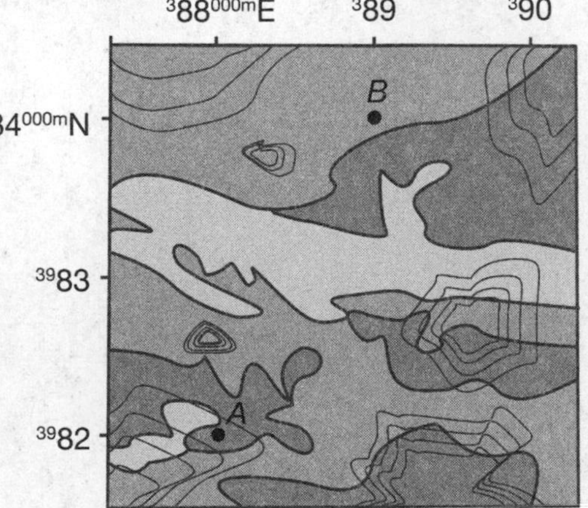

2. Let your line segment *AB* be the hypotenuse of a right triangle. Draw the legs of this right triangle and label the point where the sides meet as point *C*. What are the coordinates in kilometers of point *C*?

Investigate Problem 1

How do the coordinates of point C relate to the coordinates of points A and B? Use complete sentences in your answer.

13

3. Write an expression that you can use to find the distance between point A and point C in kilometers. Then, find this distance. Use a complete sentence to explain how you found your answer.

4. Write an expression that you can use to find the distance between point B and point C in kilometers. Then find this distance. Use a complete sentence to explain how you found your answer.

5. Find the distance between point A and point B. Round your answer to the nearest tenth. Show your work and use a complete sentence in your answer.

6. Complete the summary of the steps that you took to find the distance between points A and B.

$$AC^2 + BC^2 = AB^2$$

$$(\square - \square)^2 + (\square - \square)^2 = AB^2$$

$$\square^2 + \square^2 = AB^2$$

$$\square + \square = AB^2$$

$$\square = AB^2$$

$$\sqrt{\square} = AB$$

13

Investigate Problem 1

7. **Just the Math: The Distance Formula** We can use your method for finding the distance between points A and B to write the **Distance Formula:** if (x_1, y_1) and (x_2, y_2) are two points in the coordinate plane, then the distance d between (x_1, y_1) and (x_2, y_2) is given by

$$d = \sqrt{(x_2 - x_1)^2 + (y_2 - y_1)^2}.$$

The formula is illustrated in the figure below. We indicate that distance is positive by using the absolute value symbol.

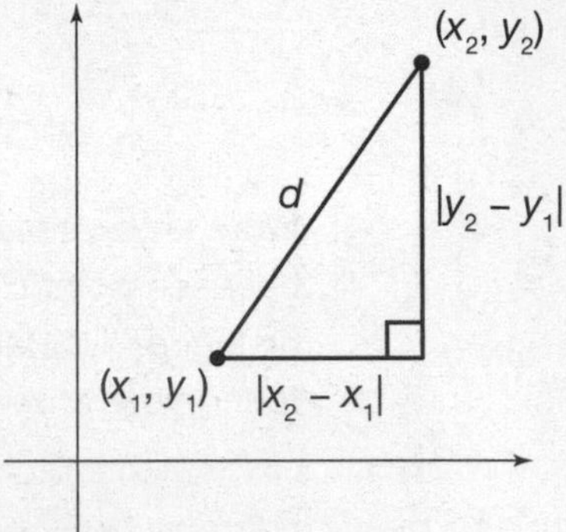

Do you think that it matters which point you identify as (x_1, y_1) and which point you identify as (x_2, y_2)? Use a complete sentence to explain your reasoning.

8. Find the distance between each pair of points. Round your answer to the nearest tenth if necessary. Show your work.

(0, 0) and (3, 4)

(1, 5) and (4, 8)

(0, −2), (3, 3)

(−1, 4), (3, 2)

13

Problem 2 Are We (Halfway) There Yet?

Consider the points A, B, and C labeled on the map at the right.

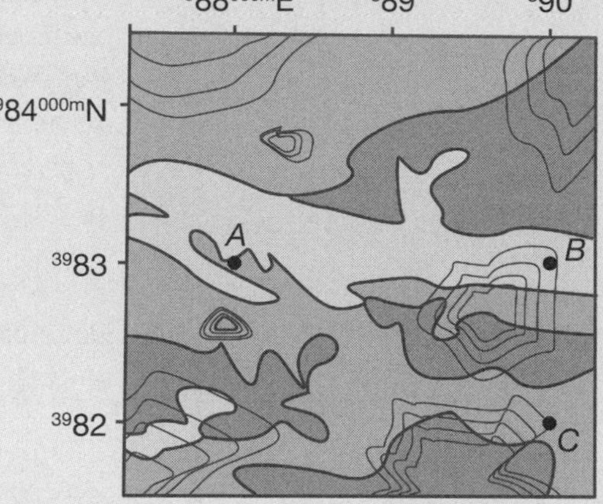

A. What is the distance between points A and B in kilometers? Show your work and use a complete sentence in your answer.

B. The point halfway between points A and B is called the **midpoint.** How many kilometers from point A is the midpoint? Show your work and use a complete sentence in your answer.

C. What are the coordinates in kilometers of the point from part (B)? Plot this point and label it as point D on the map above. Show your work and use a complete sentence in your answer.

D. Use complete sentences to describe how you would find the midpoint of a horizontal line segment.

E. Consider the horizontal line segment with endpoints (x_1, y) and (x_2, y). Complete the steps below to find the x-coordinate of the midpoint.

$$\frac{x_2 - x_1}{2} + x_1 = \frac{x_2 - x_1}{2} + \frac{\qquad}{2}$$ Write expressions with common denominator.

$$= \frac{\qquad\qquad}{2}$$ Add numerators.

$$= \frac{\qquad}{2}$$ Simplify.

The midpoint is located at $\left(\underline{\qquad}, \quad \right)$.

13

Problem 2 Are We (Halfway) There Yet?

F. Now find the coordinates in kilometers of the midpoint between points *B* and *C*. Show all your work and use a complete sentence in your answer. Plot this point and label it as point *E* on the map on the previous page.

G. Use complete sentences to describe how you would find the midpoint of a vertical line segment.

H. Consider the vertical line segment with endpoints (x, y_1) and (x, y_2). Complete the steps below to find the *y*-coordinate of the midpoint.

$$\frac{y_2 - y_1}{2} + y_1 = \frac{y_2 - y_1}{2} + \frac{\quad}{2}$$ Write expressions with common denominator.

$$= \frac{\qquad}{2}$$ Add numerators.

$$= \frac{\qquad}{2}$$ Simplify.

The midpoint is located at $\left(\quad , \underline{\qquad} \right)$.

Investigate Problem 2

1. What do you think are the coordinates in kilometers of the midpoint between points *A* and *C*? Plot this point and label it as point *F* on the map on the previous page. Use complete sentences to explain your reasoning.

Use complete sentences to explain how can you use the Distance Formula to verify your answer.

13

Investigate Problem 2

Use your method described on the previous page to verify your answer to Question 1.

2. **Just the Math: The Midpoint Formula** If (x_1, y_1) and (x_2, y_2) are two points in the coordinate plane, then the **midpoint** of the line segment that joins these two points is given by

$$\left(\frac{x_1 + x_2}{2}, \frac{y_1 + y_2}{2}\right).$$

Use the **Midpoint Formula** to find the midpoint of the line segment that connects points A and C on the map in Problem 2. Show all your work.

How does this midpoint compare to the one you found in Question 1? Use a complete sentence in your answer.

3. Find the midpoint of the line segment that has the given points as its endpoints. Show your work.

(0, 4) and (2, 5)

(10, 5) and (8, 0)

(–1, 6) and (7, –2)

(–5, 6) and (–5, –8)

13.3 "Old" Mathematics

Completing the Square and Deriving the Quadratic Formula

13

Objectives

In this lesson, you will:

- Solve quadratic equations by completing the square.
- Derive the Quadratic Formula.

Key Terms

- perfect square trinomial
- factor
- complete the square
- Quadratic Formula

SCENARIO When you used the Quadratic Formula in Lesson 8.6, did you wonder where the formula came from or why it works? Quadratic equations have been around since ancient times. Al-Kwārizī, an Islamic mathematician who lived from 780 A.D. to 850 A.D., wrote a text that included methods for solving quadratic equations. In his book, Al-Kwārizī used geometric figures to justify his methods.

Problem 1 Creating a Perfect Square

In previous lessons, you learned how to factor a trinomial of the form $a^2 + 2ab + b^2$ as the perfect square $(a + b)^2$. Now we will construct a perfect square by using a geometric model.

A. Consider the expression $x^2 + 10x$. This sum can be represented geometrically by the figure below. Write the area of each piece in the center of the piece.

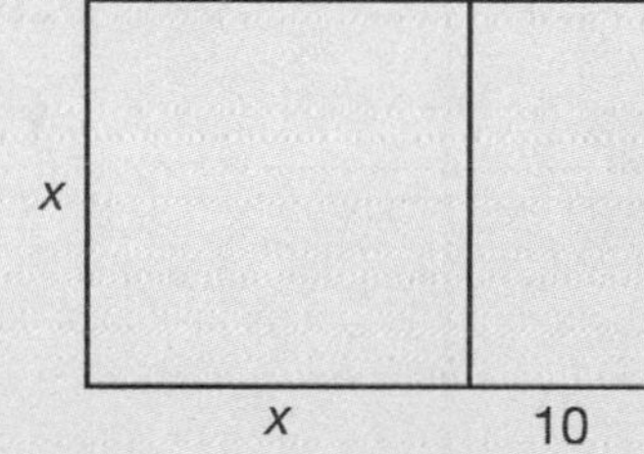

B. Let's rebuild this figure so that it is more in the shape of a square by splitting the rectangle in half and rearranging the pieces. Label the side length of each piece and write the area of each piece in the center of the piece.

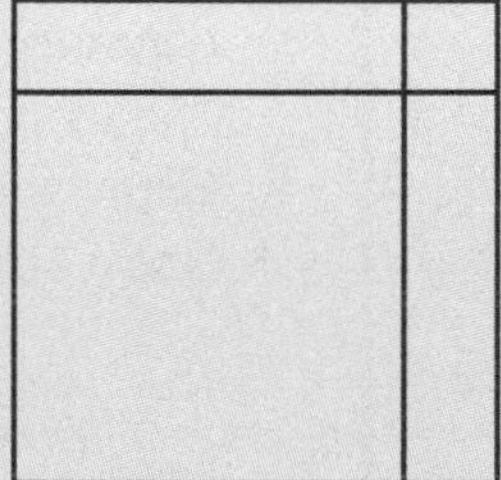

C. Do the two figures represent the same expression? How do you know? Use a complete sentence in your answer.

D. Complete the figure so that it is a square. Label the area of the piece you added.

13

Problem 1 Creating a Perfect Square

E. Add this area to your expression. What is the expression?

F. Factor this expression.

G. Use complete sentences to explain how to *complete the square* on the expression $x^2 + bx$ where b is an integer.

Take Note

A **perfect square trinomial** is a trinomial that can be factored as a square of a difference or sum of binomials:

$a^2 + 2ab + b^2 = (a + b)^2$ or
$a^2 - 2ab + b^2 = (a - b)^2$.

Investigate Problem 1

1. Use a geometric figure to complete the square (or create a perfect square trinomial) for each expression. Then **factor** the trinomial.

$x^2 + 8x$

$x^2 + 5x$

2. You can use the idea of completing the square to help you solve quadratic equations. Consider the equation $x^2 + 10x - 11 = 0$. The trinomial in this equation cannot be factored as it is written. But how can we make $x^2 + 10x$ a perfect square trinomial? Use a complete sentence in your answer.

Because we know that we can make $x^2 + 10x$ into a perfect square trinomial, we will get this expression by itself on one side of the equation $x^2 + 10x - 11 = 0$.

$x^2 + 10x = \boxed{}$

Investigate Problem 1

13

Now, add the number to each side of the equation that will make $x^2 + 10x$ a perfect square trinomial. Complete the steps below.

$x^2 + 10x + \square = 11 + \square$ Add same number to each side.

$x^2 + 10x + \square = \square$ Add.

$(\square)^2 = \square$ Factor trinomial.

We can extend the method of extracting square roots to solve this equation. Complete each step below.

$x + 5 = \square$ or $x + 5 = \square$

$x + 5 = \square$ or $x + 5 = \square$

$x = \square$ or $x = \square$

Check your work by substituting each solution into the original equation. Show your work.

3. Solve each equation by completing the square and then extracting square roots. Show all your work.

$x^2 + 8x - 9 = 0$

$x^2 + 20x + 36 = 0$

13

Investigate Problem 1

$x^2 - 14x + 13 = 0$

4. The method that you used to solve the equations in Question 2 is not the best method for *all* quadratic equations. For instance, you would probably not want to use this method to solve the equation $53x^2 + 104x - 51 = 0$. That is why we have the Quadratic Formula. Consider the equation $ax^2 + bx + c = 0$, where $a \neq 0$. Complete the steps below to discover how the *Quadratic Formula* was formed by completing the square.

$ax^2 + bx + c = 0$	Write original equation.
$ax^2 + bx = \square$	Subtract c from each side.
$x^2 + \square x = \square$	Divide each side by a.
$x^2 + \frac{b}{a}x + \square = -\frac{c}{a} + \square$	Add $\left(\frac{b}{2a}\right)^2$ to each side.
$\square = -\frac{c}{a} + \left(\frac{b}{2a}\right)^2$	Factor left-hand side.
$\left(x + \frac{b}{2a}\right)^2 = -\frac{c}{a} + \square$	Simplify.
$\left(x + \frac{b}{2a}\right)^2 = \square + \frac{b^2}{4a^2}$	Write expression with common denominator.
$\left(x + \frac{b}{2a}\right)^2 = \square$	Add and write numerator in standard form.
$\square = \pm\sqrt{\square}$	Extract square roots.
$x + \frac{b}{2a} = \pm\frac{\sqrt{b^2 - 4ac}}{\square}$	Simplify radical.
$x = \square \pm \frac{\sqrt{b^2 - 4ac}}{2a}$	Subtract $-\frac{b}{2a}$ from each side.
$x = \frac{-b \pm \sqrt{b^2 - 4ac}}{2a}$	Write right side as single fraction.

13.4 Learning to Be a Teacher

Vertex Form of a Quadratic Equation

13

Objectives

In this lesson, you will:

- Write quadratic equations in standard form.
- Write quadratic equations in factored form.
- Write quadratic equations in vertex form.

Key Terms

- standard form
- factored form
- vertex form

SCENARIO A college student is in school to learn how to be a teacher. An assignment for one of his classes is to create an interactive project that helps students learn about the different shapes of quadratic functions. He plans to make an interactive animation of water coming out of a garden hose so that the water's path is in the shape of a parabola. In the animation, students can change the numbers in a quadratic equation and see how the shape of the water's path changes.

Problem 1 Choosing a Quadratic Form

It has been a while since the college student has worked with quadratic equations, so he looks over material from old notes. According to his notes, there are three forms of a quadratic equation: the *standard form,* the *factored form,* and the *vertex form.* He has an example in his notes of a function represented by each of the forms:

Standard form: $y = x^2 - 4x + 3$

Factored form: $y = (x - 3)(x - 1)$

Vertex form: $y = (x - 2)^2 + (-1)$

A. How would you show that all of the equations represent the same function? Use a complete sentence in your answer.

Use your method to show that all of the equations represent the same function. Show all your work.

B. Without graphing the equation, what can you determine about the graph by looking at the equation in standard form? Use complete sentences in your answer.

C. Without graphing the equation, what can you determine about the graph by looking at the equation in factored form? Use a complete sentence in your answer.

13

Problem 1 Choosing a Quadratic Form

D. Create a graph of the quadratic function on the grid below. First, choose your bounds and intervals. Be sure to label your graph clearly.

Variable quantity	Lower bound	Upper bound	Interval

E. What is the vertex of the graph? Is it obvious why the last form is called the vertex form? Use complete sentences in your answer.

Investigate Problem 1

1. **Just the Math: Vertex Form of a Quadratic Equation** The **vertex form of a quadratic equation** is an equation of the form $y = a(x - h)^2 + k$ where (h, k) is the vertex of the graph of the equation.

Investigate Problem 1

13

1. Identify the vertex of the graph of each equation.

$y = (x - 3)^2 + 9$ $y = (x - 1)^2 - 2$

$y = (x + 4)^2 + 8$ $y = (x + 7)^2 - 5$

2. How is the vertex form of a quadratic equation different from the standard form? Use a complete sentence in your answer.

In Problem 1, you wrote an equation in standard form by simplifying the expressions in the vertex form of the equation. How do you think an equation that is written in standard form could be written in vertex form? Use a complete sentence to explain your reasoning.

3. Consider the quadratic equation from Problem 1 in standard form: $y = x^2 - 4x + 3$. What number should you add to $x^2 - 4x$ to make a perfect square trinomial?

Add this number to each side of the quadratic equation in standard form.

Why did you have to add the number to each side of the equation? Use a complete sentence in your answer.

Now factor your perfect square trinomial.

Finally, write your equation in vertex form.

4. Write the equation $y = x^2 + 2x + 5$ in vertex form. Show your work. Then identify the vertex of the graph of the equation.

Investigate Problem 1

5. The college student has to determine which form of the equation to use in the interactive project. He will make his decision after creating several graphs and comparing the three forms of each function. Write each equation in the other two forms. Then graph each equation in the given form.

Standard form: $y = x^2 + 2x - 15$

Factored form: ____________________

Vertex form: ____________________

Investigate Problem 1

Standard form: ____________________

Factored form: $y = (x - 2)(x - 4)$

Vertex form: ____________________

13

13

Investigate Problem 1

Standard form: ____________________

Factored form: ____________________

Vertex form: $y = (x + 4)^2 - 9$

6. Which form of a quadratic equation do you think the college student should choose for his interactive project? He has the following options:

In the standard form $y = ax^2 + bx + c$, students would be able to change *a*, *b*, and *c* in the animation.

In the factored form $y = a(x - p)(x - q)$, students would be able to change *a*, *p*, and *q* in the animation.

In the vertex form $y = a(x - h)^2 + k$, students would be able to change *a*, *h*, and *k* in the animation.

Explain your reasoning. Use complete sentences in your answer.

13.5 Screen Saver

Graphing by Using Parent Functions

Objectives

In this lesson, you will:

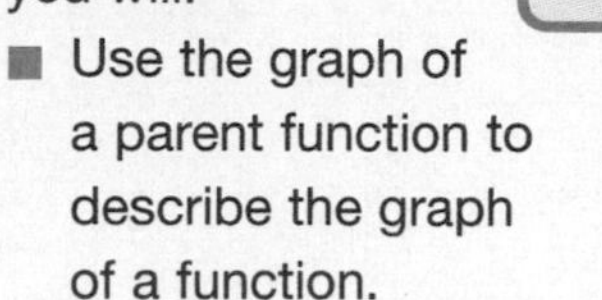

- Use the graph of a parent function to describe the graph of a function.

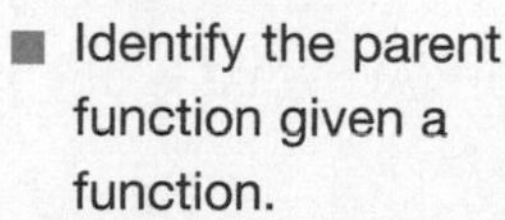

- Identify the parent function given a function.
- Write equations of functions based on the graphs of functions.

Key Terms

- parent function
- translation
- reflection

SCENARIO Your friend is learning how to create a screen saver by moving a mathematical figure around on the screen. She chooses to use a parabola and will start with the graph of $y = x^2$. Each step of her program will require her to display the graph of a different quadratic function to show the movement.

Problem 1 Right, Left, Up, and Down

A. First, your friend must decide how the parabola will move around on the screen. Create the graph of $y = x^2$ on the grid below.

B. Create a graph of $y = x^2 + 2$ on the grid in part (A). What is the vertex of the graph of $y = x^2 + 2$?

How does this graph compare to the graph of $y = x^2$? Use a complete sentence in your answer.

Write $y = x^2 + 2$ in vertex form.

13

Problem 1 Right, Left, Up, and Down

C. Create a graph of $y = x^2 - 2$ on the grid in part (A). What is the vertex of the graph of $y = x^2 - 2$?

How does this graph compare to the graph of $y = x^2$? Use a complete sentence in your answer.

Write $y = x^2 - 2$ in vertex form.

D. Create a graph of $y = (x + 2)^2$ on the grid in part (A). What is the vertex of the graph of $y = (x + 2)^2$?

How does this graph compare to the graph of $y = x^2$? Use a complete sentence in your answer.

Write $y = (x + 2)^2$ in vertex form.

E. Create a graph of $y = (x - 2)^2$ on the grid in part (A). What is the vertex of the graph of $y = (x - 2)^2$?

How does this graph compare to the graph of $y = x^2$? Use a complete sentence in your answer.

Write $y = (x - 2)^2$ in vertex form.

Investigate Problem 1

1. How can you obtain the graph of $y = x^2 + n$ when n is positive by using the graph of $y = x^2$? Use a complete sentence in your answer.

Investigate Problem 1

How can you obtain the graph of $y = x^2 + n$ when n is negative by using the graph of $y = x^2$? Use a complete sentence in your answer.

13

2. How can you obtain the graph of $y = (x - n)^2$ when n is positive by using the graph of $y = x^2$? Use a complete sentence in your answer.

How can you obtain the graph of $y = (x - n)^2$ when n is negative by using the graph of $y = x^2$? Use a complete sentence in your answer.

3. Explain how you can use the graph of $y = x^2$ to draw the graph of $y = (x - 1)^2 + 4$. Use a complete sentence in your answer.

Explain how you can use the graph of $y = x^2$ to draw the graph of $y = (x + 2)^2 + 3$. Use a complete sentence in your answer.

Explain how you can use the graph of $y = x^2$ to draw the graph of $y = (x - 3)^2 - 1$. Use a complete sentence in your answer.

Explain how you can use the graph of $y = x^2$ to draw the graph of $y = (x + 5)^2 - 2$. Use a complete sentence in your answer.

Use complete sentences to explain how you found your answers to Question 3.

13

Investigate Problem 1

4. Your friend's parabola will move as described below in the table. She will later add intermediate steps to make the movement smooth. Your friend will start with the graph of $y = (x - 5)^2 + 8$. In each step, write the equation that will graph the parabola described. Then identify the vertex.

Step	Movement	Equation	Vertex
0	none	$y = (x - 5)^2 + 8$	(5, 8)
1	left two units, up two units		
2	left four units down ten units		
3	right three units, down ten units		
4	right three units, up ten units		

Problem 2 Squish, Stretch, and Flop

Your friend is also considering other changes to the parabola as it moves around on the screen.

A. Begin with the graph of $y = x^2$. Create a graph of $y = x^2$ on the grid below.

Problem 2 Squish, Stretch, and Flop

B. Now, create a graph of $y = 2x^2$ on the grid in part (A). How does this graph compare to the graph of $y = x^2$? Use a complete sentence in your answer.

13

C. Create a graph of $y = \frac{1}{2}x^2$ on the grid in part (A). How does this graph compare to the graph of $y = x^2$? Use a complete sentence in your answer.

D. Create a graph of $y = -x^2$ on the grid in part (A). How does this graph compare to the graph of $y = x^2$? Use a complete sentence in your answer.

E. Describe the effect that a constant being multiplied by x^2 has on the graph of $y = x^2$. Use complete sentences in your answer.

Investigate Problem 2

1. How can you obtain the graph of $y = ax^2$ by using the graph of $y = x^2$ when $|a|$ is greater than 1? Use a complete sentence in your answer.

How can you obtain the graph of $y = ax^2$ by using the graph of $y = x^2$ when $|a|$ is less than 1? Use a complete sentence in your answer.

2. How can you obtain the graph of $y = -x^2$ by using the graph of $y = x^2$? Use a complete sentence in your answer.

13

Investigate Problem 2

3. **Just the Math: Parent Functions** The graph of $y = x^2$ is called a **parent function** because the function $y = x^2$ represents the most basic quadratic function.

In Problem 1 you worked with *translations*. **Translations** are shifts (left, right, up, or down) of the graph of the parent function. In parts (B) and (C) of Problem 2, the graphs that you drew were either wider or narrower than the graph of the parent function. Finally, in part (D) of Problem 2, you **reflected,** or created the mirror image of the graph of the parent function, over the x-axis.

For each function below, identify the parent function. Then describe how the graph of the given function relates to the graph of the parent function. Use complete sentences in your answer.

$y = 10x^2$

Parent function: ______________________________

Relationship: ______________________________

____

$y = (x - 4)^2$

Parent function: ______________________________

Relationship: ______________________________

____

$y = -2x^2$

Parent function: ______________________________

Relationship: ______________________________

____

$y = 3x^2 + 2$

Parent function: ______________________________

Relationship: ______________________________

____

Investigate Problem 2

4. The graph of $y = x^2$ has been transformed into the graph below. Write an equation for the graph in vertex form.

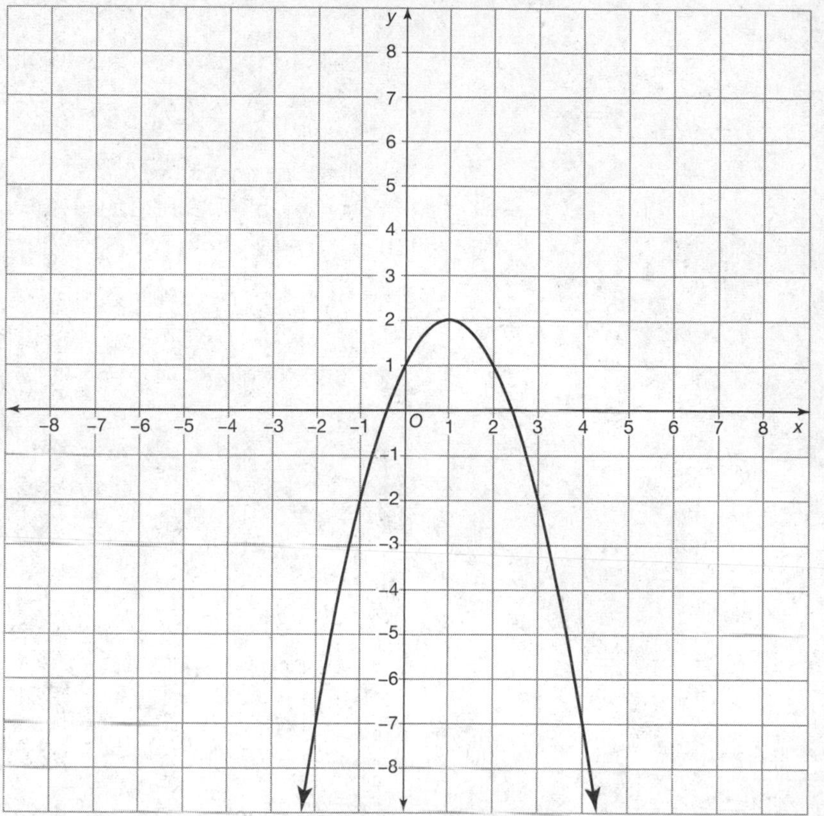

5. Your friend wants to program the movement of the parabola as described below in the table. She will later add intermediate steps to make the movement smooth. Your friend will begin with the graph of $y = x^2$. In each step, write the equation that will graph the parabola described. Then identify the vertex.

Step	Movement	Equation	Vertex
0	none	$y = x^2$	(0, 0)
1	reflection in *x*-axis		
2	right one unit, down two units		
3	left three units, down two units		

13

13.6 Science Fair

Introduction to Exponential Functions

Objectives

In this lesson, you will:

- Write and graph exponential functions.
- Identify translations of exponential functions.

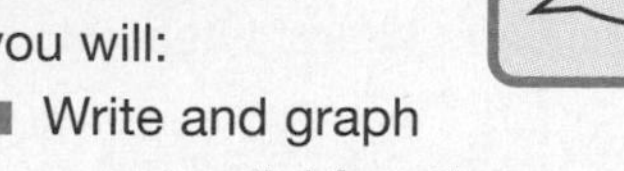

Key Term

- exponential function

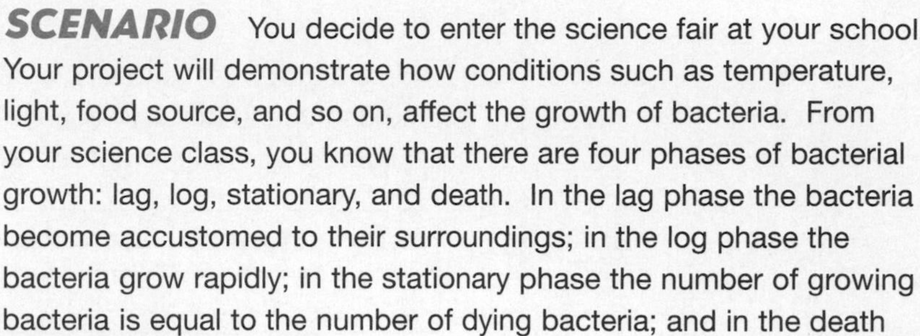

SCENARIO You decide to enter the science fair at your school. Your project will demonstrate how conditions such as temperature, light, food source, and so on, affect the growth of bacteria. From your science class, you know that there are four phases of bacterial growth: lag, log, stationary, and death. In the lag phase the bacteria become accustomed to their surroundings; in the log phase the bacteria grow rapidly; in the stationary phase the number of growing bacteria is equal to the number of dying bacteria; and in the death phase the bacteria die off.

Problem 1 Growing Bacteria

In your first experiment, you record the following data for the log phase of the bacterial growth.

Time since beginning of log phase (in hours)	Number of bacteria	
0	1	
1	2	
2	4	
3	8	
4	16	
5	32	

A. Assuming that the bacterial growth continues in this manner, how many bacteria will there be six hours after the beginning of the log phase? Use a complete sentence to explain how you found your answer.

B. Is there a pattern in the numbers of bacteria? If so, what is the pattern? Use a complete sentence in your answer.

C. Find the prime factorization of each number of bacteria. Record your results in the third column of the table.

Problem 1 Growing Bacteria

D. Write a function that gives the population, or number of bacteria, in terms of time. Let x be the amount of time in hours and let y be the number of bacteria.

E. Create a graph that shows the population as a function of time on the grid below. First, choose your bounds and intervals. Be sure to label your graph clearly.

Variable quantity	Lower bound	Upper bound	Interval

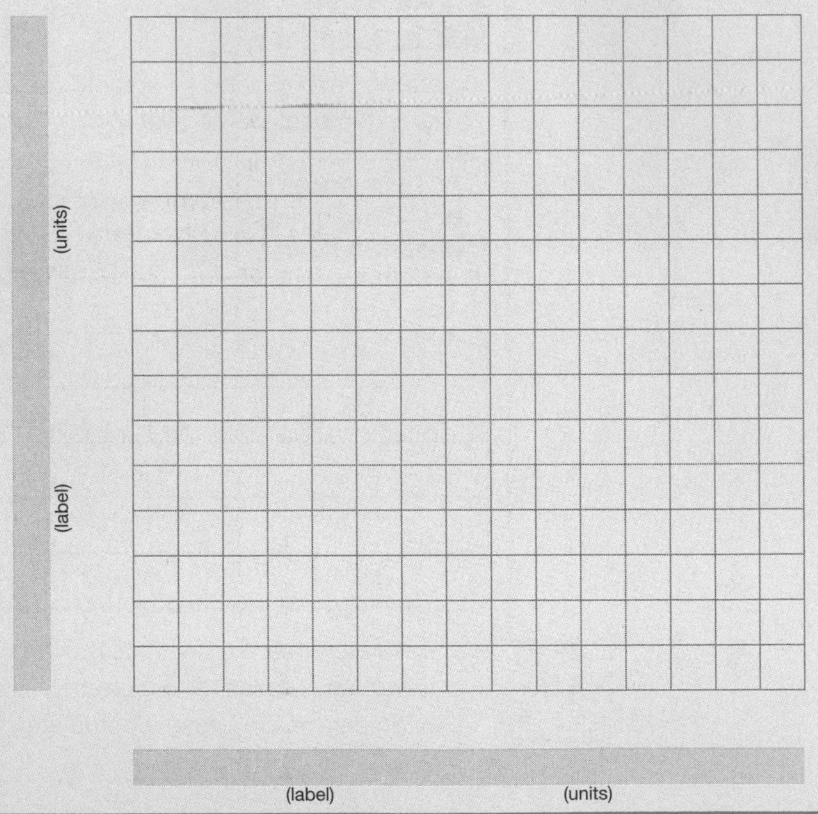

Investigate Problem 1

1. What is the domain of your function in the problem situation? Use a complete sentence in your answer.

Investigate Problem 1

13

What does the domain of your function represent in the problem situation?

What factors do you think will affect the length of the log phase? Use complete sentences in your answer.

What is the range of your function in the problem situation? Use a complete sentence in your answer.

2. **Just the Math: Exponential Functions** The function that you wrote in part (D) is an example of an *exponential function.* An **exponential function** is a function of the form $f(x) = a^x$ where $a > 0$ and $a \neq 1$. Why do you think that 1 is excluded as a base? Use a complete sentence in your answer.

3. Complete the table of values below for three different exponential functions.

x	$f(x) = 2^x$	$f(x) = 3^x$	$f(x) = \left(\frac{1}{2}\right)^x$
−3			
−2			
−1			
0			
1			
2			
3			

13

Investigate Problem 1

4. Graph each of the functions in Question 3 together on the grid.

5. Describe the graph of $f(x) = a^x$ when $a > 1$. Use a complete sentence in your answer.

Describe the graph of $f(x) = a^x$ when $0 < a < 1$. Use a complete sentence in your answer.

6. What do think happens to the graph of $f(x) = a^x$ ($a > 1$) as a gets larger? Use a complete sentence in your answer.

What do you think happens to the graph of $f(x) = a^x$ ($0 < a < 1$) as a gets smaller? Use a complete sentence in your answer.

Investigate Problem 1

7. What is the domain of an exponential function of the form $f(x) = a^x$? Use a complete sentence in your answer.

What is the range of an exponential function of the form $f(x) = a^x$? Use a complete sentence in your answer.

8. Complete the table of values below for the functions $f(x) = 2^x$, $g(x) = 2^x + 1$, and $h(x) = 2^x - 3$.

x	$f(x) = 2^x$	$g(x) = 2^x + 1$	$h(x) = 2^x - 3$
0			
1			
2			
3			
4			

How do you think the graphs of g and h are related to the graph of f? Use complete sentences to explain.

9. Complete the table of values below for the functions $f(x) = 2^x$, $g(x) = 2^{x+2}$, and $h(x) = 2^{x\ 1}$.

x	$f(x) = 2^x$	$g(x) = 2^{x+2}$	$h(x) = 2^{x-1}$
0			
1			
2			
3			
4			

How do you think the graphs of g and h are related to the graph of f? Use complete sentences to explain.

13

13.7 Money Comes and Money Goes

Exponential Growth and Decay

Objectives

In this lesson, you will:

- Write and use an exponential growth model.
- Write and use an exponential decay model.

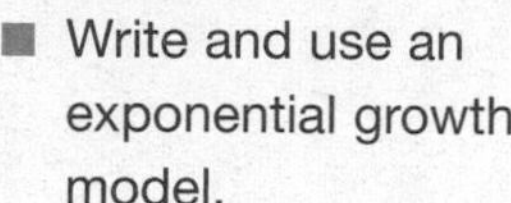

Key Terms

- simple interest
- compound interest
- exponential growth
- growth rate
- growth factor
- exponential decay
- decay rate
- decay factor

Take Note

The simple interest formula is $I = Prt$ where I is the interest earned in dollars, P is principal (the amount of money put into the account) in dollars, r is the interest rate in decimal form, and t is the time in years.

SCENARIO The value of money, cars, homes, and so on can change, for the better or for the worse. For instance, you could put your money into a savings account and earn interest on your money. You could also buy stock in a company and the value of your stock could rise or fall.

Problem 1 Compound Can Be Better than Simple

A. Suppose that you invest \$100 into a savings account that earns 3% interest for 3 years. Find the amount of simple interest that you earned at the end of the 3 year period. Show your work and use a complete sentence in your answer.

How much money do you have altogether? Use a complete sentence in your answer.

B. Find the amount of simple interest earned by depositing \$100 into an account that earns 3% interest for 1 year. Show your work and use a complete sentence in your answer.

How much money do you have altogether? Use a complete sentence in your answer.

C. Take the total amount of money that you have from part (B) and put it back into the same account for another year. Find the amount of simple interest that you earned after this year. Show your work and use a complete sentence in your answer.

How much money do you have altogether? Use a complete sentence in your answer.

13

Problem 1 Compound Can Be Better than Simple

D. Take the total amount of money that you have from part (C) and put it back into the same account for one more year. Find the amount of simple interest that you earned after this year. Show your work and use a complete sentence in your answer.

How much money do you have altogether? Use a complete sentence in your answer.

E. How does the total amount of money that you have in part (A) compare to the total amount of money that you have in part (D)?

In parts (B) through (D), the interest was **compounded.** In other words, the interest is earned not only on the principal, but on interest that was previously earned.

Take Note

The amount of money in an account is often called the balance of the account.

Investigate Problem 1

1. Create a table of values that shows the balance of the account in terms of time. The third and fourth columns of the table will be completed later.

Time (years)	Balance (dollars)	Balance in terms of previous balance	Balance in terms of original balance
0			
1			
2			
3			

2. For successive years, what percent of the previous balance is the new balance? Show your work. Round to the nearest whole percent if necessary.

Year 0 to year 1: ____________________

Year 1 to year 2: ____________________

Year 2 to year 3: ____________________

Investigate Problem 1

What do you notice about the percents? Use a complete sentence in your answer.

13

3. Write each balance in the table in terms of the previous balance. Record your answers in the third column of the table.

4. Write each balance in the table in terms of the original balance of the account. Record your answers in the fourth column of the table.

5. Write a function for the account balance y in dollars in terms of the time t in years since the account was opened.

6. **Just the Math: Exponential Growth Model** The function that you wrote in Question 5 is an *exponential growth model*. The general form of an **exponential growth model** is the equation $y = C(1 + r)^t$ where C is the original amount (of money, people, and so on) before any growth occurs, r is the **growth rate** in decimal form, $(1 + r)$ is the **growth factor,** t is the amount of time, and y is the new amount. What is the growth rate of your model in Question 5? What is the growth factor? Show your work and use a complete sentence in your answer.

7. You invest \$500 into a savings account that earns 2% interest, compounded yearly. Write a model for the account balance y after t years.

Take Note

In later courses, you will learn that compoundings can take place more often than yearly. When you compound interest yearly, you should use the exponential growth model in Question 6.

13

Investigate Problem 1

8. Complete the table of values that shows the account balance as a function of the number of years the account is open.

Quantity Name	Time	Account balance
Unit		
Expression		
	0	
	1	
	2	
	5	
	10	
	15	

9. Create a graph that shows the account balance as a function of time on the grid below. First, choose your bounds and intervals. Be sure to label your graph

Variable quantity	Lower bound	Upper bound	Interval

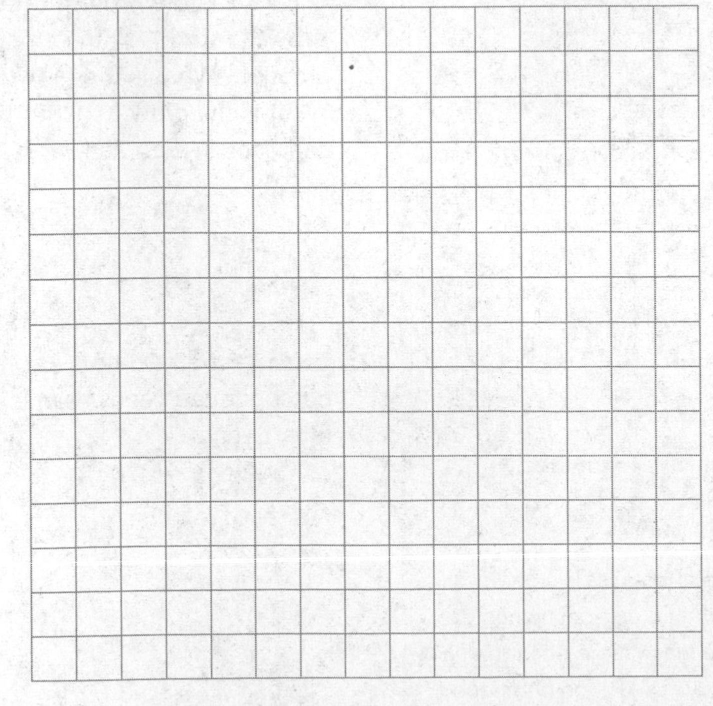

(label) (units)

Investigate Problem 1

13

10. Use your graph to determine how long you have to keep the account open in order to have a balance of $575. Use a complete sentence in your answer.

Use your graph to determine how long you have to keep the account open in order to have a balance of $650. Use a complete sentence in your answer.

Use your graph to determine the account balance after three years. Use a complete sentence in your answer.

11. Suppose that Lupe invests $1500 into a savings account that earns 4% simple interest. Domingo invests the same amount of money into a savings account that earns 4% interest compounded yearly. If neither Lupe nor Domingo has removed any money from their account after 10 years, how much money is in each account? Which account has earned more interest? Show your work and use complete sentences to explain your reasoning.

13

Problem 2 Losing Value

Whenever you buy an item like a car or a computer, the value of the item depreciates, or decreases, because once you start using the item, it is no longer in its original condition.

The value of a new car from the time it is bought over a five year period is shown in the table at the right.

Time (years)	Value (dollars)
0	15,000.00
1	9000.00
2	5400.00
3	3240.00
4	1944.00
5	1166.40

A. Create a graph that shows the car's value as a function of time on the grid below. First, choose your bounds and intervals. Be sure to label your graph clearly.

Variable quantity	Lower bound	Upper bound	Interval

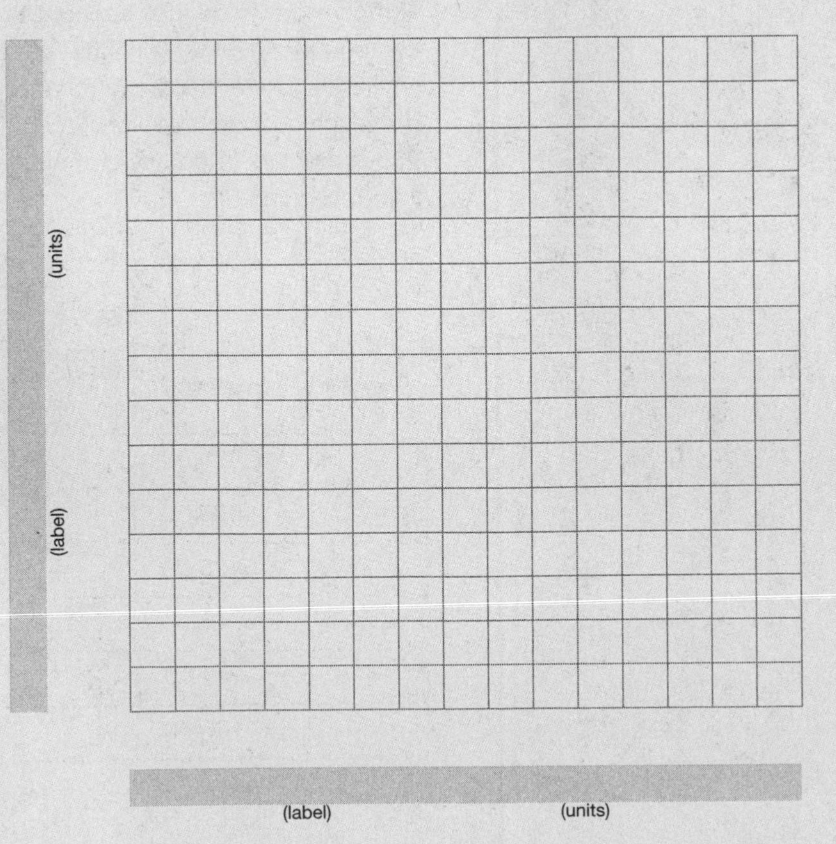

Problem 2 Losing Value

B. What kind of function would you use to model your graph? Use complete sentences to explain your reasoning.

13

Investigate Problem 2

1. For successive years, what percent of the previous value is the new value? Show your work.

Year 0 to year 1: ______________

Year 1 to year 2: ______________

Year 2 to year 3: ______________

Year 3 to year 4: ______________

Year 4 to year 5: ______________

What do you notice about the percents? Use a complete sentence in your answer.

2. Write each value in the table in terms of the previous value. Record your answers in the third column of the table.

Time (years)	Value (dollars)	Value in terms of previous value	Value in terms of original value
0	15,000.00		
1	9000.00		
2	5400.00		
3	3240.00		
4	1944.00		
5	1166.40		

13

Investigate Problem 2

3. Write each value in the table in terms of the original value of the car. Record your answers in the fourth column of the table.

4. Write a function for the value y of the car in dollars in terms of the time t in years since the car was bought.

5. **Just the Math: Exponential Decay Model** The function that you wrote in Question 4 is an *exponential decay model*. The general form of an **exponential decay model** is the equation $y = C(1 - r)^t$ where $0 < r < 1$, C is the original amount before any decay occurs, r is the **decay rate** in decimal form, $(1 - r)$ is the **decay factor,** t is the amount of time, and y is the new amount. What is the decay rate of your model in Question 4? Show your work and use a complete sentence in your answer.

6. According to this model, will the value of the car ever be $0? Why or why not? Use complete sentences in your answer.

   Is this reasonable? Explain your reasoning. Use a complete sentence in your answer.

7. How are the exponential growth model and exponential decay model similar? How are they different? Use complete sentences in your answer.

13.8 Camping

Special Topic: Logic

Objectives

In this lesson, you will:

- Prove a statement using a direct proof.
- Prove a statement using an indirect proof.
- Find a counterexample.

Key Terms

- logical reasoning
- proof
- direct proof
- counterexample
- indirect proof

SCENARIO A camping tent manufacturer has a writer on staff to create instruction sheets for the company's tents, one of which is shown below. The instruction sheets must include a list of all of the tent parts, diagrams, and written assembly instructions. Not only must the assembly instructions be in the correct order, but they must also be clearly written.

Problem 1 What's Your Order

The writer has the following parts list and diagram.

Parts

1 tent body
1 tent fly-cover
7 tent stakes
4 tent poles

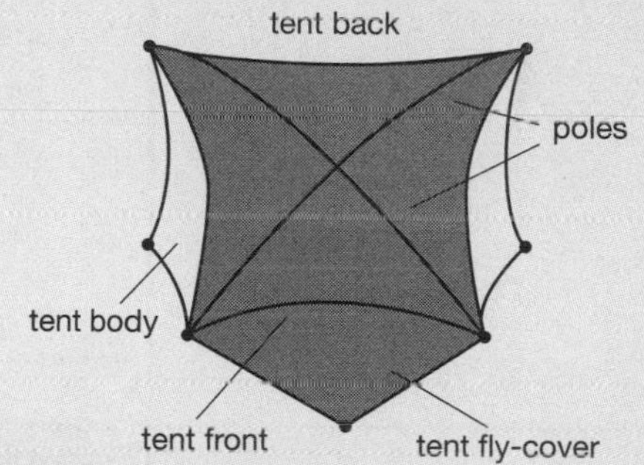

During a meeting with the tent designer, the writer comes up with the following steps, in no particular order.

a) Attach tent fly-cover over top of tent and put stake through loop and pound stake into the ground.

b) Assemble two pairs of tent poles.

c) Put stakes through the two loops at tent front and pound the stakes into the ground.

d) Select a site to place tent.

e) Pull tent fabric tight on one side of tent and put the stake through the loop at tent side and pound the stake into the ground.

f) Unpack tent and lay it on the ground where you want it so that the tent floor is on the bottom.

g) Pull tent fabric tight toward the back and put stakes through the two loops at tent back and pound the stakes into the ground.

h) Thread both tent poles through loops on top of tent.

i) Pull tent fabric tight on other side of tent and put a stake through the loop at tent side and pound the stake into the ground.

13

Problem 1 What's Your Order

A. What do you think should be the first step in the instructions? Why? Use complete sentences in your answer.

B. What do you think should be the last step in the instructions? Why? Use complete sentences in your answer.

C. Write the order of the steps for the instructions. You can identify the order by using the letters shown in Problem 1.

D. Could any of the steps be moved in your order so that the tent is still properly assembled? If so, identify the steps and explain why and where they could be moved. Use complete sentences in your answer.

Investigate Problem 1

Take Note

When you write a logical series of steps to demonstrate a statement, you are writing a **proof.**

1. When you completed the correct order of the tent assembly steps in Problem 1, you were using **logical reasoning.** You also use logical reasoning to simplify an expression or to prove a mathematical statement. To prove a mathematical statement means to use logical steps to show that the statement is true. Consider the statement

$(a + b)(a^2 - ab + b^2) = a^3 + b^3.$

The steps below, in no particular order, can be used to prove that this statement is true.

$= a^3 + b^3$	Additive Inverse
$= a(a^2) - a(ab) + a(b^2) + a^2b - b(ba) + b(b^2)$	Commutative Prop. of Mult.
$= a^3 - a^2b + ab^2 + a^2b - ab^2 + b^3$	Commutative Prop. of Mult.
$= a(a^2 - ab + b^2) + b(a^2 - ab + b^2)$	Distributive Prop.
$= a^3 - a^2b + a^2b + ab^2 - ab^2 + b^3$	Commutative Prop. of Addition
$= a(a^2) - a(ab) + a(b^2) + b(a^2) - b(ab) + b(b^2)$	Distributive Prop.
$= a^3 - a^2b + ab^2 + a^2b - b^2a + b^3$	Product of Powers

Investigate Problem 1

Write a proof that shows the steps in the correct order.

13

Take Note

Recall that you learned some of the rules of algebra in Lessons 4.4 and 4.5 and you used properties of exponents in Chapter 9.

2. **Just the Math: Direct Proof** The proof in Question 1 is a **direct proof.** Not only do you have to put the steps in the correct order, but you also have to use the rules of algebra. Use a direct proof to show that the following statement is true. Show all your work and give your reason for each step.

   $(a^2 - b^2)(a^2 + b^2) = a^4 - b^4$

3. **Just the Math: Counterexample** Your friend claims that the statement $(m + n)^2 = m^2 + n^2$ is true. You claim that it is false. Give an example that uses real numbers to show that the statement is false. An example that shows that a statement is not true is called a **counterexample.**

   Do you think that the statement $a - (b - c) = (a - b) - c$ is true? If so, give a proof. If not, give a counterexample.

Investigate Problem 1

4. **Just the Math: Indirect Proof** In some cases, it is better to prove that a statement is true by using an **indirect proof.** To indirectly prove that a statement is true, you begin by assuming that the conclusion, or end result, of the statement is false. If you can show that this assumption leads to an impossible result, then you have indirectly proven that the statement must be true.

Consider the following statement: If p^2 is an even integer, then p must be an even integer.

To indirectly prove that this statement is true, we will assume that the conclusion, p is an even integer, is false. So, assume that p is an odd integer.

If p is an odd integer, then it has the form $2n + 1$ where n is an integer (an even integer has the form $2n$ where n is an integer). Complete the following steps to finish the proof.

$p^2 = (\_\_\_\_\_\_\_\_)^2$ Substitute $2n + 1$ for p.

$p^2 = \_\_\_\_\_\_\_\_\_\_\_\_$ Find the product.

Does the expression $4n^2 + 4n$ represent an even number or an odd number? Use a complete sentence to explain your reasoning.

Is the expression $4n^2 + 4n + 1$ an even number or an odd number? Use a complete sentence to explain your reasoning.

What can you conclude about p^2? Use a complete sentence in your answer.

How does this answer complete the indirect proof? Use a complete sentence in your answer.

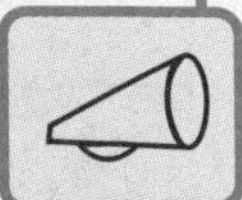

Take Note

To say than an even integer has the form $2n$ where n is an integer is the same as saying that an even integer is an integer that is divisible by 2.

Glossary

absolute deviation

The absolute deviation is the absolute value of the difference between a data value and the mean of the data set.

Example

The mean of the data set 2, 3, 9, and 13 is 6.75.

The data value 2 has an absolute deviation of 4.75.

The data value 3 has an absolute deviation of 3.75.

The data value 9 has an absolute deviation of 2.25.

The data value 13 has an absolute deviation of 6.25.

absolute value

The absolute value of a number is the distance between zero and the point that represents the number on a real number line. The absolute value of a number is always greater than or equal to zero.

Example

$|5| = 5$ because 5 is 5 units from 0 on the number line.
$|-3| = 3$ because -3 is 3 units from 0 on the number line.

additive identity

The additive identity is a number such that when you add it to a second number, the sum is the second number.

Example

The additive identity is the number 0. $0 + 2 = 2$

additive inverse

The additive inverse of a number is the number such that the sum of the given number and its additive inverse is 0 (the additive identity).

Example

The additive inverse of 5 is -5 because $5 + (-5) = 0$.

algebraic equation

An algebraic equation is an expression used to generalize a problem situation, formed by writing an equals sign between two algebraic expressions.

Example

The statement $10 = 2x + 3$ is an equation.

algebraic expression

An algebraic expression is a mathematical phrase consisting of numbers, variables, and operations.

Example

If one pizza costs $7 and a pizza shop charges a $2.50 delivery charge, the cost of buying one or more pizzas can be represented by the algebraic expression $7p + 2.50$, where p is the number of pizzas purchased.

area

The area of a figure is the number of square units needed to cover the figure.

Example

The area of the rectangle is 18 square units.

The area of the triangle is 10 square units.

The area of circle is about 19.63 square units.

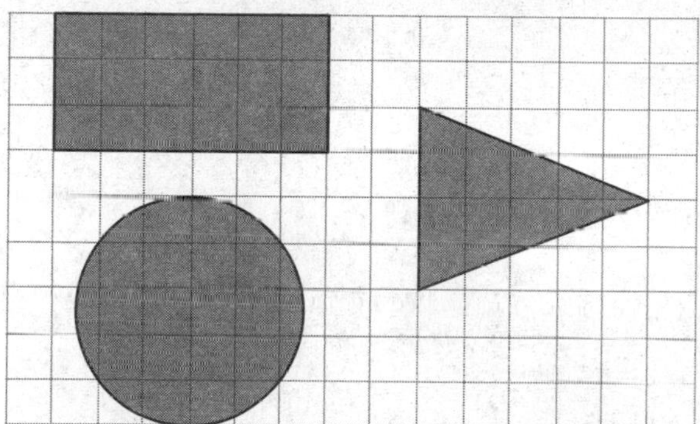

area model

An area model is a method for multiplying two polynomials. Each polynomial represents a side length. The area of the rectangle is the product of the polynomials.

Example

The product of the polynomials $3x$ and $4x + 1$ can be represented by using an area model. The product is equal to the area, which is $12x^2 + 3x$.

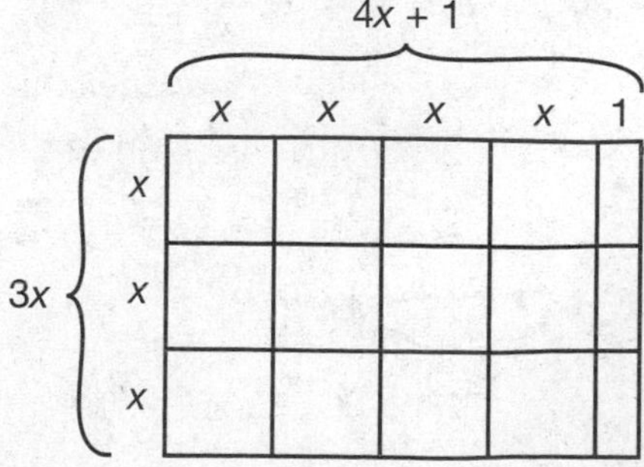

Glossary

area of a square

The area of a square is equal to the side length of the square multiplied by itself: $A = (s)(s) = s^2$.

Example

In square *ABCD*, the length of each side is 12 centimeters. So, the area of the square is $A = (12)(12) = 144$ square centimeters.

axis of symmetry

An axis of symmetry is a line that passes through a figure and divides the figure into two symmetrical parts that are mirror images of each other.

Example

Line *K* is the axis of symmetry of the parabola.

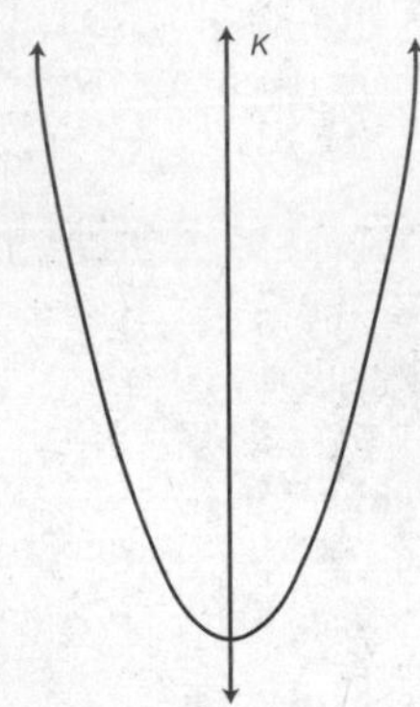

balance

A balance is the amount of money in an account.

Example

Carla opens a checking account with $200. She writes a check for $50. The balance of her checking account is $150.

bar graph

A bar graph is a graph that uses parallel bars to represent data. The heights of the bars represent quantities from the data set.

Example

The bar graph represents John's earnings over a four-week period.

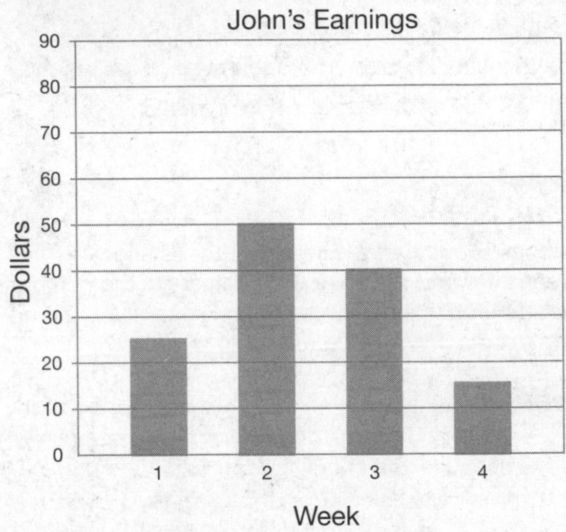

base of a power

The base of a power is the repeated factor in a power.

Example

In the expression 3^5, the number 3 is the base. $3^5 = (3)(3)(3)(3)(3) = 243$.

biased sample

A biased sample is a sample that does not accurately represent all of a population.

Example

A survey is conducted asking students their favorite class. Only students in the math club are surveyed. The sample of students is a biased sample.

bimodal

A data set is bimodal if two values occur in the data set the same number of times.

Example

The data set 1, 1, 3, 3, 4, 5, 7 is bimodal.

binomial

A binomial is a polynomial with exactly two terms.

Example

The polynomial $3x + 5$ is a binomial.

bounds

The lower and upper bounds determine the portion of a graph that you will see. The data that you are graphing should be greater than the lower bounds and less than the upper bounds.

Example

In this graph, the lower bound for the x-axis is 0 and the upper bound for the x-axis is 300. The lower bound for the y-axis is 0 and the upper bound for the y-axis is 225.

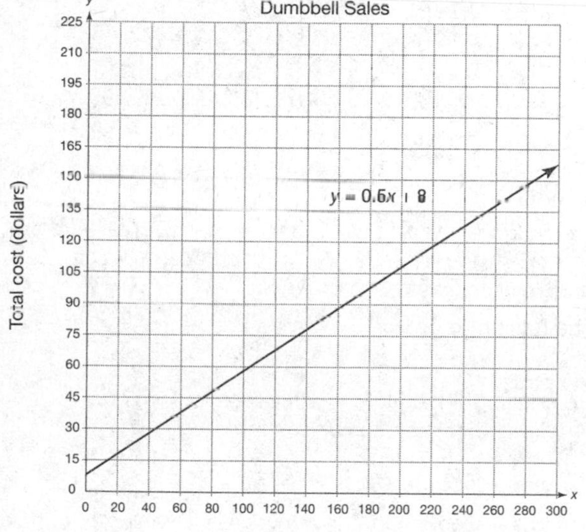

box-and-whisker plot

A box-and-whisker plot is a visual display of data that organizes the data values into four groups using the upper and lower bounds, the median, and the upper and lower quartiles.

Example

The box-and-whisker plots compare the test scores from two algebra classes.

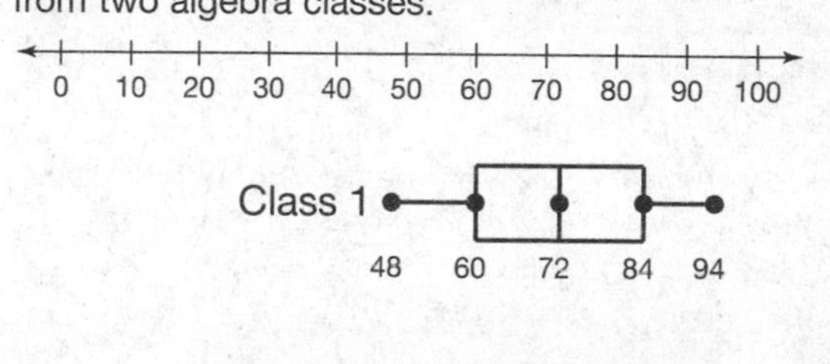

Cartesian coordinate system

A Cartesian coordinate system is a method of representing the location of a point using an ordered pair of real numbers of the form (x, y).

Example

Point J is represented by the ordered pair (5, 4).

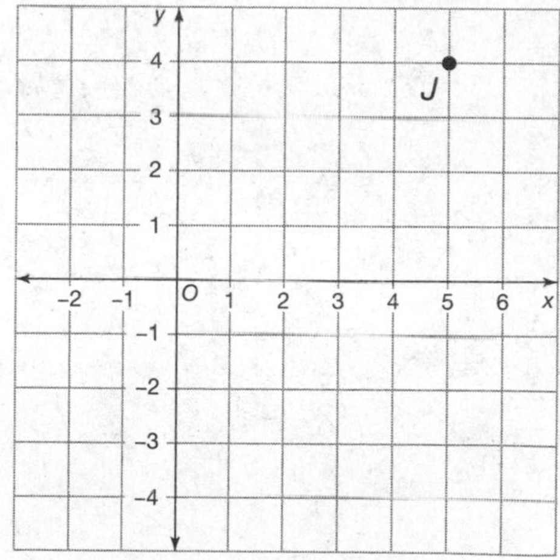

closure property

The closure property states that a set of numbers is closed under an operation if the result of the operation on two numbers in the set is a number in the set.

Example

The set of whole number numbers is closed under addition. The sum of any two whole numbers is always another whole number.

Glossary

coefficient

In a term containing a number multiplied by one or more variables, the number is the coefficient of the term.

Example

The term $3x^5$ has a coefficient of 3.

combination

A combination is a selection of objects from a group of objects for which the order of the items chosen does not matter.

Example

Choosing two pizza toppings from five possible toppings is a combination.

combination of distinct objects taken *r* at a time

A combination of *n* distinct objects taken *r* at a time is the number of groupings of *n* objects taken *r* at a time and is given by ${}_nC_r = \dfrac{n!}{(n-r)!r!}$.

Example

You choose two pizza toppings from five possible toppings.

$$
\begin{aligned}
{}_nC_r &= \frac{n!}{(n-r)!r!} \\
&= \frac{5!}{(5-2)!2!} \\
&= \frac{5!}{3!2!} \\
&= \frac{120}{(6)(2)} \\
&= \frac{120}{12} \\
&= 10
\end{aligned}
$$

combine like terms

To combine like terms is to add or subtract like terms.

Example

The expression $5x + 3x$ can be simplified to $8x$ by combining like terms.

commission

A commission is a fee or a percent of sales that are paid to a sales representative or an agent for services rendered.

Example

A sales person is to receive a 5% commission on her sales. Suppose that she sells $500 worth of merchandise. Her commission will be $25: 5% of 500 = (0.05)(500) = 25.

common factor

A common factor is a whole number that is a factor of two or more integers or expressions.

Example

The whole number 2 is a common factor of 6 and 8.

complementary events

Two events are complementary if one event or the other event must occur, but not both.

Example

A coin landing heads up and a coin landing tails up are complementary events.

completing the square

Completing the square is a process for writing a quadratic expression in vertex form.

Example

To write the equation $y = x^2 + 10x + 2$ in vertex form, perform the following steps.

$$
\begin{aligned}
y &= x^2 + 10x + 2 \\
y &= x^2 + 10x + 25 + 2 - 25 \\
y &= (x + 5)^2 - 23
\end{aligned}
$$

composite number

A composite number is a whole number greater than 1 that is divisible by 1, itself, and at least one other positive number.

Example

The first five composite numbers are 4, 6, 8, 9, and 10.

compound event

A compound event is an event that is made up of two or more simple events.

Example

Choosing two socks from a drawer is a compound event.

compound inequality

A compound inequality is formed by two inequalities that are connected by the word "and" or the word "or."

Example

The statement $x > 5$ or $x > -5$ is a compound inequality.

compound interest

Compound interest is interest on both the principal and previously earned interest.

Example

Sonya opens a savings account with $100. She earns $4 in interest the first year. The compound interest y is found by using the equation $y = 100(1 + 0.04)^t$, where t is the time in years.

congruent figures

Two figures are congruent if they have the same size and the same shape.

Example

Triangle ABC and triangle DEF are congruent triangles.

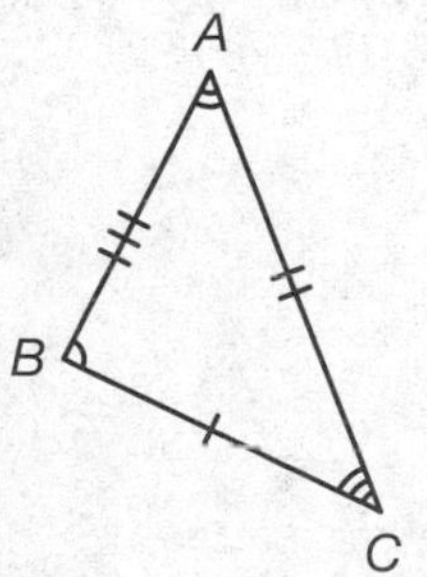

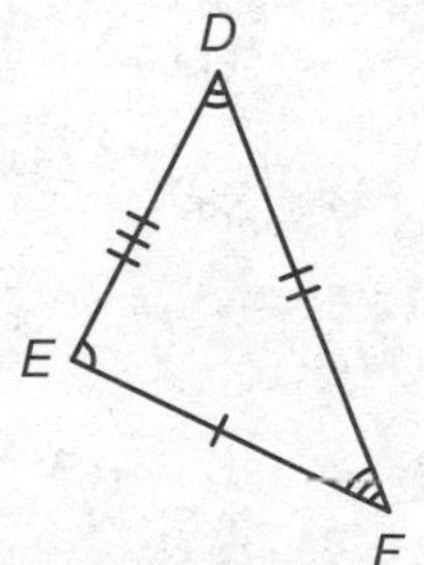

conjecture

A conjecture is a possible explanation that can be tested by further investigation.

Example

Stating that more people in a school are right-handed is a conjecture.

constant ratio

A constant ratio is a ratio that has a constant value.

Example

A recipe for fruit punch specifies 1 cup of cranberry juice for every 2 cups of apple juice. The ratio of the amount of cranberry juice to the amount of apple juice is a constant ratio.

converse

The converse of an if-then statement is the statement that results from interchanging the hypothesis (the "if" part) and the conclusion (the "then" part) of the original statement.

Example

The converse of the statement "If $a = 0$ or $b = 0$, then $ab = 0$" is "If $ab = 0$, then $a = 0$ or $b = 0$."

converse of the Pythagorean theorem

The converse of the Pythagorean Theorem states that if a, b, and c are sides of a triangle and $a^2 + b^2 = c^2$, then the triangle is a right triangle.

Example

In triangle ABC, the lengths of the sides are 5 inches, 10 inches, and 12 inches. To determine whether the triangle is a right triangle, substitute the side lengths into the Pythagorean theorem.

$$a^2 + b^2 = c^2$$
$$5^2 + 10^2 \stackrel{?}{=} 12^2$$
$$25 + 100 \stackrel{?}{=} 144$$
$$125 \neq 144$$

The expression is false, so the triangle is not a right triangle.

Glossary

coordinate plane

A coordinate plane is a plane formed by the intersection of a vertical real number line and a horizontal real number line. The vertical number line is the y-axis and the horizontal number line is the x-axis. The number lines intersect at right angles and the point of intersection is the origin.

Example

The origin is labeled on the coordinate plane below.

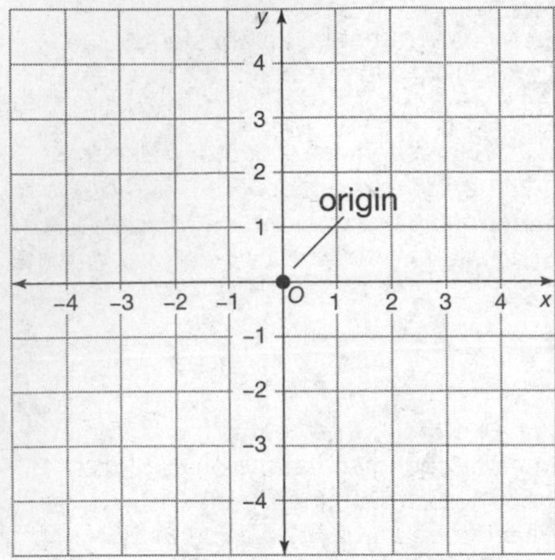

correlation

A correlation exists between the x- and y-values of a data set when it is appropriate to use a line of best fit to approximate a collection of points.

Example

A correlation does not exist for this data set.

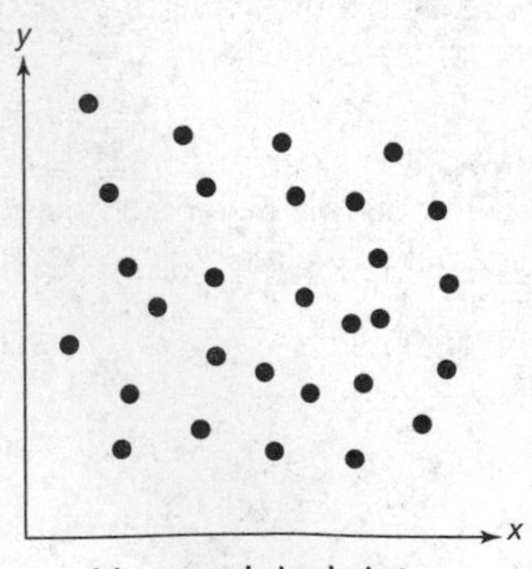

Uncorrelated data

correlation coefficient

The correlation coefficient, r, indicates how close the data are to forming a straight line. If the value of r is between 0 and 1, the linear regression equation has a positive slope. If the value is between 0 and -1, the linear regression equation has a negative slope. The closer r is to 1 or -1, the closer the data are to being in a straight line.

Example

The correlation coefficient for the data is –0.9935. The value is negative so the equation has a negative slope. The value is close to –1 so the data is very close to forming a straight line.

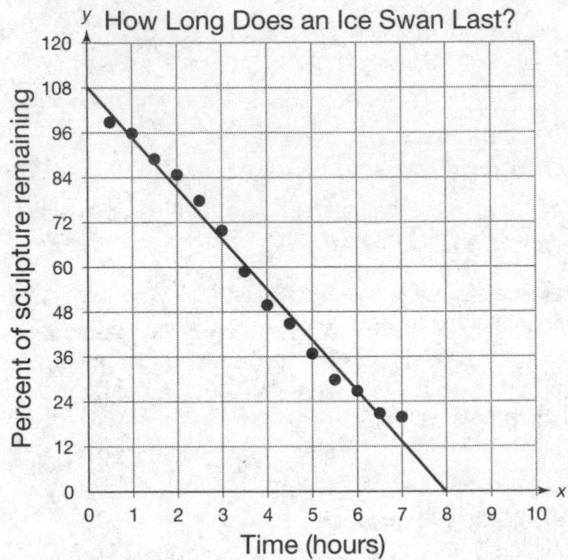

corresponding sides

Corresponding sides of two similar or congruent figures are pairs of sides that are in the same relative position in both figures.

Example

Side lengths AB and DE are corresponding sides in similar triangles ABC and DEC.

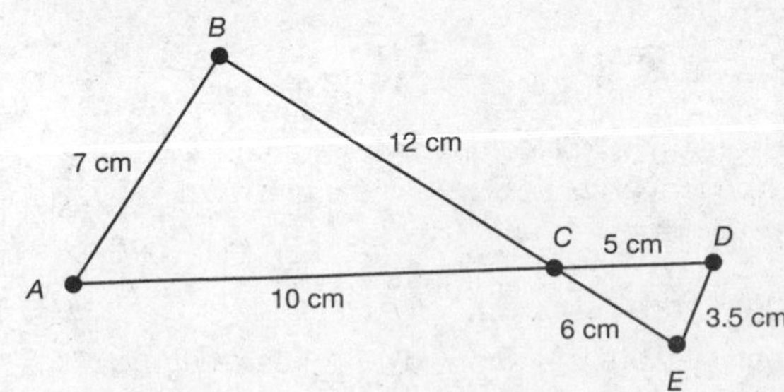

Glossary

counterexample

A counterexample is an example that shows that a statement is not true.

Example

Your friend claims that you add fractions by adding the numerators and adding the denominators.

A counterexample is $\frac{1}{2} + \frac{1}{2}$. The sum of these two fractions is 1. Your friend's method results in $\frac{2}{4}$, or $\frac{1}{2}$. Your friend's method is incorrect.

cube root

The cube root of a given number is a number that, when cubed, equals the given number.

Example

The cube root of 8 is 2.

decay factor

The decay factor is the expression $(1 - r)$ in the exponential decay equation.

Example

Your uncle bought a car for $20,000. The value of the car decreases 30% each year. A model for the value of the car after t years is $y = 20{,}000(1 - 0.3)^t$.

The decay factor is 0.70.

decay rate

The decay rate is the variable r in the exponential decay equation, written in decimal form.

Example

Your uncle bought a car for $20,000. The value of the car decreases 30% each year. A model for the value of the car after t years is $y = 20{,}000(1 - 0.3)^t$.

The decay rate is 0.30.

degree of a polynomial

The degree of a polynomial in one variable is the exponent of that variable with the largest numerical value.

Example

The polynomial $2x^3 + 5x^2 - 6x + 1$ has a degree of 3.

demand

The demand is the amount of a good that is used.

Example

The demand for oil in the world can be modeled by the equation $y = 360.1x + 15.179$, where x is the time, in years, since 1965 and y is the demand for oil, in millions of barrels.

dependent events

Dependent events are events in which the outcome of one event affects the outcome of the other event.

Example

Choosing a sock from a drawer, keeping the sock, and choosing another sock from the drawer are dependent events.

dependent variable

A dependent variable, or output value of a function, is a variable whose value is determined by an independent variable, or input value of a function.

Example

In the relationship between driving time and distance traveled, distance is represented by the dependent variable d because the value of d depends on the value of the driving time t.

deviation

The deviation of a data value is the difference between a data value and the mean of the data set.

Example

The mean of the data set 2, 3, 9, and 13 is 6.75.

The data value 2 has a deviation of –4.75.

The data value 3 has a deviation of –3.75.

The data value 9 has a deviation of 2.25.

The data value 13 has a deviation of 6.25.

dilation

A dilation is a transformation of a figure in which the figure stretches or shrinks with respect to a fixed point. The scale factor of a dilation is the ratio of a side length of the dilated figure to the original figure. An enlargement or reduction of a photo is an example of a dilation.

Example

The original light hexagon is dilated to produce the dark hexagon by a scale factor of 2.

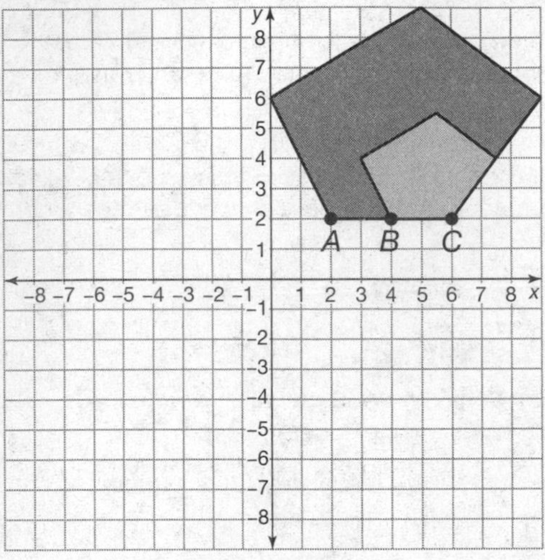

direct proof

To prove that a statement is true by using a direct proof, put all the steps in order using mathematical rules.

Example

To prove the statement $(a - b)(a^2 + ab + b^2) = a^3 - b^3$, use the following direct proof.

$(a - b)(a^2 + ab + b^2)$

$= a(a^2 + ab + b^2) - b(a^2 + ab + b^2)$

Distributive property

$= a(a^2) + a(ab) + a(b^2) - b(a^2) - b(ab) - b(b^2)$

Distributive Property of Multiplication Over Addition

$= a^3 + a^2b + ab^2 - a^2b - ab^2 - b^3$

Product of Powers

$= a^3 - b^3$

Additive Inverse

direct variation

Direct variation is the relationship between two quantities x and y having a constant ratio; one quantity varies directly with the other.

Example

The relationship between the variables x and y in the equation $y = 2x$ is a direct relationship.

discriminant

In a quadratic equation $ax^2 + bx + c = 0$, the discriminant is equal to the expression $b^2 - 4ac$.

Example

In the quadratic equation $x^2 + 2x - 24 = 0$, the discriminant is equal to $2^2 - 4(1)(-24)$, or 100.

distance formula

The distance formula can be used to find the distance between two points.

The distance between points (x_1, y_1) and (x_2, y_2) is $d = \sqrt{(x_2 - x_1)^2 + (y_2 - y_1)^2}$.

Example

To find the distance between the points (–1, 4) and (2, –5), substitute the coordinates into the Distance Formula.

$d = \sqrt{(x_2 - x_1)^2 + (y_2 - y_1)^2}$

$d = \sqrt{(2 + 1)^2 + (-5 - 4)^2}$

$d = \sqrt{3^2 + (-9)^2}$

$d = \sqrt{9 + 81}$

$d = \sqrt{90}$

$d \approx 9.49$

So, the distance between the points (–1, 4) and (2, –5) is approximately 9.49 units.

distribution

A distribution is the way in which the data are distributed, such as being spread out or clustered together.

Example

Skewed to the Right

symmetric

distributive property

The distributive property states that for any numbers a, b, and c it is true that $a(b + c) = ab + ac$.

Example

The distributive property can be used to write the expression $2(x + 4)$ as $2x + 8$.

domain of a function

The domain of a function is the set of all input values for the function.

Example

The domain of the function $y = 2x$ is the set of all real numbers.

equivalent equations

Two equations are equivalent if they have the same solution or solutions.

Example

The equations $x + y = 1$ and $2x + 2y = 2$ are equivalent.

estimation

Estimation is the process of finding the approximate value of an expression, often done through rounding.

Example

To estimate 697 + 309, round 697 to 700 and round 309 to 300. Then you can estimate that 697 + 309 is approximately 700 + 300, or 1000.

evaluate an expression

To evaluate an expression, find the value of the expression by replacing each variable with a given value and then simplifying the result.

Example

To evaluate $3x + 6$ when $x = 5$, replace the x by 5, and then simplify.

$$\begin{aligned}(3)(5) + 6 &= 15 + 6\\ &= 21\end{aligned}$$

event

A simple event is a collection of outcomes of an experiment. An outcome is one possible result of an experiment.

Example

Flipping a coin or rolling a number cube is a simple event.

excluded value

An excluded value is a number that causes the denominator of a rational expression to equal zero.

Example

The excluded value for the rational expression $\frac{2x + 1}{x - 3}$ is $x = 3$.

experiment

An experiment is a test to demonstrate a known truth.

Example

You want to find the probability of a coin landing heads up. One experiment is flipping a coin 100 times and recording the results.

experimental probability

An experimental probability is a probability that is based on repeated trials of an experiment.

Example

You want to find the probability of a coin landing heads up. You flip a coin 100 times and record the results. The coin lands heads up 55 times and lands tails up 45 times. The experimental probability of the coin landing heads up is $\frac{55}{100}$.

exponent of a power

The exponent of a power is the number of times that the factor is repeated.

Example

In the expression 10^3, the number 3 is the exponent. This indicates that the base 10 is used as a factor 3 times: $10^3 = (10)(10)(10) = 1000$.

exponential decay model

The general form of an exponential decay model is the equation $y = C(1 - 4)^t$ where $0 < r < 1$, C is the original amount before any decay occurs, r is the decay rate in decimal form, $(1 - r)$ is the decay factor, t is the amount of time, and y is the new amount.

Example

Your uncle bought a car for \$20,000. The value of the car decreases 30% each year. A model for the value of the car after t years is $y = 20{,}000(1 - 0.3)^t$.

exponential function

An exponential function is a function of the form $f(x) = a^x$ where $a > 0$ and $a \neq 1$.

Example

The function $y = 2^x$ is an exponential function.

exponential growth model

The general form of an exponential growth model is the equation $y = C(1 + r)^t$ where C is the original amount before any growth occurs, r is the growth rate in decimal form, $(1 + r)$ is the growth factor, t is the amount of time, and y is the new amount.

Example

You invest \$1000 into a savings account that earns 2.5% interest, compounded annually. A model for the account balance after t years is $y = 1000(1 + 0.025)^t$.

expression

An expression is any symbolic mathematical phrase that may include constants, variables, and operators.

Examples

Three expressions are shown below.

$5y$ $\quad 4x - 2$ $\quad 6^3 + 8$

extracting square roots

Extracting square roots is the process of recognizing that $x = \sqrt{b}$ and $x = -\sqrt{b}$ satisfy the equation $x^2 = b$.

Example

The equation $x^2 = 10$ has two solutions; $x = \sqrt{10}$ and $x = -\sqrt{10}$.

extreme

An extreme is the greatest and least value of a data set. The greatest value is called the upper extreme and the least value is called the lower extreme.

Example

The upper extreme of the numbers 1, 5, 7, 10, 14 is 14. The lower extreme is 1.

extremes of a proportion

The extremes of a proportion are the two outside quantities of a proportion.

Example

In the proportion 3 dimes: 5 quarters:: 15 dimes: 25 quarters, the extremes are the outside quantities 3 dimes and 25 quarters.

factor an expression

To factor an expression is to use the distributive property in reverse.

Example

The expression $2x + 4$ can be factored as $2(x + 2)$.

factor of a number

A factor of a number is a number that evenly divides the given number with no remainder.

Example

The number 24 has eight factors: 1, 2, 3, 4, 6, 8, 12, and 24.

factor of a polynomial

A factor of a polynomial is a polynomial that evenly divides the given polynomial with no remainder.

Example

The polynomial $x^2 + 5x + 6$ has two factors: $x + 2$ and $x + 3$.

factorial

The factorial of a number n is the product of all of the positive integers less than or equal to n. The factorial of n is expressed using the notation $n!$

Example

$5! = 5 \cdot 4 \cdot 3 \cdot 2 \cdot 1 = 120$

factoring a polynomial

Factoring is the process of expressing a polynomial as the product of monomials and binomials.

Example

The polynomial $x^2 + 5x + 6$ can be written in factored form as $(x + 2)(x + 3)$.

factoring out a common factor

Factoring out a common factor is a method of factoring a polynomial where the polynomial is written as the product of the common factor of all terms on the remaining polynomial.

Example

$2x^3 - 6x^2 + 8x = 2x(x^2 - 3x + 4)$

fair game

A fair game is a game in which each player has an equally likely chance of winning.

Example

You are playing a two-player game with your friend using two six-sided number cubes. In each round, one player is the roller and one player is the recorder. If the sum of the numbers on a roller's turn is even, the roller gets one point. If the sum of the numbers on a roller's turn is odd, the recorder gets one point. The winner of the round is the player who has the most points after 20 rolls.

The probability that the roll results in an even number is $\frac{18}{36}$, or $\frac{1}{2}$.

The probability that the roll results in an odd number is $\frac{18}{36}$, or $\frac{1}{2}$.

After 20 rolls, you can expect 10 even rolls and 10 odd rolls which results in 10 points for the roller and 10 points for the recorder. This game is fair.

favorable outcome

A favorable outcome is a specific outcome chosen for a particular event.

Example

You are finding the probability of rolling an even number with a six-sided number cube. There are three favorable outcomes: rolling a 2, 4, or 6.

first quartile

The first quartile, Q_1, is the median of the lower half of the data.

Example

In the data set 13, 17, 23, 24, 25, 29, 31, 45, 46, 53, 60, the median, 29, divides the data into two halves. The first quartile, 23, is the median of the lower half of the data.

13 17 23 24 25 29 31 45 46 53 60

lower quartile (23) — median (29) — upper quartile (46)

FOIL pattern

The FOIL pattern is a method for finding the product of two binomials by multiplying the first terms, the outer terms, the inner terms, and the last terms.

Example

$(x - 1)(2x + 5) = 2x^2 + 5x - 2x - 5 = 2x^2 + 3x - 5$

function

A function is a relation in which for every input there is exactly one output.

Example

The equation $y = 2x$ is a function. Every value of x has exactly one corresponding y-value.

function notation

Function notation is a notation used to write functions such that the dependent variable is replaced with the name of the function.

Example

In the function $f(x) = 0.75x$, f is the name of the function, x represents the domain, and $f(x)$ represents the range.

fundamental counting principle

The fundamental counting principle states that if you have m choices for one event and n choices for another event, then the number of choices for both events is $m \cdot n$.

Example

You flip a coin and then roll a six-sided number cube. There are 2 choices for flipping a coin and 6 choices for rolling the number cube. The number of choices for both events is $2 \cdot 6$, or 12.

geometric probability

A geometric probability is the ratio of a desired length, area, or volume to the total length, area, or volume.

Example

A circular dartboard has a radius of 6.75 inches. The radius of the circular bull's-eye is 0.5 inch. To find the probability of hitting the bull's-eye, find the ratio of the area of the bull's-eye to the total area of the dart board.

$$\text{Probability} = \frac{\text{Area of bull's-eye}}{\text{Area of dart board}} \approx \frac{3.14(0.5)^2}{3.14(6.75)^2}$$

$$= \frac{(0.5)^2}{(6.75)^2} = \frac{0.25}{45.5625} = 0.0055$$

So, the probability of hitting the bull's-eye is 0.0055, or 0.55%.

graph

A graph is a visual representation of the relationship between two sets of values as points in a coordinate plane.

Example

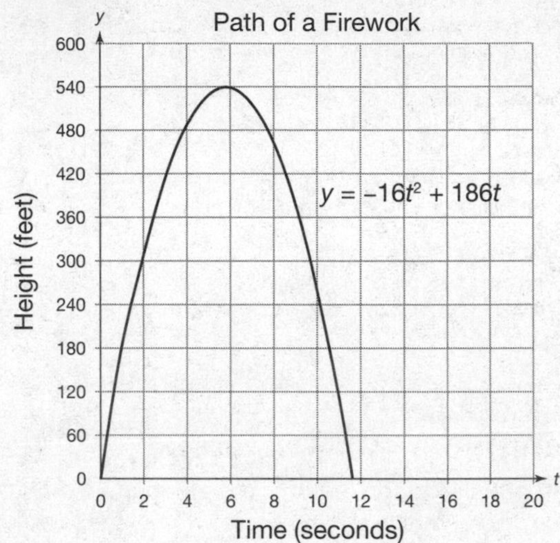

graph of an inequality

The graph of an inequality in one variable is the set of all points that make the inequality true.

Example

The inequality $x > 5$ is represented by the graph shown.

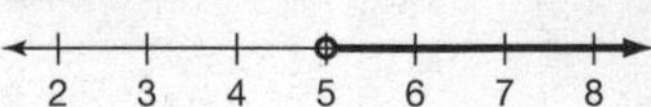

greatest common factor

The greatest common factor of two whole numbers is the largest whole number that is a factor of both numbers. The greatest common factor is abbreviated as GCF.

Example

The whole number 3 is the greatest common factor of 6 and 9.

gross pay

Gross pay is the total amount of money an employee earns before any taxes or deductions are subtracted.

Example

Nadia's gross pay was $2400 per month.

Glossary

growth factor

The growth factor is the expression $(1 + r)$ in the exponential growth equation.

Example

You invest $1000 into a savings account that earns 2.5% interest, compounded annually. A model for the account balance after t years is $y = 1000(1 + 0.025)^t$.

The growth factor is 1.025.

growth rate

The growth rate is the variable r in the exponential growth equation, written in decimal form.

Example

You invest $1000 into a savings account that earns 2.5% interest, compounded annually. A model for the account balance after t years is $y = 1000(1 + 0.025)^t$.

The growth rate is 0.025.

half-plane

A half-plane is the graph of a linear inequality or half a coordinate plane.

Example

The shaded portion of the graph is a half-plane.

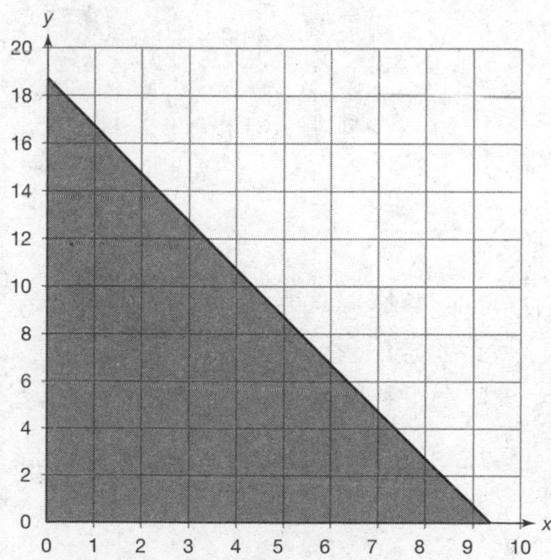

hypotenuse of a right triangle

In a right triangle, the hypotenuse is the side of the triangle that is opposite the right angle.

Example

In triangle ABC, angle A is the right angle, so side BC is the hypotenuse. In triangle DEF, angle F is the right angle, so side DE is the hypotenuse.

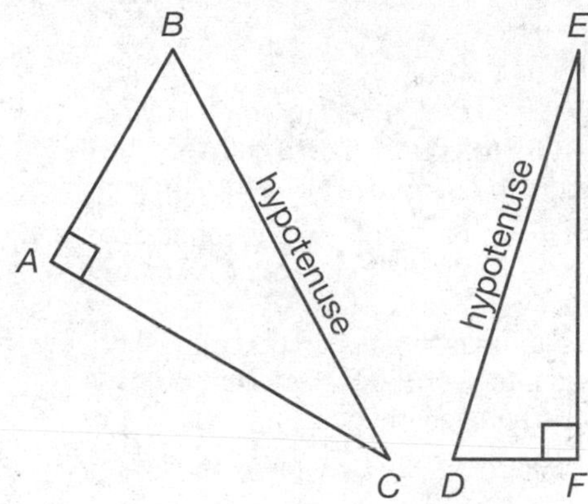

income

Income is the amount of money that a company earns.

Example

A company makes $10,000 before expenses are considered. The company's expenses are $8000. The company's income is $10,000.

independent events

Independent events are two events in which the outcome of the first event does not affect the probability of the second event.

Example

Choosing a sock from a drawer, replacing the sock, and choosing another sock from the drawer are independent events.

independent variable

An independent variable, or input value, is a variable whose value is not determined by another variable.

Example

In the relationship between driving time and distance traveled, time is represented by the independent variable t because the value of t does not depend on any variable.

index

An index is a number used to indicate what root is to be determined. It is placed above and to the left of the radical sign.

Example

In the radical expression $\sqrt[4]{16}$, 4 is the index.

indirect proof

To prove that a statement is true using an indirect proof, assume that the conclusion is false. If the assumption leads to an impossible result, then the statement must be true.

Example

To prove the statement "If p^2 is an odd integer, then p must be an odd integer" using an indirect proof, assume that p is an even integer.

If p is an even integer, it can be written as $p = 2n$.

$p^2 = (2n)^2$
$p^2 = 4n^2$

The expression $4n^2$ is even because it can be written as $2(2n^2)$. If $4n^2$ is even then p^2 must be even. This is impossible because p^2 is given as odd.

So, the statement "If p^2 is an odd integer, then p must be an odd integer" must be true.

inequality

An inequality is a statement that one expression is less than, less than or equal to, greater than or equal to, or greater than another expression. The inequality symbols are <, >, ≤, and ≥.

Example

The statement $y < 2x + 5$ is an inequality.

inequality symbol

An inequality symbol is one of the symbols for less than (<), greater than (>), less than or equal to (≤), or greater than or equal to (≥).

input value

An input value is the first coordinate of an ordered pair in a relation.

Example

The ordered pair (5, 8) has an input value of 5.

integer

An integer is any of the numbers –4, –3, –2, 1, 0, 1, 2, 3, 4, 5, ... Integers include all of the whole numbers and their additive inverses.

Examples

The numbers –12, 0, and 30 are integers.

intercept

An intercept is the point where a graph intersects the x- or y-axis.

Example

In the graph below, the points x-intercept is 1 and the y-intercept is –3.

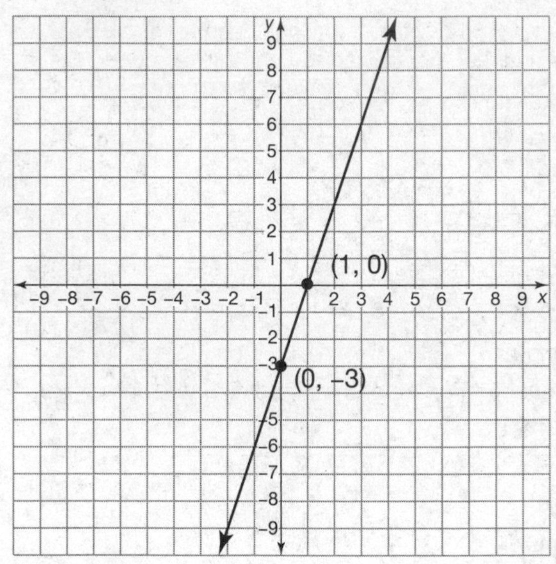

interest

Interest is the amount that is charged for borrowing money or the amount that is earned from saving money.

Example

Derek earned $13.58 in interest from his savings account.

Glossary

interquartile range

The interquartile range, IQR, is the difference between the upper and lower quartiles.

Example

In the data set 13, 17, 23, 24, 25, 29, 31, 45, 46, 53, 60, the median, 29, divides the data into two halves. The first quartile, 23, is the median of the lower half of the data. The third quartile, 46, is the median of the upper half of the data. The interquartile range is 46 – 23, or 23.

inverse operations

Inverse operations are operations that undo each other.

Example

The operations of addition and subtraction are inverse operations.

irrational number

An irrational number is a number that cannot be written as $\frac{a}{b}$, where a and b are integers.

Example

The number π is an irrational number.

label

A label is a written description that identifies an object.

Example

In the graph, the label on the x-axis is "Time (hours)" and the label on the y-axis is "Earnings (dollars)."

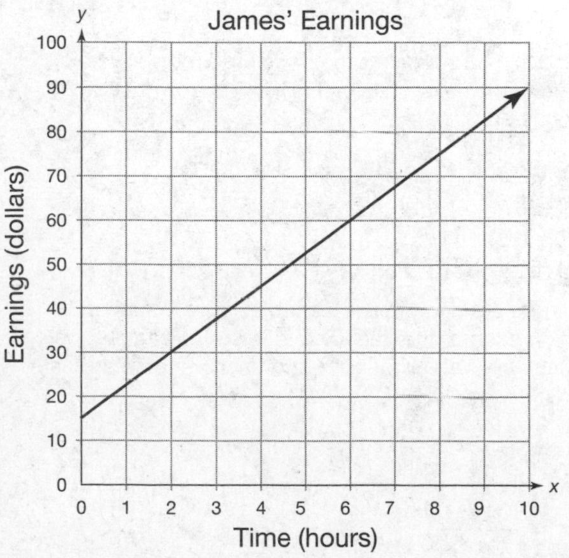

least squares method

The least squares method is a method used to find the equation of the line of best fit.

Example

Most graphing calculators use the least squares method to calculate the line of best fit.

legs of a right triangle

In a right triangle, the legs are the two sides of the triangle that form the right angle.

Example

In triangle ABC, angle A is the right angle, so sides AB and AC are the legs of the triangle.

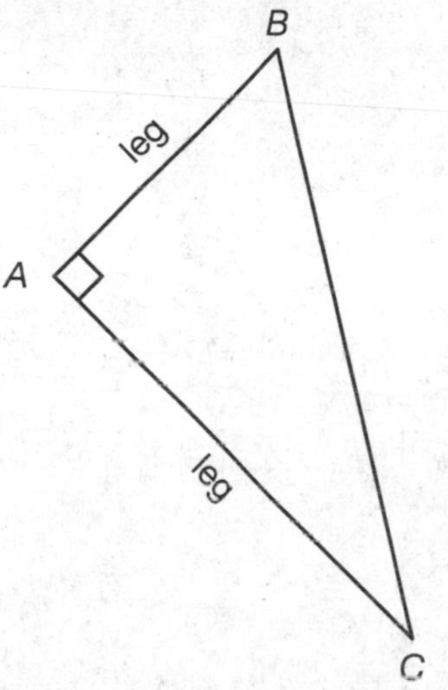

Glossary

line of best fit

A line of best fit is a line that is used to approximate the data as close to as many points as possible.

Example

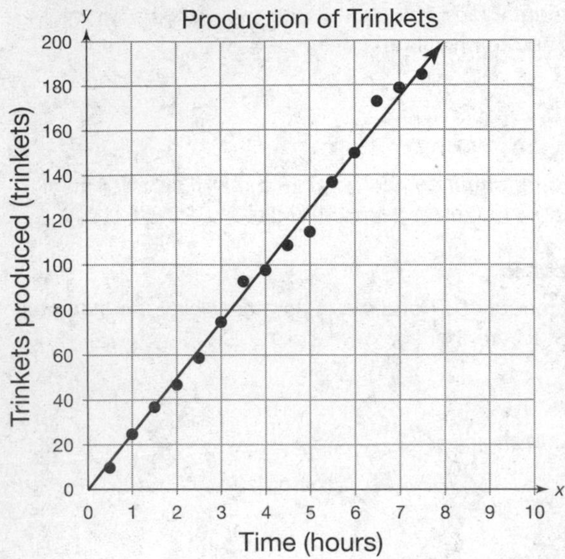

line of symmetry

A line of symmetry is an imaginary line that divides a graph into two parts that are mirror images of each other.

Example

Line K is the line of symmetry of the parabola.

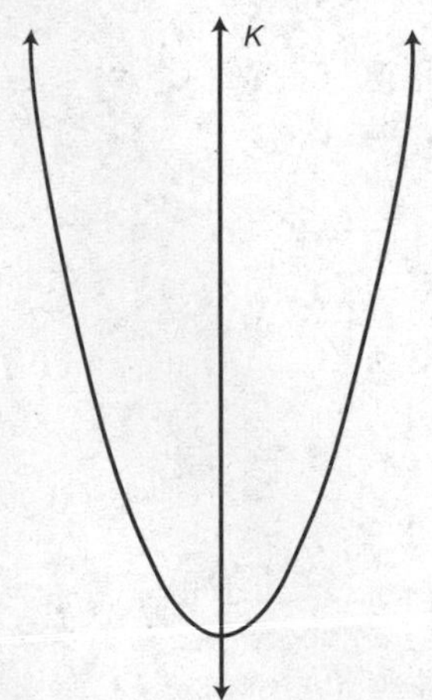

line plot

A line plot is a graph that has an X above each number on a number line that appears in the data set.

Example

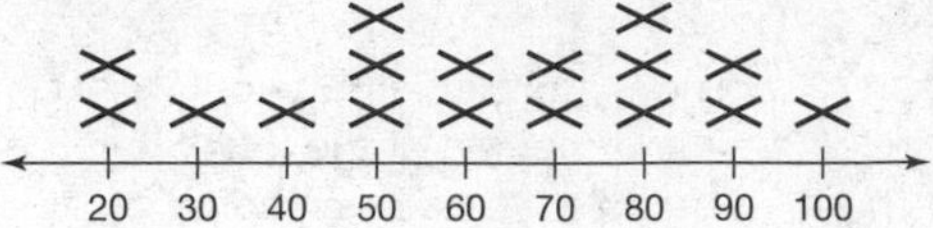

linear combination

A linear combination is an equation that is the result of adding two equations to each other.

Example

The linear combination of the equations $2x + 3y = 5$ and $x - 3y = -1$ is $3x = 4$.

linear combinations method

The linear combinations method is a process to solve a system of equations by adding two equations to each other resulting in an equation with one variable.

Example

Solve the following system of linear equations using linear combinations.

$6x - 5y = 3$
$2x + 2y = 12$

To solve the system by using linear combinations, first multiply the second equation by –3. Then, add the equations and solve for the remaining variable. Finally, substitute $y = 3$ into the first equation and solve for x.

$6x - 5y = 3$	$6x - 5y = 3$	$6x - 5(3) = 3$
$2x + 2y = 12$	$-6x - 6y = -36$	$6x - 15 = 3$
	$-11y = -33$	$6x = 18$
	$y = 3$	$x = 3$

So, the solution of the system is (3, 3).

linear equation in two variables

A linear equation in two variables is an equation in which each of the variables is raised to the first power (such as x, rather than x^2) and each variable appears at most once.

Example

The equation $y = 2x + 1$ is a linear equation.

linear factor

A linear factor is a factor that is a linear expression.

Example

The polynomial $x^2 + 5x + 6$ has two linear factors: $x + 2$ and $x + 3$.

linear function

A linear function is a function whose graph is a non-vertical straight line.

Example

$f(x) = 3x + 2$ is a linear function.

linear inequality in two variables

A linear inequality in two variables is any inequality that can be written in one of these forms: $ax + by > c$, $ax + by < c$, $ax + by \geq c$, or $ax + by \leq c$.

Example

The inequality $3x + 4y > 7$ is a linear inequality.

linear regression equation

A linear regression equation is the equation of the line of best fit.

Example

The linear regression equation for the data is $y = 25x$.

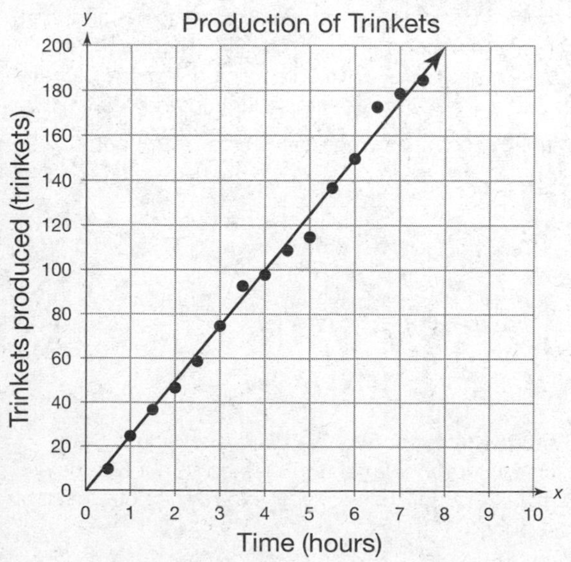

linear system

A linear system is two or more linear equations in the same variables.

Example

The equations $y = 3x + 7$ and $y = -4x$ are a system of linear equations.

literal equation

A literal equation is an equation that contains two or more variables to represent known quantities.

Example

The equations $I = Prt$ and $A = lw$ are literal equations.

maximum point

The maximum point of the graph of a function is the ordered pair on the graph with the greatest y-coordinate.

Example

The ordered pair (4, 2) is the maximum point of the graph of the function $y = -\frac{1}{2}x^2 + 4x - 6$.

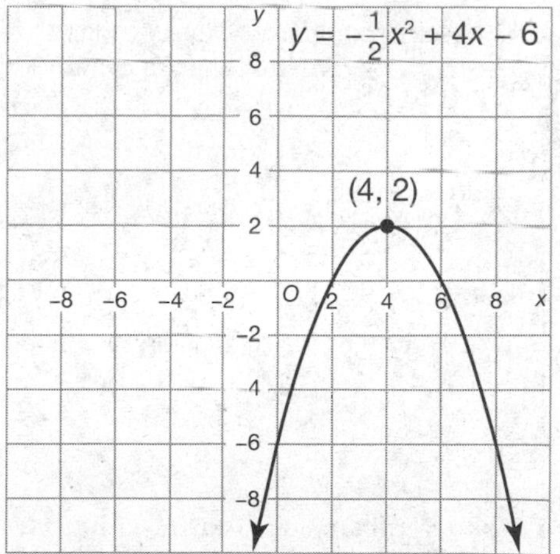

mean

The mean of a data set is the sum of all of the values of the data set divided by the number of values in the data set. The mean is also called the average.

Example

The mean of the numbers 7, 9, 13, 4, and 7 is $\frac{7 + 9 + 13 + 4 + 7}{5}$, or 8.

mean absolute deviation

The mean absolute deviation is the average of the absolute deviations for all data values.

Example

The mean of the data set 2, 3, 9, and 13 is 6.75.

The data value 2 has an absolute deviation of 4.75.

The data value 3 has an absolute deviation of 3.75.

The data value 9 has an absolute deviation of 2.25.

The data value 13 has an absolute deviation of 6.25.

The mean absolute deviation is

$\frac{4.75 + 3.75 + 2.25 + 6.25}{4}$, or 4.25.

mean deviation

The mean deviation is the average of the deviations for all data values.

Example

The mean of the data set 2, 3, 9, and 13 is 6.75.

The data value 2 has a deviation of –4.75.

The data value 3 has a deviation of –3.75.

The data value 9 has a deviation of 2.25.

The data value 13 has a deviation of 6.25.

The mean deviation is

$\frac{-4.75 - 3.75 + 2.25 + 6.25}{4}$, or 0.

means of a proportion

The means of a proportion are the two inside quantities of a proportion.

Example

In the proportion 4 girls: 7 boys:: 8 girls: 14 boys, the means are the inside quantities 7 boys and 8 girls.

measure of central tendency

A measure of central tendency is a single value that represents a typical value in a data set.

Example

The mean, median, and mode are the most common measures of central tendency.

median

The median of a data set that is arranged in numerical order is either the middle value (when the number of data values is odd), or the average of the two middle values (when the number of data values is even).

Example

The median of the numbers 1, 5, 7, 10, 14 is 7.

midpoint

The midpoint of a segment is the point that divides the segment into two congruent segments.

Example

Because point *B* is the midpoint of segment *AC*, segment *AB* is congruent to segment *BC*.

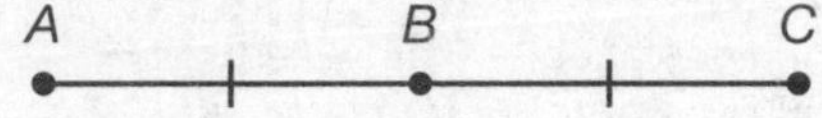

midpoint formula

The midpoint formula can be used to find the midpoint between two points. The midpoint between (x_1, y_1) and (x_2, y_2) is $\left(\frac{x_1 + x_2}{2}, \frac{y_1 + y_2}{2}\right)$.

Example

To find the midpoint between the points (–1, 4) and (2, –5), substitute the coordinates into the Midpoint Formula.

$$\left(\frac{x_1 + x_2}{2}, \frac{y_1 + y_2}{2}\right) = \left(\frac{-1 + 2}{2}, \frac{4 - 5}{2}\right)$$
$$= \left(\frac{1}{2}, \frac{-1}{2}\right)$$

So, the midpoint between the points (–1, 4) and (2, –5) is $\left(\frac{1}{2}, -\frac{1}{2}\right)$.

minimum point

The minimum point of the graph of a function is the ordered pair on the graph with the least y-coordinate.

Example

The ordered pair (1, –4) is the minimum point of the graph of the function $y = \frac{2}{3}x^2 - \frac{4}{3}x - \frac{10}{3}$.

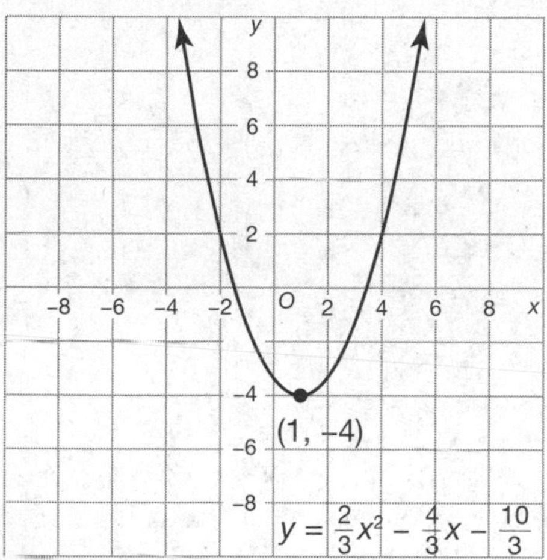

mode

The mode is the number (or numbers) that occurs most often in a data set. If there is no number that occurs most often, the data set has no mode.

Example

The mode of the numbers 1, 3, 3, 5, 8, 10, 17 is 3.

model of a data set

A model of a data set is a line of best fit and its equation.

Example

The equation of the line of best fit is $y = 25x$.

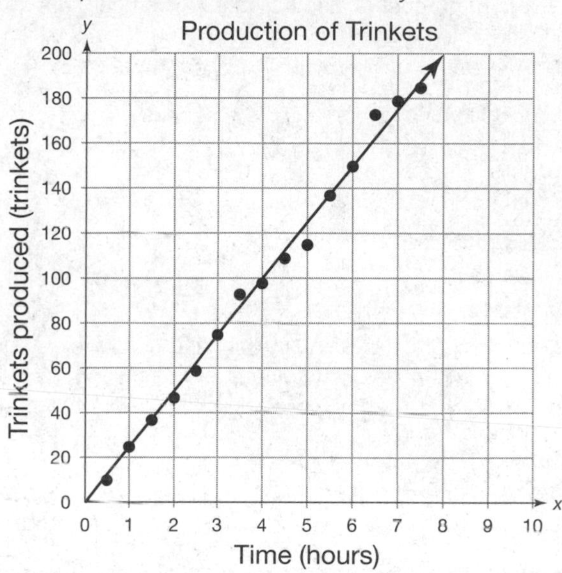

monomial

A monomial is an expression that consists of a single term that is either a constant, a variable, or a product of a constant and one or more variables. A monomial is a polynomial with one term.

Example

The expressions $5x$, 7, $-2xy$, and $13x^3$ are monomials.

multiplicative identity

The multiplicative identity is a number such that when you multiply it by a second number, the product is the second number.

Example

The multiplicative identity is the number 1.

$1 \cdot 5 = 5$

Glossary

multiplicative inverse

The multiplicative inverse of a number $\frac{a}{b}$ is the number $\frac{b}{a}$. The product of any nonzero number and its multiplicative inverse is 1. The multiplicative inverse of a number is also called its reciprocal.

Example

The multiplicative inverse of $\frac{2}{3}$ is $\frac{3}{2}$ because $\left(\frac{2}{3}\right)\left(\frac{3}{2}\right) = 1$.

natural number

The set of natural numbers, or counting numbers, consists of all positive whole numbers beginning with 1.

Example

The numbers 1, 2, 3, 4, ... are natural numbers.

negative exponent

A negative exponent is an exponent in a power. A power of a whole number with a negative exponent represents a number that is less than 1.

Example

In the expression x^{-2}, -2 is a negative exponent.

negative square root

A negative square root is one of the two square roots of a positive number.

Example

The negative square root of 25 is -5.

negatively correlated

Points are negatively correlated when the line of best fit has a negative slope.

Example

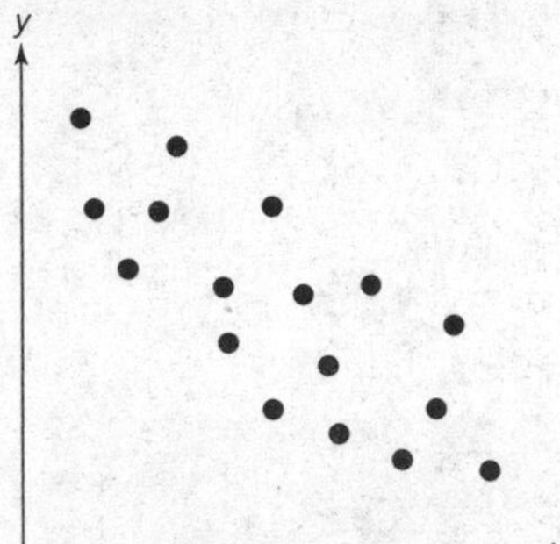

Negatively correlated data

net pay

Net pay is the amount of money that an employee earns after deductions are subtracted from the employee's gross pay.

Example

An employee earns $2400 per month of gross pay. Deductions of $432 in taxes and $164 in insurance are subtracted from this amount. So, the employee's net pay is $2400 − $432 − $164 = $1804.

*n*th percentile

The *n*th percentile for a data set is the value for which *n* percent of the numbers in the set are less than that value.

Example

A student scored 987 points on a standardized test. The score is in the 60th percentile because 60% of the test scores were less than 987.

*n*th term

The *n*th term is a convention used to generate or represent terms of a sequence.

Example

A sequence is given by $a_n = 7n$.

The first term is $a_1 = 7(1) = 7$.

The second term is $a_2 = 7(2) = 14$.

number line

A number line is a line on which a unique point is assigned to every real number.

Example

The point on the number line below corresponds to the rational number 1.5.

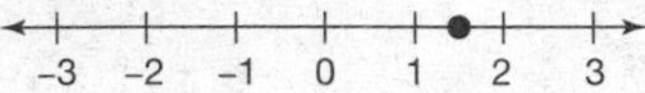

numerical expression

A numerical expression is a mathematical phrase consisting of numbers and operations to be performed.

Example

$2(1 + 5) - 6$ is a numerical expression.

odds against an event

The odds against an event is the ratio of the number of unfavorable outcomes to the number of favorable outcomes.

Example

The odds against rolling a number that is a multiple of 3 with a six-sided number cube is $\frac{4}{2}$.

odds in favor of an event

The odds in favor of an event is the ratio of the number of favorable outcomes to the number of unfavorable outcomes.

Example

The odds of rolling a number that is a multiple of 3 with a six-sided number cube is $\frac{2}{4}$.

one-step equation

A one-step equation is an equation that requires only one operation to solve.

Example

The equation $x + 5 = 8$ is a one-step equation. It can be solved by subtracting 5 from each side of the equation.

opposite of a number

The opposite of a number is the number that is the same distance from zero but on the opposite side of zero on a number line.

Example

The opposite of –3 is 3. Both numbers are 3 units from 0 on the number line.

order of operations

The order of operations is a set of rules that ensure that the result of combining numbers and operations, such as addition and multiplication, is the same every time. The order of operations is:

1. Evaluate expressions inside grouping symbols, such as ( ) or [ ].
2. Evaluate powers.
3. Multiply and divide from left to right.
4. Add and subtract from left to right.

Example

To evaluate the expression $(3 + 4)^2 + 5 \cdot 2$, perform the operations in this order. Evaluate expressions inside the parentheses first.

$$\begin{aligned}(3 + 4)^2 + 5 \cdot 2 &= 7^2 + 5 \cdot 2 \\ &= 49 + 5 \cdot 2 \\ &= 49 + 10 \\ &= 59\end{aligned}$$

Glossary

ordered pair

An ordered pair is a pair of numbers of the form (x, y) that represents a unique position in the coordinate plane. The first number in the ordered pair is the x-coordinate and the second number is the y-coordinate.

Example

The ordered pairs (4, 2) and (–2, –3) are shown in the coordinate plane.

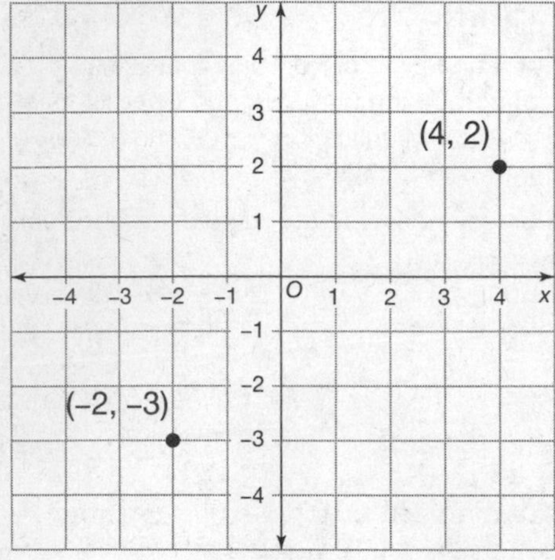

origin

The origin is the point where the x-axis and y-axis intersect in the coordinate plane. The ordered pair that represents the origin is (0, 0).

Example

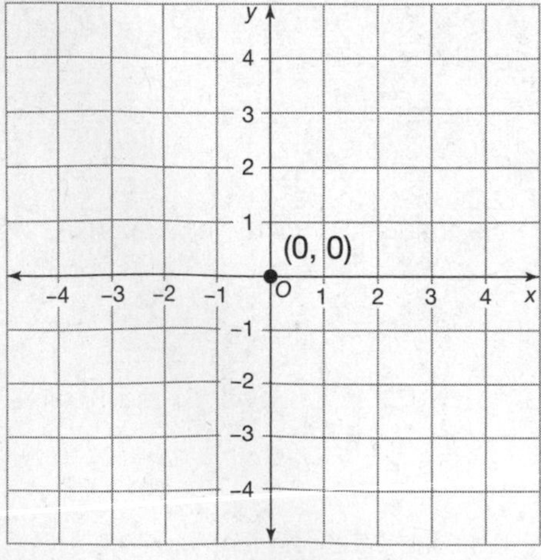

outcome

An outcome is a possible result of an event.

Example

Flipping a coin has two outcomes: heads and tails.

outlier

An outlier is a data value that is much less or much greater than the other values in the data set.

Example

The data set 1, 1, 3, 3, 4, 4, 5, 1000 has outlier of 1000.

output value

An output value is the second coordinate of an ordered pair in a relation.

Example

The ordered pair (5, 8) has an output value of 8.

parabola

A parabola is the U-shaped graph of a quadratic function of the form $y = ax^2 + bx + c$, where $a \neq 0$.

Example

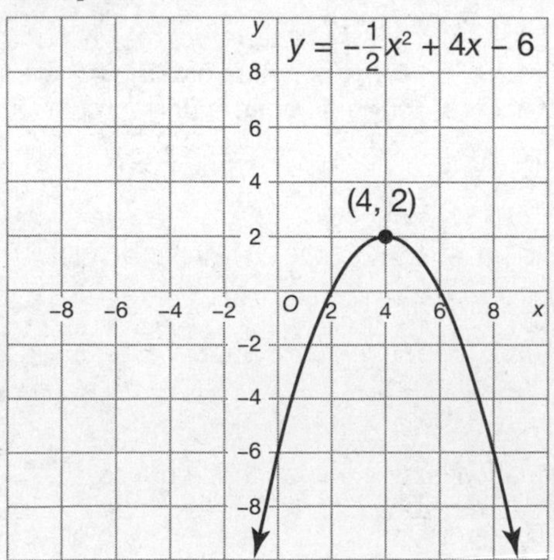

parallel

Two lines in the same plane are parallel to each other if they do not intersect.

Example

Lines *m* and *n* are parallel.

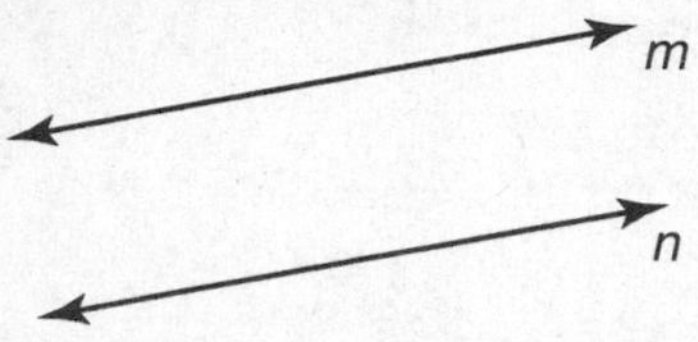

parallelogram

A parallelogram is a quadrilateral in which both pairs of opposite sides are parallel.

Example

In parallelogram *ABCD*, opposite sides *AB* and *CD* are parallel; opposite sides *AD* and *BC* are parallel.

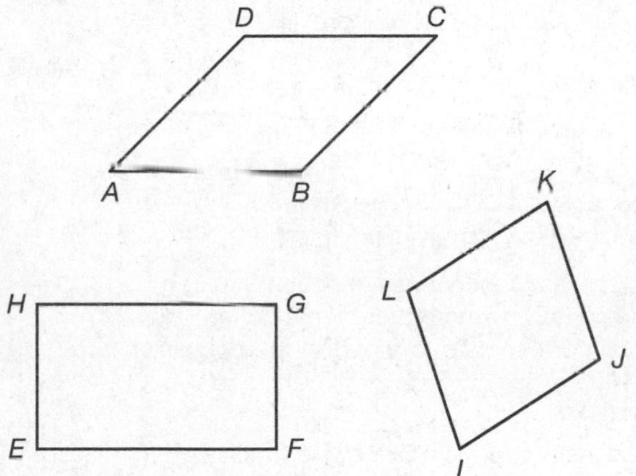

parent function

A parent function is the most basic function of a family of functions.

Example

The parent linear function is $y = x$. The parent quadratic function is $y = x^2$.

pattern

A pattern is an ordered sequence of numbers, shapes, or other objects that are arranged according to a rule.

Examples

The pattern a, b, a, b, a, b, a, b, ... is the sequence of alternating letters a and b.

The pattern 0, 1, 4, 9, 16, 25, 36, 49, ... is the sequence of the squares of whole numbers.

percent

A percent is a ratio whose denominator is 100. One percent of a quantity is $\frac{1}{100}$ of the quantity.

Example

You buy a notebook for $4.00 and pay a sales tax of 7%. The sales tax is equal to $\frac{7}{100}$ of $4.00, or $.28.

percent equation

A percent equation is an equation of the form $a = \frac{p}{100}b$, where p is the percent and the numbers being compared are a and b. A percent equation can also be written in the form $a = pb$ where p is the percent in decimal form and the numbers that are being compared are a and b.

Example

A store is having a sale. All merchandise is 75% of the original price. The equation $y = \frac{75}{100}x$ is a percent equation where x represents the original price and y represents the discounted price.

percentile

A percentile divides a data set into 100 equal parts.

perfect square

A perfect square is a whole number whose square root is also a whole number.

Example

The numbers 1, 4, 9, and 16 are perfect squares.

Glossary

perfect square trinomial

A perfect square trinomial is a trinomial of the form $ax^2 + 2ab + b^2$ or $ax^2 - 2ab + b^2$. A perfect square trinomial can be written as the square of a binomial.

Example

The trinomial $x^2 + 6x + 9$ is a perfect square trinomial and can be written as $(x + 3)$ squared.

perimeter of a square

The perimeter of a square is the sum of all the side lengths.

Example

The perimeter of square *ABCD* is (4)(5) or 20 centimeters.

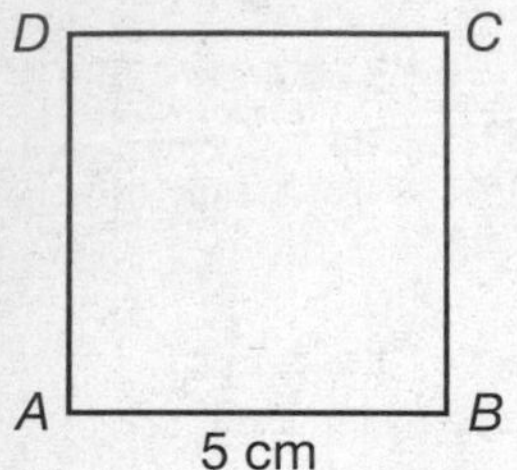

permutation

A permutation is an arrangement of a set of items for which the order of the items is important.

Example

Selecting the order in which students will give presentations is a permutation.

perpendicular

Perpendicular lines are two lines that intersect to form a right angle. The slopes of perpendicular lines are negative reciprocals of each other.

Example

Lines *m* and *k* are perpendicular lines.

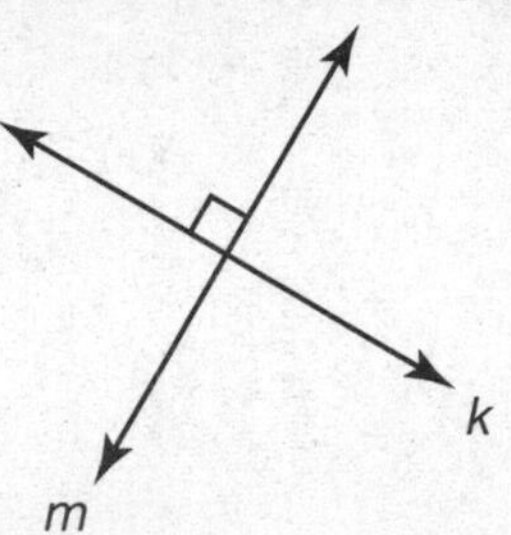

pi

π is the symbol that is used to represent the ratio of a circle's circumference to its diameter. π is an irrational number and its value is approximately 3.14.

Example

$\pi = 3.14159265358979323846...$

piecewise function

A piecewise function is a function that can be represented by more than one function, each of which corresponds to a part of the domain.

Example

The function $f(x)$ is a piecewise function.

$$f(x) = \begin{cases} x + 5 & x \le -2 \\ -2x + 1 & -2 < x \le 2 \\ 2x - 9 & x > 2 \end{cases}$$

Glossary

point of intersection

The point of intersection is the location on a graph where two lines or functions intersect indicating that the values at that point are the same.

Example

The point of intersection is the point (100, 300).

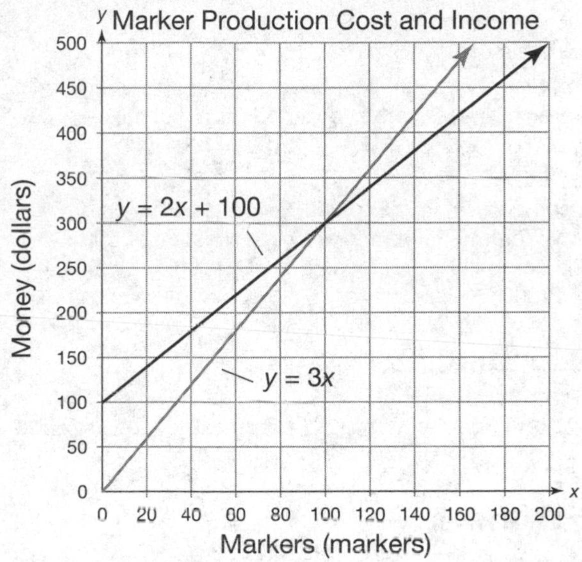

point-slope form of a linear equation

The point-slope form of a linear equation that passes through the point (x_1, y_1) and has slope m is $y - y_1 = m(x - x_1)$.

Example

A line passing through the point (1, 2) with a slope of $\frac{1}{2}$ can be written in point-slope form as $y - 2 = \frac{1}{2}(x - 1)$.

polynomial

A polynomial is an expression of the form

$a_0 + a_1x + a_2x^2 + ... + a_nx^n$

where the coefficients $(a_0, a_1, a_2, ...)$ are real numbers or complex numbers and the exponents are nonnegative integers.

Example

The expression $3x^3 + 5x^2 - 6x + 1$ is a polynomial.

population

A population is the entire group of people or items from which information is gathered.

Example

The population of math students in your school is every student in your school who is enrolled in a math class.

positive exponent

A positive exponent is an exponent in a power.

Example

In the expression x^2, 2 is a positive exponent.

positive square root

A positive square root is one of the two square roots of a positive number.

Example

The positive square root of 25 is 5.

positively correlated

Points are positively correlated when the line of best fit has a positive slope.

Example

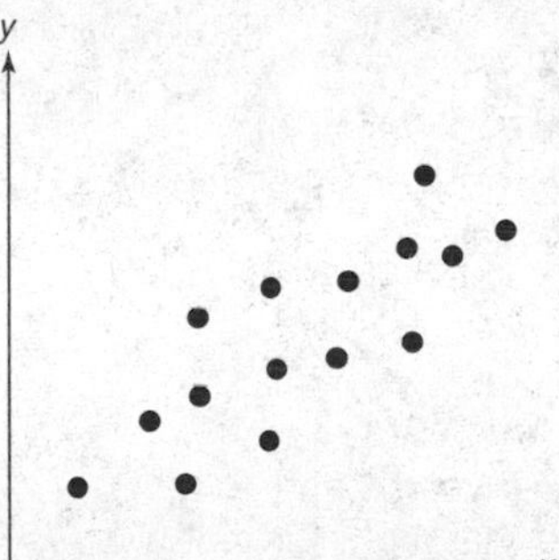

Positively correlated data

power

A power is an expression in which a number or variable is raised to an exponent. A power is a notation used to represent repeated multiplication.

Example

The expression 2^5 is a power.

prime factorization

The prime factorization of a number is the representation of the number as a product of prime numbers.

Example

The prime factorization of 24 is $2 \cdot 2 \cdot 2 \cdot 3$ or $2^3 \cdot 3$.

prime number

A prime number is a whole number that is greater than 1 and has exactly two whole number factors, 1 and itself.

Example

The first five prime numbers are 2, 3, 5, 7, and 11.

principal

The principal is an amount of money that is borrowed or invested, represented by P.

Example

Sharon deposits $500 into a new checking account. The principal is $500.

principal square root

The positive square root is called the principal square root.

Example

An expression such as $\sqrt{49}$ indicates that you should find the principal square root of 49.

probability

A probability is a number between 0 and 1 that is a measure of the likelihood that a given event will occur. The probability of an event when all outcomes are equally likely is equal to the number of desired outcomes divided by the number of possible outcomes.

Example

The probability of rolling an even number with a six-sided number cube is $\frac{3}{6}$, or $\frac{1}{2}$.

product

A product is the result of multiplying one quantity by another.

Example

The product of 2 and 6 is 12.

profit

Profit is the amount of money that remains after the production costs are subtracted from income.

Example

A company makes $10,000 before expenses are considered. The company's expenses are $8000. The company's profit would be $10,000 − $8000 or $2000.

proof

A proof is a logical series of steps to demonstrate a statement.

Example

To prove the statement $(a - b)(a^2 + ab + b^2) = a^3 - b^3$, use the following direct proof.

$(a - b)(a^2 + ab + b^2)$

$= a(a^2 + ab + b^2) - b(a^2 + ab + b^2)$

Distributive property

$= a(a^2) + a(ab) + a(b^2) - b(a^2) - b(ab) - b(b^2)$

Distributive Property of Multiplication Over Addition

$= a^3 + a^2b + ab^2 - a^2b - ab^2 - b^3$

Product of Powers

$= a^3 - b^3$

Additive Inverse

proportion

A proportion is an equation that states that two ratios are equal.

Examples

The equation $\frac{4}{8} = \frac{1}{2}$ is a proportion. The equation $\frac{x}{12} = \frac{5}{60}$ is a proportion.

Glossary

Pythagorean Theorem

The Pythagorean Theorem states that if a and b are the legs of a right triangle, and c is the hypotenuse, then the sum of the squares of the lengths of the legs equals the square of the length of the hypotenuse: $a^2 + b^2 = c^2$.

Example

In triangle ABC, angle C is the right angle, so side BC is a leg, side AC is a leg, and side AB is the hypotenuse.

$$a^2 + b^2 = c^2$$
$$3^2 + b^2 = 8^2$$
$$9 + b^2 = 64$$
$$b^2 = 64 - 9$$
$$b^2 = 55$$
$$b = \sqrt{55}$$

So, the length of side AC is $\sqrt{55}$, or approximately 7.42 centimeters.

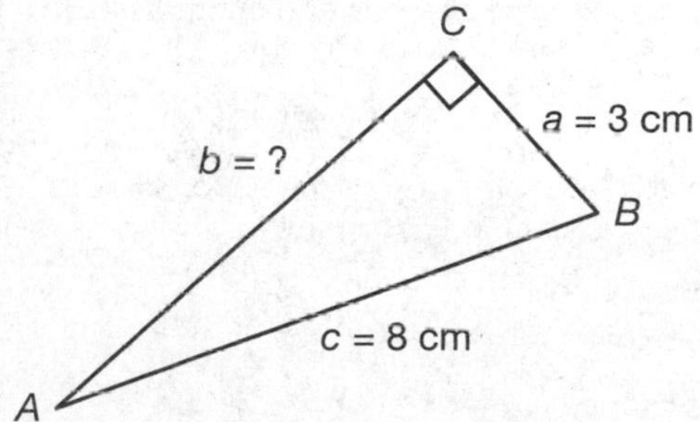

quadratic formula

The Quadratic Formula is a formula used to find the solutions of a quadratic equation. For a quadratic equation of the form $ax^2 + bx + c = 0$, the solutions can be found using the Quadratic Formula

$$x = \frac{-b \pm \sqrt{b^2 - 4ac}}{2a}.$$

Example

To use the Quadratic Formula to find the solutions of $x^2 + 2x - 24 = 0$, use $a = 1$, $b = 2$, and $c = -24$.

$$x = \frac{-2 \pm \sqrt{(2)^2 - 4(1)(-24)}}{2(1)}$$
$$= \frac{-2 \pm \sqrt{100}}{2}$$
$$= \frac{-2 \pm 10}{2}$$
$$x = \frac{-2 + 10}{2} \quad \text{or} \quad x = \frac{-2 - 10}{2}$$
$$= 4 \quad \text{or} \quad = -6$$

So, the solutions of $x^2 + 2x - 24 = 0$ are –6 and 4.

quadratic function

A quadratic function is a function that can be written in the form $f(x) = ax^2 + bx + c$, where a, b, and c are real numbers and a is not equal to zero.

Example

The equations $y = x^2 + 2x + 5$ and $y = -4x^2 - 7x + 1$ are quadratic functions.

quartile

The three quartiles divide a data set into four equal parts. The middle quartile is the median. The other two values are the upper quartile and the lower quartile.

Example

In the data set 13, 17, 23, 24, 25, 29, 31, 45, 46, 53, 60, the median, 29, divides the data into two halves. The first quartile, 23, is the median of the lower half of the data. The third quartile, 46, is the median of the upper half of the data.

13 17 23 24 25 29 31 45 46 53 60

↑ lower quartile (23) ↑ median (29) ↑ upper quartile (46)

quotient

A quotient is the number that results from the division of one number by another. The quotient is the answer of a division problem.

Example

The quotient of the division problem $96 \div 12 = 8$ is the number 8.

radical symbol

A radical symbol is the symbol used to write a square root.

Example

The square root of 25 can be written using a radical symbol as $\sqrt{25}$.

radicand

A radicand is the quantity under a radical sign in an expression.

Example

In the radical expression $\sqrt{25}$, 25 is the radicand.

radius

The radius is the distance from the center of a circle to a point on the circle.

Example

In the circle, *O* is the center and the length of segment *OA* is the radius.

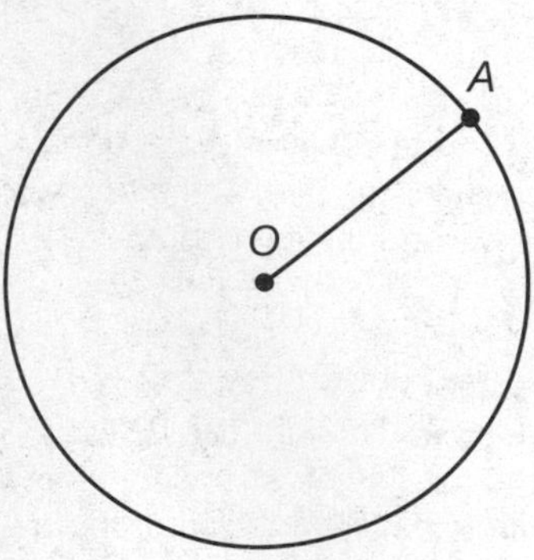

randomly chosen

To be randomly chosen means that no particular rule was used to choose a person.

Example

Choosing 100 fans at random to participate in a survey from crowd of 5000 people is an example of being randomly choosen.

range of a data set

The range of a data set is the difference between the greatest number and the least number in the data set.

Example

The range of the numbers 1, 5, 7, 10, 14 is $14 - 1$, or 13.

range of a function

The range of a function is the set of all output values for the function.

Example

The range of the function $y = x^2$ is the set of all numbers greater than or equal to zero.

rate

A rate is a ratio in which the units of the quantities being compared are different.

Example

A car uses 20 gallons of gasoline to drive 600 miles. The car's fuel consumption rate is

$\frac{600 \text{ miles}}{20 \text{ gallons}} = \frac{30 \text{ miles}}{1 \text{ gallon}}$ or 30 miles per gallon.

rate of change

Rate of change is a comparison of two quantities with different units that are changing.

Example

The speed of a car, measured in miles per hour, is a rate of change.

ratio

A ratio is a way to compare two quantities that are measured in the same units by using division. The ratio of two numbers *a* and *b*, with the restriction that *b* cannot equal zero, can be written in three ways.

a to *b*

$a : b$

$\frac{a}{b}$

Example

In Central High School, there are 4 boys for every 5 girls. The ratio of boys to girls can be written as 4 boys to 5 girls, 4 boys: 5 girls, or $\frac{4 \text{ boys}}{5 \text{ girls}}$.

rational exponent

A rational exponent is an exponent that is a rational number.

Example

In the expression $x^{2/3}$, $\frac{2}{3}$ is a rational exponent

rational expression

A rational expression is an expression that can be written as the quotient of two nonzero polynomials.

Example

The expression $\frac{2x + 1}{x - 3}$ is a rational expression.

rational number

A rational number is a number that can be written as the quotient of two integers.

Example

The number 0.5 is a rational number because it can be written as the fraction $\frac{1}{2}$.

real number

The real numbers consist of all rational numbers and irrational numbers. Real numbers can be represented on the real number line.

Example

The numbers -3, 11.4, $\frac{1}{2}$, and $\sqrt{5}$ are real numbers.

real number system

The real number system is comprised of the real numbers together with their properties and operations.

reciprocals

Two non-zero numbers are reciprocals if their product is 1.

Example

The fractions $\frac{2}{3}$ and $\frac{3}{2}$ are reciprocals.

reflection

A reflection is a transformation in which a figure is reflected, or flipped, in a given line called the line of reflection.

Example

The triangle on the right is a reflection of the triangle on the left.

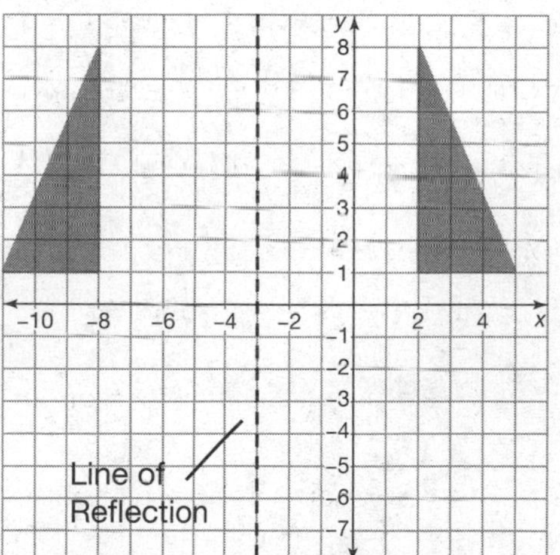

relation

A relation is any set of ordered pairs.

Example

The set of points {(0, 1), (1, 8), (2, 5), (3, 7)} is a relation.

Glossary

remainder

The remainder is the whole number left over in a division problem if the divisor does not divide the dividend evenly.

Example

When 17 is divided by 3, the remainder is 2.

repeating decimal

A repeating decimal is a decimal with one or more digits that repeat indefinitely. A repeating decimal can be represented by placing a bar over the repeating digits.

Example

The fraction $\frac{1}{3}$ can be written as the repeating decimal $0.\overline{3}$.

restricting the domain

Restricting the domain is a process of eliminating excluded values from the domain of a rational expression.

Example

The domain of the rational expression $\frac{2x + 1}{x - 3}$ is all real numbers except $x = 3$.

rise

The rise is the vertical change of a line.

Example

The slope of the line that passes through the points (1, 4) and (3, 8) is 2 because the rise is 4 units and the run is 2 units.

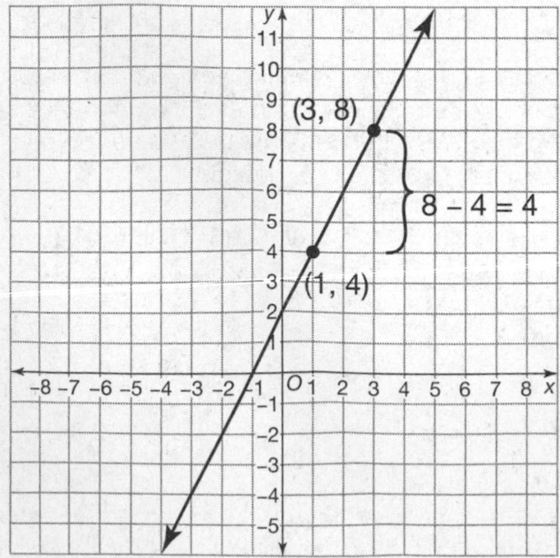

root of a number

A root of a number or nth root of a number b is a solution of the equation $x^n = b$.

Example

The fourth root of 16 is 2 because $2^4 = 16$.

run

The run is the horizontal change of a line.

Example

The slope of the line that passes through the points (1, 4) and (3, 8) is 2 because the rise is 4 units and the run is 2 units.

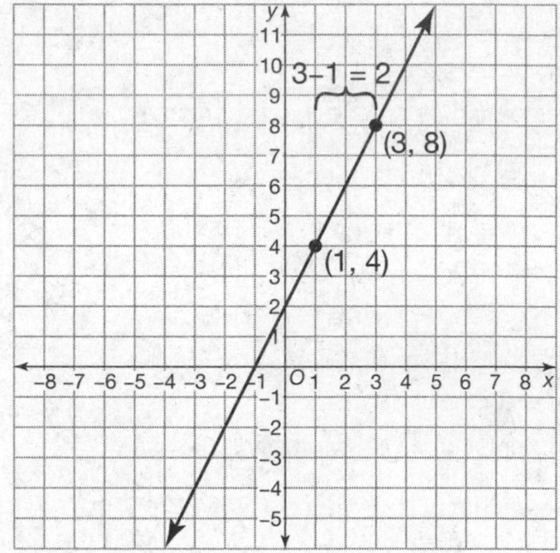

sample

A sample is a group of items that are selected at random from a larger group of items called the population.

Example

If the population of a study concerning health care includes everyone born in the United States from 1995 to 2005, then everyone born on May 22 of each year from 1995 to 2005 is a sample.

sample size

The sample size is the number of people that are surveyed.

Example

A newspaper reporter surveys 100 people. The sample size is 100.

sample space

A sample space of a random experiment is the set of all possible outcomes of the experiment.

Example

The sample space for flipping a coin twice consists of four outcomes: Heads-Heads, Heads-Tails, Tails-Heads, and Tails-Tails.

sample standard deviation

The sample standard deviation, s, is the square root of the sample variance.

Example

The mean of the data set 2, 3, 9, and 13 is 6.75.

The data value 2 has a deviation of –4.75.

The data value 3 has a deviation of –3.75.

The data value 9 has a deviation of 2.25.

The data value 13 has a deviation of 6.25.

The sample variance is equal to $\frac{80.75}{3}$, or approximately 26.92.

The sample standard deviation is the square root of 26.92, or approximately 5.19.

sample variance

The sample variance, s^2, is found by dividing the variance by one less than the number of data values in the set.

Example

The mean of the data set 2, 3, 9, and 13 is 6.75.

The data value 2 has a deviation of –4.75.

The data value 3 has a deviation of –3.75.

The data value 9 has a deviation of 2.25.

The data value 13 has a deviation of 6.25.

The variance is $(-4.75)^2 + (-3.75)^2 + 2.25^2 + 6.25^2$, or 80.75.

The sample variance is equal to $\frac{80.75}{3}$, or approximately 26.92.

sampling method

A sampling method is a method for selecting people or items from a population for a survey. Types of sampling methods are random sampling, stratified sampling, systematic sampling, convenience sampling, and self-selected sampling.

Example

Choosing 100 fans at random to participate in a survey from a crowd of 5000 people is an example of random sampling.

scatter plot

A scatter plot is a graph in the coordinate plane in which values of x and y are plotted as points (x, y).

Example

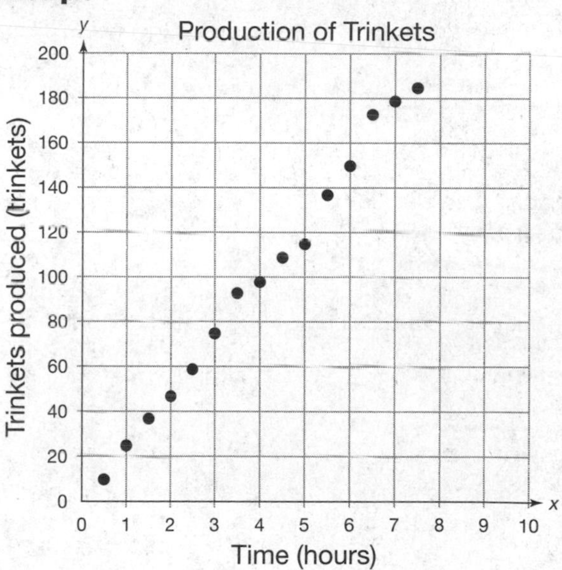

scientific notation

Scientific notation is a way of writing very large or very small numbers. A number written in scientific notation has the form $c \times 10^n$, where c is greater than or equal to 1 and less than 10 and n is an integer.

Example

The number 1,000,000,000 can be written in scientific notation as 1×10^9.

Glossary

second quartile

The second quartile, Q_2, is the median of a data set.

Example

In the data set 13, 17, 23, 24, 25, 29, 31, 45, 46, 53, 60, the median, 29, is the second quartile.

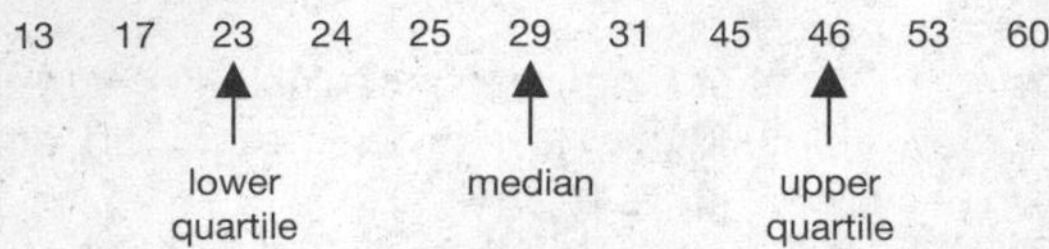

sequence

A sequence is an ordered set of objects or numbers.

Example

The numbers 1, 1, 2, 3, 5, 8, 13 are a sequence.

set notation

Set notation is an indication that a group of numbers is part of a set, including enclosing the numbers in curly braces: { }.

Example

The set of even whole numbers is written using set notation as {2, 4, 6, 8, 10, ...}.

similar figures

Two figures are similar if they have the same shape, but not necessarily the same size.

Example

Triangle *ABC* is similar to triangle *DEF*

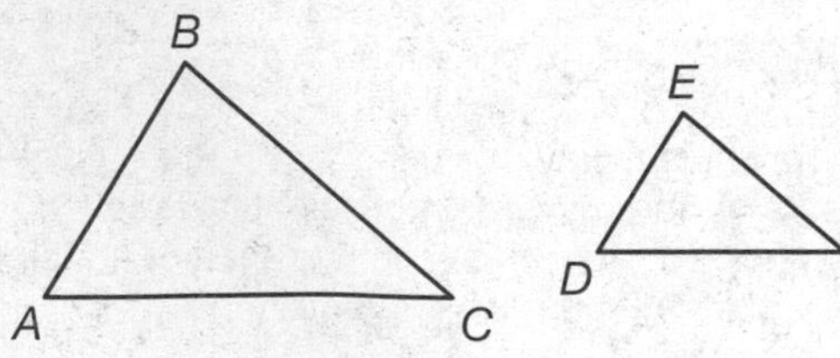

simple event

A simple event is a collection of outcomes of an experiment. An outcome is one possible result of an experiment.

Example

Flipping a coin or rolling a number cube is a simple event.

simple interest

Simple interest is when interest is paid only as a percent of the principal. To find simple interest, multiply the principal P by the annual interest rate r written as a decimal and the time t in years: $I = Prt$.

Example

Tonya deposits $200 in a 3-year certificate of deposit that earns 4% interest. The amount of interest that Tonya earns can be found using the simple interest formula.

$I = (200)(0.04)(3)$

$I = 24$

Tonya earns $24 interest.

simplify an expression

To simplify an expression, rewrite the expression as an equivalent yet briefer expression that is easier to work with.

Example

The expression 2(4 + 5) can be simplified as 18.

slope

The slope of a non-vertical line is the ratio of the vertical change to the horizontal change.

Example

The slope of the line that passes through the points (3, –6) and (2, –4) is –2 because the vertical change is –2 units and the horizontal change is 1 unit.

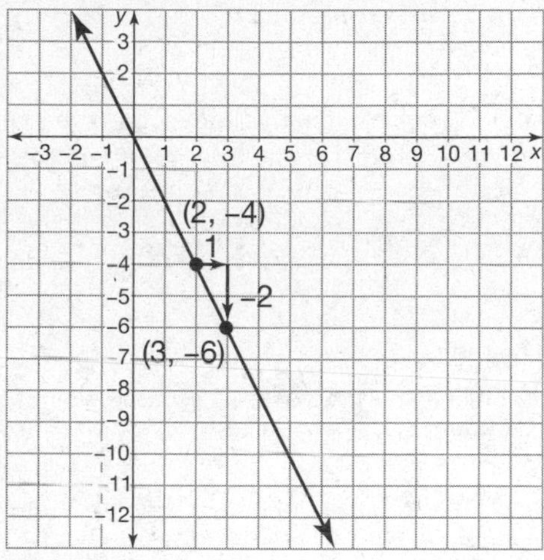

slope-intercept form of a linear equation

The slope-intercept form of a linear equation is $y = mx + b$, where m is the slope of the line and b is the y-intercept of the line.

Example

The linear equation $y = 2x + 1$ is written in slope-intercept form. The slope of the line is 2 and the y-intercept is 1.

solution of a linear system

A solution of a linear system is an ordered pair (x, y) that is a solution of both equations in the system.

Example

The equations $y = 3x + 7$ and $y = -4x$ are a system of equations. The solution to the system of equations is the intersection point (–1, 4).

solution of an equation

The solution of an equation is a number that, when substituted for the variable, makes the equation true.

Example

The solution of the equation $3x + 4 = 25$ is 7 because 7 makes the equation true: $3(7) + 4 = 25$, or $25 = 25$.

solve an inequality

To solve an inequality, find the values of the variable that make the inequality true.

Example

The inequality $x + 5 > 6$ can be solved by subtracting 5 from each side of the inequality. The solution is $x > 1$. Any number greater than 1 will make the inequality $x + 5 > 6$ true.

square of a binomial difference

The square of a binomial difference $(a - b)^2$ is equal to $a^2 - 2ab + b^2$.

Example

$(x - 3)^2 = x^2 - 6x + 9$

square of a binomial sum

The square of a binomial sum $(a + b)^2$ is equal to $a^2 + 2ab + b^2$.

Example

$(x + 3)^2 = x^2 + 6x + 9$

square root

A number b is a square root of a if $b^2 = a$.

Example

The square roots of 25 are 5 and –5.

standard form of a linear equation

The standard form of a linear equation is $ax + by = c$, where a, b, and c are constants and a and b are not both zero.

Example

The linear equation $2x + 3y = 5$ is written in standard form.

standard form of a number

A number in standard form is a number written as a numeral. In standard form, the position of the digit represents the place value of the digit.

Example

The number 243 is written in standard form. The digit 2 is in the hundreds place, the digit 4 is in the tens place, and the digit 3 is in the ones place.

standard form of a polynomial

A polynomial in standard form is written with the terms in descending order, starting with the term with the greatest degree and ending with the term with the least degree.

Example

The polynomial $2x^2 + x^4 + 1 + 5x - 2x^3$ can be written in standard form as $x^4 - 2x^3 + 2x^2 + 5x + 1$.

stem-and-leaf plot

A stem-and-leaf plot is a visual display of data that is organized by digits. Each data value is separated into a stem and a leaf. The leading digits of the data value are represented by the stem and the last digit is represented by the leaf.

Example

A stem-and-leaf plot can be drawn to represent test scores.

55, 62, 73, 75, 76, 79, 80, 83, 86, 87, 87, 88, 88, 89, 89, 89

The tens' place represents the stem and the ones' place represents the leaves.

Stems	Leaves
1	
2	
3	
4	
5	5
6	2
7	3 5 6 9
8	0 3 6 7 7 8 8 9 9 9

Key: 7 | 3 = 73

substitution method

The substitution method is a process of solving a system of equations by substituting a variable in one equation by an equal expression.

Example

Solve the following system of equations by using the substitution method:

$$x - 3y = 4$$

$$2x + 5y = -14$$

First, solve the first equation for x. Then, substitute in the second equation. Next, substitute $y = -2$ into the equation $x - 3y = 4$. The solution of the system is $(-2, -2)$.

success

A success is a trial having the desired outcome.

Example

You want to find the probability of a coin landing heads up. One experiment is flipping a coin 100 times and recording the results. Each coin flip that lands heads up is a successful trial.

sum

A sum is the result of adding one quantity to another.

Example

The sum of 26 and 13, 26 + 13, is the number 39.

supply

The supply is the amount of a good that is available.

Example

The supply of oil in the world can be modeled by the equation $y = 324.3x + 15.856$, where x is the time, in years, since 1965 and y is the supply of oil, in millions of barrels.

survey

A survey is an investigation of a characteristic of a population to gather information.

Example

A newspaper takes a survey to determine which mayoral candidate is favored.

system of linear equations

A system of linear equations is two or more linear equations in the same variables.

Example

The equations $y = 3x + 7$ and $y = -4x$ are a system of equations.

system of linear inequalities

A system of linear inequalities is two or more linear inequalities in the same variables.

Example

The inequalities $y > 3x + 7$ and $y < -4x$ are a system of linear inequalities.

tax rate

A tax rate is the percent used to calculate the amount of money taken out of your gross pay.

Example

John lives in a township that has a tax rate of 2% so 2% of John's pay is taken out for local taxes.

term

A term is a member of a sequence. The first term is the first object or number in the sequence; the second term is the second object or number in the sequence; and so on.

Example

In the sequence 2, 4, 6, 8, 10, the first term is 2, the second term is 4, and the third term is 6.

terms of an expression

The terms of an expression are the parts that are added together. A term may be a number, a variable, or a product of a number and a variable or variables.

Example

The polynomial $2x + 3y + 5$ has three terms: $2x$, $3y$, and 5.

theoretical probability

A theoretical probability is a probability that is based on knowing all of the possible outcomes that are equally likely to occur.

Example

The theoretical probability of a coin landing heads up is $\frac{1}{2}$.

third quartile

The third quartile, Q_3, is the median of the upper half of the data .

Example

In the data set 13, 17, 23, 24, 25, 29, 31, 45, 46, 53, 60, the median, 29, divides the data into two halves. The third quartile, 46, is the median of the upper half of the data.

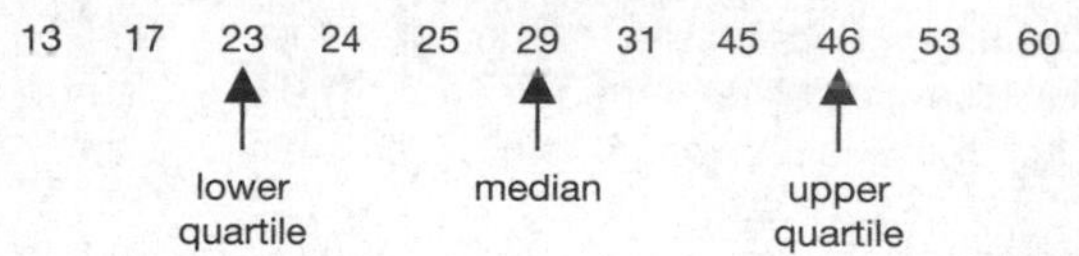

tolerance

A tolerance is the amount by which a quantity is allowed to vary from the normal or target quantity.

Example

A centimeter ruler has a tolerance of $\frac{1}{10}$ centimeter, or 1 millimeter.

transformation

A transformation is an operation that maps, or moves a figure, called the preimage, to form a new figure, called the image. Three types of transformations are reflections, rotations, and translations.

Example

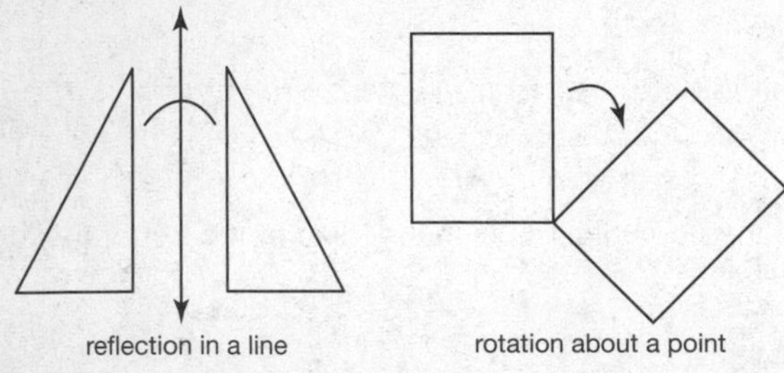

reflection in a line

rotation about a point

translation

A translation is a transformation in which a figure is shifted so that each point of the figure moves the same distance in the same direction. The shift can be in a horizontal direction, a vertical direction, or both.

Example

The top trapezoid is a vertical translation of the bottom trapezoid by 5 units.

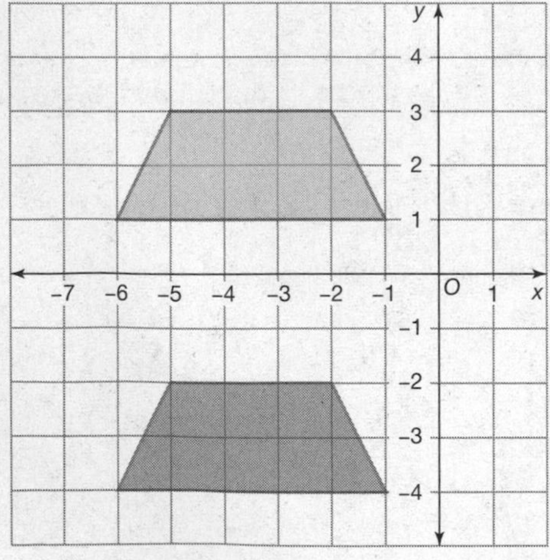

trapezoid

A trapezoid is a quadrilateral with exactly one pair of parallel sides. The parallel sides are called bases and the nonparallel sides are called legs. The perpendicular distance between the bases is the height of the trapezoid.

Example

Quadrilateral *ABCD* is a trapezoid. The height is 4 meters, the length of base *AD* is 12 meters, and the length of base *BC* is 6 meters.

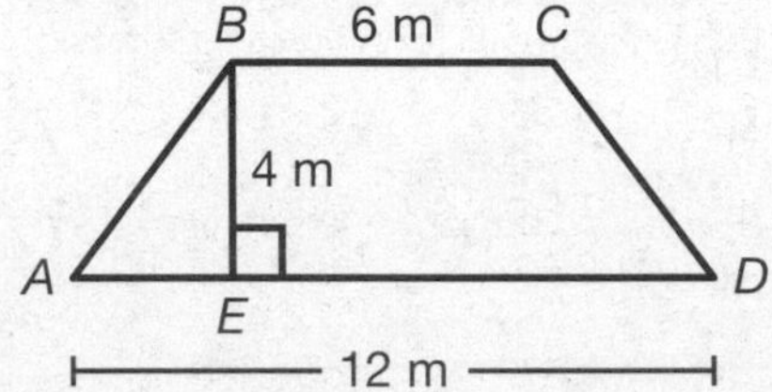

tree diagram

A tree diagram is a visual display that represents the outcomes for a series of events.

Example

The tree diagram shows the sample space for flipping a coin three times.

H
H
T
H
H
T
T

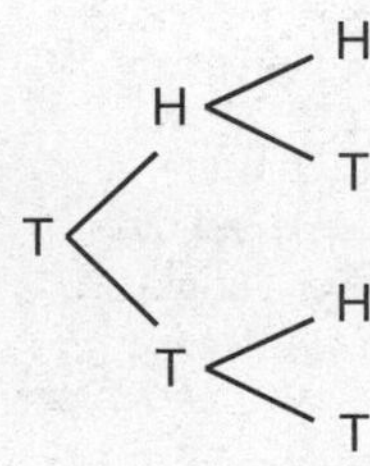

trial

A trial is one instance of an experiment.

Example

You want to find the probability of a coin landing heads up. One experiment is flipping a coin 100 times and recording the results. Each coin flip is a trial.

triangle

A triangle is a three-sided polygon that is formed by joining three points called vertices with line segments.

Example

In triangle *ABC* below, vertices *A*, *B*, and *C* are joined by segments *BA*, *AC*, and *CB*.

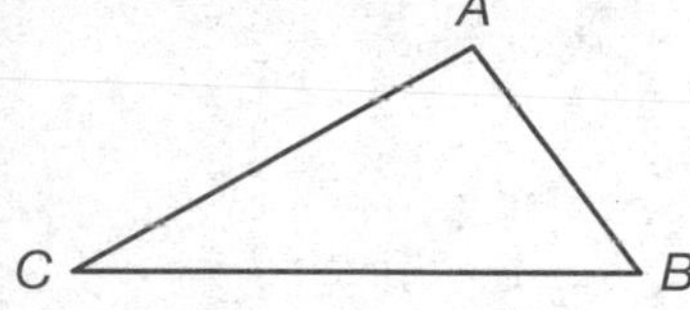

trimodal

A data set is trimodal if three values occur in the data set the same number of times.

Example

The data set 1, 1, 3, 3, 4, 4, 5, 7 is trimodal.

trinomial

A trinomial is a polynomial that consists of three terms.

Example

The polynomial $5x^2 - 6x + 9$ is a trinomial.

two-step equation

A two-step equation is an equation that requires two steps to solve.

Example

The equation $2x + 1 = 5$ is a two-step equation. It can be solved by subtracting 1 from both sides of the equation and then dividing both sides of the equation by 2.

undefined division

An undefined division is division by zero.

Example

The expression $6 \div 0$ is undefined.

unit

A unit is a standard measurement of one, such as one inch, one pound, or one second.

Examples

A unit of money is one dollar. A unit of distance is one foot.

unit rate

A unit rate is the rate per one given unit.

Example

The rate $\frac{150 \text{ miles}}{3 \text{ hours}}$ can be written as the unit rate of 50 miles per hour:

$$\frac{(150 \div 3) \text{ miles}}{(3 \div 3) \text{ hours}} = \frac{50 \text{ miles}}{1 \text{ hour}}.$$

value of an expression

The value of an expression is the result that is obtained when the indicated operations are carried out.

Example

The value of $9^{-1/2}$ is $\frac{1}{3}$. The value of $3x^2 + 6$ when $x = 2$ is 18.

variable

A variable is a letter or symbol that represents an unspecified member of a set.

Example

In the expression $2x + 3$, the letter "x" is a variable.

Glossary

Venn diagram

A Venn diagram uses circles to show how elements among sets of numbers or objects are related.

Example

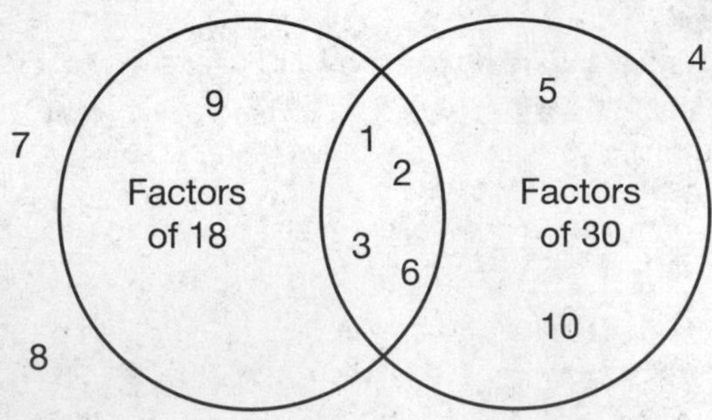

vertex form of a quadratic equation

The vertex form of a quadratic equation is an equation of the form $y = a(x - h)^2 + k$ where (h, k) is the vertex of the graph of the equation.

Example

The quadratic equation $y = 2(x - 5)^2 + 10$ is written in vertex form. The vertex of the graph is the point (5, 10).

vertex of a parabola

The vertex of a parabola, which lies on the axis of symmetry, is the highest or lowest point on the parabola.

Example

The vertex of the graph of $y = \frac{2}{3}x^2 - \frac{4}{5}x - \frac{10}{3}$ is the point (1, –4), the minimum point on the parabola.

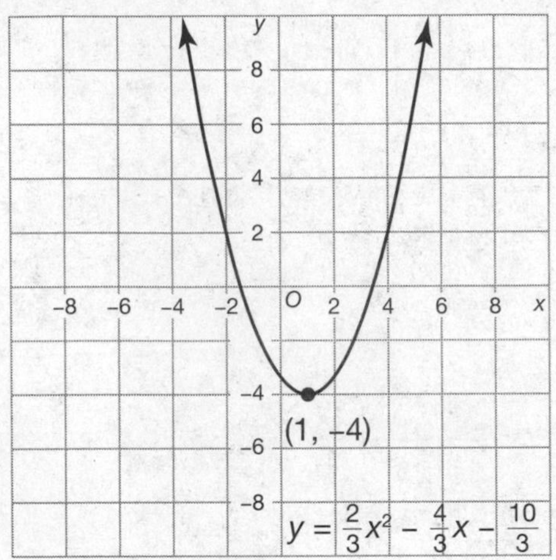

vertical line

A vertical line is a line of the form $x = a$, where a is a real number.

Example

The line represented by the equation $x = 5$ is a vertical line.

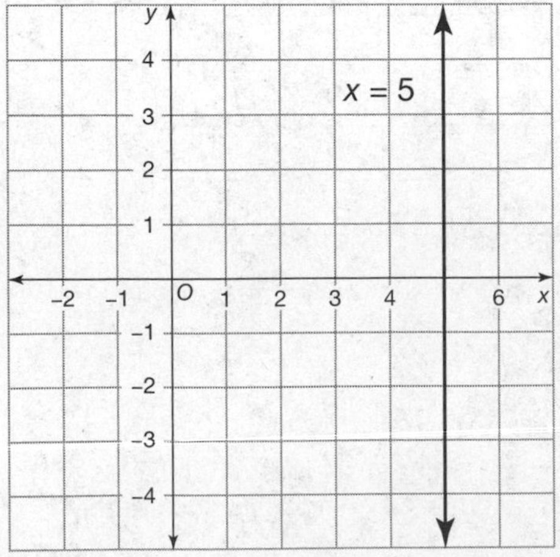

vertical line test

The vertical line test is a method of determining whether an equation is a function. It states that an equation is a function if you can pass a vertical line through any part of the graph of the equation and the line intersects the graph at most one time.

Example

The equation $y = 3x^2$ is a function, because the graph of the function passes the Vertical Line Test.

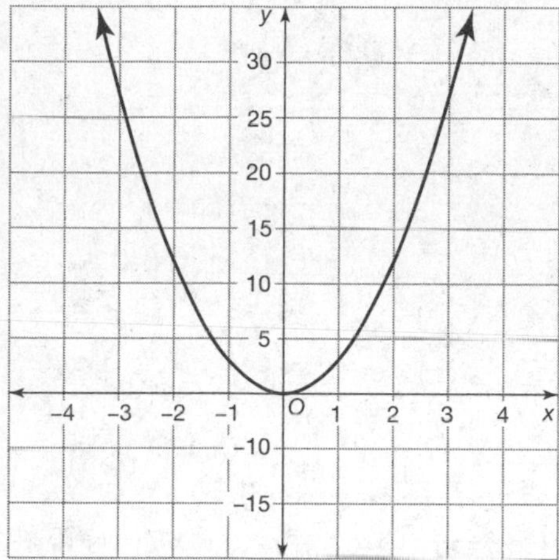

The equation $x^2 + y^2 = 9$ is not a function, because the graph of the function fails the Vertical Line Test.

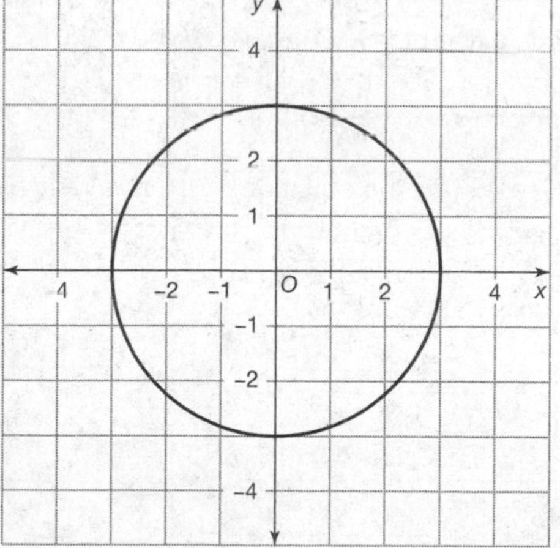

vertical motion model

A vertical motion model is an equation of the form $y = -16t^2 + vt + h$, where t is the time in seconds that the object has been moving, v is the initial velocity (speed) of the object in feet per second, h is initial height of the object in feet, and y is the height of the object in feet at time t seconds.

Example

A rock is thrown in the air at a velocity of 10 feet per second from a cliff that is 100 feet. The height of the rock is modeled by the equation $y = -16t^2 + 10t + 100$.

whole number

A whole number is any counting number or zero.

Example

The numbers 0, 1, 2, 3, … are whole numbers.

x-axis

The *x*-axis is the horizontal number line in a Cartesian coordinate system.

Example

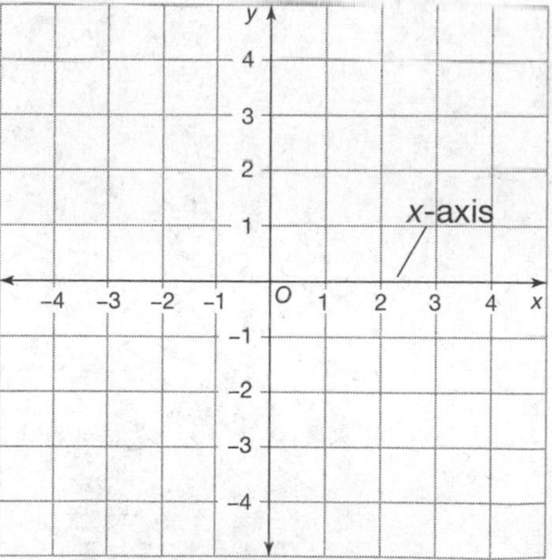

Glossary

x-coordinate

The *x*-coordinate of a point is the first number in an ordered pair. It indicates the distance of the point from the *y*-axis.

Example

In the ordered pair (5, 2), the number 5 is the *x*-coordinate.

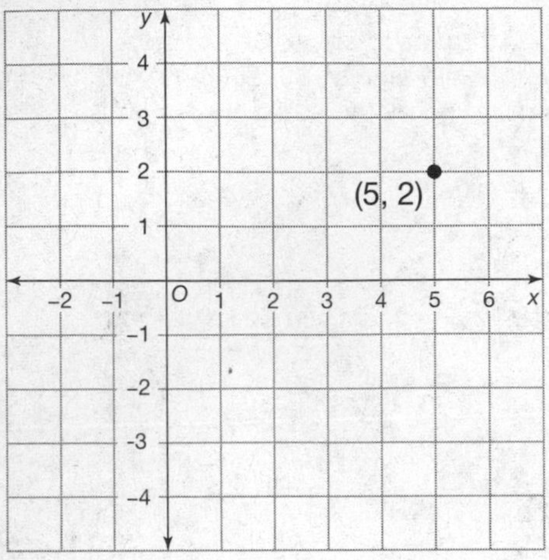

x-intercept

The *x*-intercept is the *x*-coordinate of the point where a graph crosses the *x*-axis.

Example

The *x*-intercept of the graph below is 4.

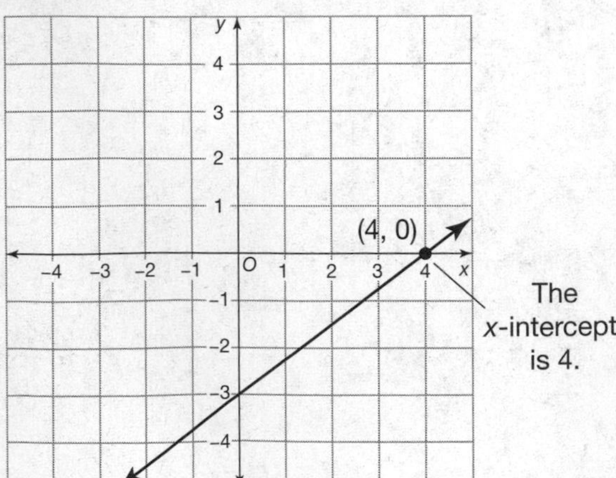

y-axis

The *y*-axis is the vertical number line in a Cartesian coordinate system.

Example

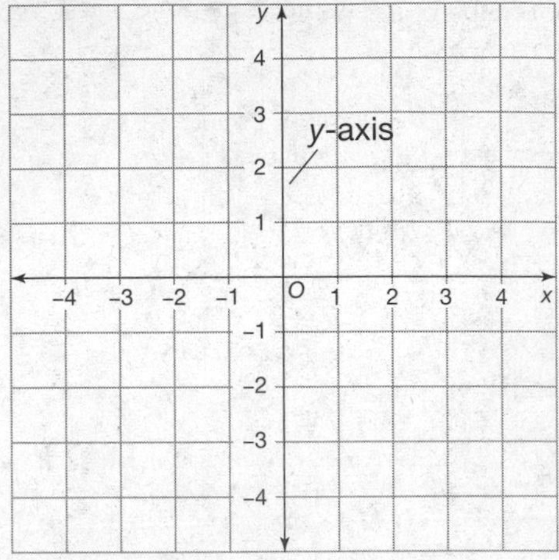

y-coordinate

The *y*-coordinate of a point is the second number in an ordered pair. It indicates the distance of the point from the *x*-axis.

Example

In the ordered pair (5, 2), the number 2 is the *y*-coordinate.

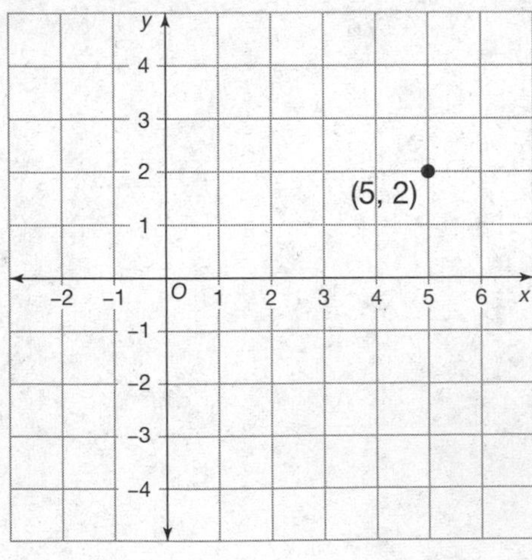

Glossary

y-intercept

The y-intercept is the y-coordinate of the point where a graph crosses the y-axis.

Example

The y-intercept of the graph below is –3.

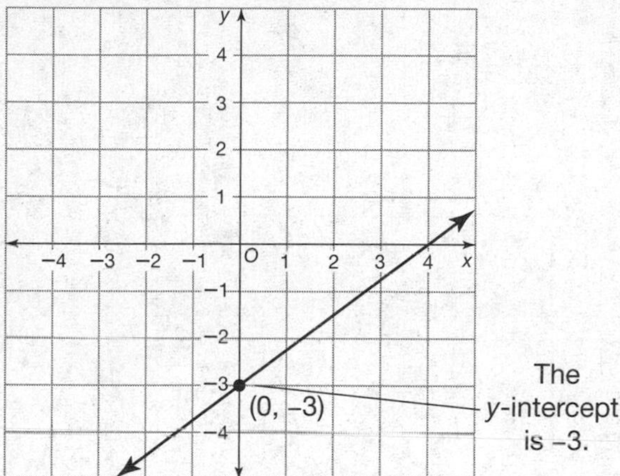

zero exponent

A zero exponent is an exponent in a power.
A nonzero power with a zero exponent is equal to 1.

Example

The expression x^0 contains a zero exponent.

Glossary

Index

Index

Index

T

U

X

Y

Z